BIG EAR

BIG EAR

John Kraus

Cygnus-Quasar Books

Published by Cygnus-Quasar Books
Powell, Ohio

Library of Congress Catalog Card Number 76-24396

Printed in U.S.A.
Beaver Press

FOREWORD

Big Ear is our adventure story of the exploration of the universe and the search for other-men. A universe so vast and mysterious it boggles the mind. An astounding, baffling, stranger-than-fiction universe of pulsars, quasars and black holes.

Big Ear is a personal, behind-the-scenes account of astronomers, engineers, inventors — humans all — their successes and failures. It is a story about the steel and aluminum structures we have raised to probe the cosmos and of our attempt to answer the question "Are we alone?"

Table of Contents

CHAPTER 1

GALENA AND CATWHISKER

"An Ohio source has the record redshift!" Mirjana announced.

"Wow! That makes it the most distant known object in the universe!" I exclaimed, "You must be kidding."

"No, I'm not," Mirjana beamed, "Cathy Imhoff called and said there's a story about OH471 in the Sunday *New York Times.*"

"Let's get a copy," I suggested.

It was Monday, the ninth of April 1973 and Mirjana Gearhart and I had met at the xerox machine in our building on the Ohio State University campus where I had gone to copy a letter and found her using the machine. We dropped everything and hurried outside to my car. As we drove to the newsstand, we talked excitedly.

OH471 was a radio source we had discovered a few years earlier with the Ohio radio telescope, a giant instrument bigger than three football fields. We assigned the name OH471 to the source as a celestial zip code that locates it in the sky. We suspected that OH471 might be unusual, so Bev Harris, of our group, helped Bryan Andrew, of a Canadian radio observatory, measure a precise position which Mirjana found to coincide with a faint star-like object in the constellation of the Lynx. We then published our findings.

Double-parking at the newsstand, I jumped out to buy the Sunday *Times.* Sure enough, on the front page was an article about "Seeing the Edge of the Universe." As I drove back to the campus, Mirjana read aloud from the *Times.*

Astronomers at the Steward Observatory in Arizona had photographed a spectrum of Mirjana's "star" and deduced that it had a redshift* of 3.4, the largest ever measured. Walter Sullivan, the *Times* Science Editor, went on to explain about the significance of the big redshift: OH471 was the most rapidly receding, most powerful and most distant object known in the universe! It was speeding away from us at 600 million miles per hour at a distance of some 12 billion light years!

A few days later the story was the number one article in *Time* magazine, which gave a philosophical and lyrically ecstatic account of man's restless desire to probe the ultimate depths of the universe and how finally he may have done just that with the "quasar OH471, the blaze marking the edge of the universe."†

Redshift, a number which relates to the distance. The bigger the redshift the greater the distance

†*Quasar,* **quasi**-stell**ar** object, an object which looks like a star but is not a star.

OH471 was the first object found with a redshift over three. It was an accomplishment like propelling the first aircraft through the sound barrier or running the first four-minute mile. Best of all it was an Ohio source. We discovered it and felt that it was a part of us, and we a part of it.

When my students and I built the Ohio radio telescope, not too many years before, we had not set out specifically to discover OH471. However, we had a feeling of great expectancy. With our telescope we had the unique privilege of "looking" out at the universe in a new and penetrating way never previously afforded man. We believed that we would discover many new and unusual things. We set out to survey the sky, make maps and produce lists of as many radio sources as possible. Our survey was at a shorter wavelength and went deeper than earlier surveys. We found many new sources and from these came such exotic gems as OH471.

Now to put things in perspective, I'd like to take you back a half century to a time when there was no radio astronomy and long before radio telescopes were even dreamed of.

*   *   *   *   *

It was 1920. Radio broadcasting was the new sensation. The first broadcasting of speech and music had started at KDKA, Pittsburgh, and a few other stations. Radio was a magic word and was rapidly replacing the older term "wireless."

Jack Binns was a national hero. He had been the radio operator on the S.S. Republic, and had sent the SOS call which brought assistance to the sinking ship, saving many lives. Prior to radio, complete isolation enshrouded a ship out-of-sight of land. Disaster might strike without anyone on nearby ships, or on the shore, being aware that anything had happened. Jack Binns had dramatized the value of radio at sea.

As a boy of 10 I was intrigued with reports that nightly broadcasts had begun from a new station WWJ in Detroit, only 40 miles from my home in Ann Arbor. There were stories that WWJ could be picked up in Ann Arbor with a simple crystal receiver. I wanted to try.

Instructions in the *Popular Science Monthly* explained that all you needed was a coil of wire, a galena crystal with a fine wire or "cat whisker," and a pair of ear phones. These were fastened together with a few pieces of wire and connected to an outside antenna. The coil consisted of several hundred turns of wire wound on a cylindrical oatmeal box or a mailing tube. The cheapest source of wire was a Model-T Ford spark coil which cost a dollar. With hatchet and screwdriver the wax and wood encased coil could be chopped and pried open and the wire unwound. A pair of ear phones was more expensive so I planned to remove the ear-piece from our household upright Bell telephone. The ear-piece was easily disconnected and a hammer then hung on the hook in its place so that the operator or "central" would not be alerted. Of course, the telephone was inoperative, but this was only a slight inconvenience for a few hours each evening.

My dad was a minerologist and he had given me some pea-sized scraps of shiny cubical black galena crystals. But I needed a "cat whisker" to make contact with the crystal so we went to Eberbach and Company, a manufacturer of scientific instruments. One of them was a device my dad had designed for measuring the specific gravity of minerals. I explained my needs to Ralph Miller, the shop foreman, who soon presented me with several inches of exceedingly fine hair-like phosphor-bronze wire and a small brass clip. The wire would serve as the "cat whisker" and the clip as the holder for the galena. Now I had everything needed for my crystal receiver. Returning home, I arranged the parts on a table next to my bedroom window and eagerly hooked them together with short pieces of wire.

For the antenna I purchased a roll of copper wire and several glazed ceramic insulators. I strung the wire with insulators from our house to an electric power pole at the back fence of our lot.

Finally I connected the antenna to the receiver. Then holding the telephone to one ear I used my free hand to probe the galena crystal with the cat whisker. Searching for a sensitive spot was tricky and often took many minutes. When I suddenly heard music or a voice, I stopped searching and held my breath lest anything disturb the delicate adjustment. Someone moving about in the same room, a door slamming in a remote part of the house, or even a passing truck, might dislodge the cat whisker from its precarious position and the set would go dead. However, the thrill of listening to the early broadcasts compensated for these frustrations.

It gave me an eerie, out-of-this-world feeling to hear the faint, but clear, voice of "Ty" Tyson announce

"This is WWJ, *The Detroit News*. The next selection will be . . . ."

It was coming without wires through seemingly empty space from 40 miles away! Programs were simple: singers, instrumentalists and an occasional speaker. There were no networks, no commercials and no regularly scheduled programs. The format was informal and extemporaneous. If you played a musical saw, you might drop into the studio unannounced and be on the air a half hour later. Typically the station came on about seven in the evening with sign-off by nine. And invariably between each item on the program came Tyson's voice

"This is WWJ, *The Detroit News* . . . ."

*　　　*　　　*　　　*　　　*

Hardly a year earlier I had listened over a radio receiver for the first time. The receiver belonged to Bob Swain who lived a few houses from me. He was a senior in high school and his knowledge of wireless seemed limitless. Bob had built a multiple-wire antenna stretching from a tall pole above the roof of his house to a huge guyed tower in his backyard. I was impressed and fascinated by Bob's antenna and regarded it as no less an engineering feat than the Brooklyn Bridge. Once I sat all afternoon at Bob's receiver with headphones pressed tightly against my ears and hearing nothing except an occasional click of static or a sputtering noise as an electric trolley car rounded a curve in the street near Bob's house.

"Just wait until after supper," Bob told me, "then you will hear the fellows with their spark transmitters."

The "fellows" Bob referred to were radio amateurs or "hams." Bob had learned the Morse code and was building a spark transmitter. Activity did pick up after supper, but just before ten everything stopped as all receivers were tuned to NAA, the powerful 2000-meter U.S. Navy station at Arlington, Virginia, which regularly transmitted time signals. Clocks were checked and reset when the long dash finally came through at precisely ten o'clock.

*　　　*　　　*　　　*　　　*

With my crystal receiver I could hear only a few broadcast stations. The most consistent was WWJ. The loudest station, though, was WCBC at the University of Michigan, built and operated by the Department of Electrical Engineering with Erwin Dreese as engineer. It was a mere 500 yards from my home but it broadcast for only an hour or so, one night a week.

Soon I built my first vacuum-tube receiver. It had a tube mounted behind a bakelite panel adorned with knobs and binding posts. The tube filament was lighted by a 6-volt automobile storage battery, which had to be recharged often. About once a week my father and I loaded it into our 4-cylinder Lycoming-powered Crow-Elkhart touring car and took it downtown to the battery service station where we left it overnight. The battery weighed about 50 pounds so the weekly trip was a chore. Hundreds of batteries in row upon row were undergoing recharging at the battery station, and my nostrils smarted from the sulphurous odor of the acid electrolyte.

A bulky 45-volt battery was also required for the tube's plate voltage supply. This was either a Burgess or Eveready type, and a new one was required about once a month. This battery could not be recharged, and old ones had to be discarded.

Reception was weak when the batteries were low, but on the evening after the storage battery had been charged and a new plate battery installed, the excitement of good listening returned. WWJ was of comfortable strength and much more distant stations were also audible.

With the coming of fall and clear, cool, crisp nights, the static disappeared and radio stations came through in profusion. With headphones glued to my head I could hear voices and music at every position on the receiver dial. It was a modern Babel, a kaleidoscope of jumbled sounds. A voice said,

"This is WBAP, Fort Worth."

Another mentioned Jefferson City, Missouri, and others gave Schenectady, Chicago, Pittsburgh, New York or New Orleans as their locations. Station identifications were frequent, and in an hour I could definitely identify and log dozens of them. As the evening wore on, I could hear stations farther and farther west.

Then one night I listened past midnight, speculating whether I might even hear California. Most of the eastern stations had signed off. I searched the dial listening intently. I heard music. The station was clear but weak. It was almost three o'clock. I waited and waited. Minutes dragged by slowly.

"Won't they ever announce?" I muttered.

Then a voice:

"This is KFI, Earl C. Anthony, Los Angeles." (Anthony was a Packard automobile dealer and a well-known pioneer broadcaster.)

My heart pounded; I had heard a voice all the way from California over 2000 miles away!

Radio waves carry their message through empty space. Communication by wires is another and older method, and I used it too, as related in the next chapter.

CHAPTER 2

THE BACKYARD TELEGRAPH

Bob Cummings and I made a telephone of two empty Campbell soup cans. We connected the cans by a tight string fastened through holes in the bottoms. I was 12, and Bob, who lived across Church Street, was 10. We installed our "telephone" between the second story windows of our houses, pulling the string high enough that automobiles passed under with ample clearance. But our telephone left much to be desired. When Bob spoke into his can all I heard was a jumbled buzz and we ended up shouting across the street. But it was fun and our antics drew a crowd of neighborhood youngsters.

The string suggested another possibility. Suppose it were used to support a small, light box which could slide on the string. Another, lower string attached to the box could then pull the box across the street. The next day Bob and I rigged our aerial conveyor system and successfully exchanged notes and trinkets.

Everything worked fine for many back-and-forth trips of the box until one noon when the upper string broke and draped itself in large loops over the lower string. The loops reached almost to the ground and an open model-T Ford speeding south on Church Street screeched to a stop just inches from the dangling string. I was flustered and embarrassed as the driver stood up in the open Ford and leaned over the windshield to get a closer look at what was "blocking" the road. We were near the University of Michigan campus and the sidewalks were crowded with students and faculty walking home for lunch. It seemed as though everyone stopped and all eyes followed the strings to the open windows where Bob and I now crouched low in an attempt to avoid detection. More automobiles were coming and I hauled in furiously on the broken string to clear the street. Soon the string was all in, the Ford moved on, and things on Church Street returned to normal. But Bob and I were shaken. Had we broken some law? Would the police come? We removed the other string and hid all evidence of the aerial conveyor system. However, our desire to communicate was not stifled.

For Christmas Bob received an inexpensive telegraph set. It consisted of two keys and two sounders which we set up at opposite ends of the attic of Bob's house. We hadn't used it long before we wondered if it would work between Bob's house and mine. We could not be sure. Some older boys on the next street had run a telegraph line between their houses and although their equipment was more expensive their line didn't work. In spite of this we decided to try and some days later I bought several rolls of wire which we strung across the street.

I was in Bob's attic with him as we made the last connections. Then I raced home and tapped on my key. Immediately Bob responded in Morse with "OK" so I sent the words "Come over." Soon I heard Bob running across our front porch. Opening the front door, he bounded in and we whooped it up. Our telegraph line worked! Samuel Morse could hardly have felt greater joy when he sent his first message over the Washington-Baltimore line.

The news of our telegraph spread rapidly. A classmate, Rob Canby, who lived several houses from me on the same side of Church Street, wanted a station. So we acquired another telegraph key and sounder for his station and made plans to run a telegraph wire between our houses. But two older boys, who lived in a house between Rob's and mine, got wind of the plans and warned us that they would not let us string a line past their house; even if we did manage to do it, they would tear it down. This posed a real problem since any direct path from Rob's house to mine crossed their lot. The best route for the wire would be via the trees which lined the street but such a line would be much too obvious. It would be better to run the wire behind the houses and we finally concluded that the best place was along the back fence. In this way it could be made very inconspicuous and might not even be noticed. However, to escape detection we would have to string the line at night.

A wooden fence marked the back of our house lot. The fence ran north and south and separated the lots on Church Street from those on the next street to the west. I had grown up on this block so I had intimate familiarity with the fence and all of the back lots that it separated. I knew where boards were loose so I could squeeze through, and where the boards were tight I knew the smoothest and best places to go over the top. Years of exploring the block, playing games of hide-and-seek, and escaping from the neighborhood bullies had made this area thoroughly mine. I knew it inch-by-inch as well or better than anyone else. I also knew, if I were seen trespassing, which housewives would greet me with a smile and a friendly wave and which would rush out shouting angry threats and shaking their fists.

So when Bob, Rob and I set out after supper on a cool, dark autumn night to run the wire from my house to Rob's, I was in familiar surroundings. From my house we strung the wire to the large box alder tree at the back of our lot and then down to the fence. It was possible to poke the wire between the horizontal beams and vertical boards of the fence so that it was very inconspicuous. It was slow work and took us several evenings to complete the job. Finally, one evening Rob's sisters gathered around him at his house to witness the first tests of the new telegraph line. We exchanged messages successfully while Bob Cummings at his station listened in to our transmissions. Bob could send messages to Rob either directly or relayed through me. We now had a burgeoning telegraph line with three stations!

After Rob had been connected I anticipated that the older boys living between Rob's house and mine might find the line and cut it. But our precautions paid off; the line was never cut.

I divided my time between the telegraph line and my radio receiver. The receiver used headphones and had two pairs so that two persons could listen. While wearing one pair I noticed that when another person was putting his pair on I could hear his voice in my headphones if his pair were close to his mouth. Could we use these headphones to talk over our telegraph line? I connected one pair of headphones across the telegraph line at my house and Bob did likewise at his house. To our delight we found that we could converse easily and with good clarity if we held one headphone close to our mouth and the other one to our ear. Our telegraph line had now become a telephone line! It worked without batteries or any external power source to the amazement of our friends. The electrical impulses were generated by the sound waves of the voice striking the diaphragm of the headphone. The same principle is used nowadays in what are called "sound powered" telephones. With telephony now available we rarely resorted anymore to telegraphy.

Soon we added two more stations, one for Bill Dowsett who lived on East University Avenue and another for John Cole on Forest Avenue. With these additions our telegraph and telephone line was quadrupled in length. It now had 5 stations on 3 different city blocks and a total line length of a half-mile.

Many times while using our telephone line I visualized the path it followed. The wire went through holes in the floor, through window casings, through trees, over streets and along back fences. The wire we had strung was a message highway over which our voices traveled around bends and turns from one house to another in an instant. It was miraculous. Even today when talking on the telephone I sometimes reflect on the path my conversation takes through cables and ducts, switchboards and many connections to the telephone at the other end.

But, I thought, what about a message from beings on a distant planet? It would travel by waves through empty space over untold miles. Would it be in a kind of Morse code or in a strange, unintelligible speech-like jargon?

We used the telegraph-telephone line for several years. Gradually the novelty wore off and our interests changed. I wanted to develop proficiency with the Morse code but the others didn't, so I began to listen to the commercial Morse code stations on the short waves and to the radio amateurs. But this is the story of the next chapter.

CHAPTER 3

48 MASON JARS

Radio — the word fascinated me. From a transmitting antenna to a receiving antenna radio waves travelled without wires. How could this be? I often wondered what it might be like to have my own transmitter and send out radio waves from my own station but the idea seemed remote and almost unattainable.

There was a way, however. First, I needed to increase my Morse code speed. Second, I needed to learn more about the way receivers and transmitters operated. Both were necessary before I could pass the government license examination for an amateur station. I read *Popular Science* and *Popular Mechanics* regularly but these magazines did not have enough specific information so I began to read the radio amateur's monthly, *QST*, and a number of books.

Evenings I listened regularly with my receiver to amateur and commercial stations. Everything was in Morse code. Slowly my code speed began to improve. I learned that it was important not to visualize the letter "V" as three dots and a dash (· · · —) but to recognize the sound of the letter, "dit dit dit dah" as "V" without thinking of individual dots or dashes, like when hearing a spoken word you don't visualize every letter used to spell it.

I joined the high school radio club. It had only nine members but it was an enthusiastic group. A few members already had stations of their own but most were beginners. Gerald Fox, a graduate student in physics at the U. of M. had charge of the club.

The club's radio station 8DAN had a 50-watt transmitter with high voltage supplied by a motor-generator which made so much noise that it had to be turned off while receiving.

I sat in at the club station during "QSOs" or conversations with other amateur stations. "Gerry" Fox was our best operator and I envied his skill and finesse. Then one day Gerry suggested that it was time for me to try my hand at being the operator. It was one thing to watch him and something else to do it myself but I agreed.

It was five in the afternoon of a late fall day as I tuned the receiver dial listening for a CQ, a general call amateurs use to solicit replies. Finally I heard one. It was loud and being sent slowly. I listened until the operator signed his call and stood by. I was tense and anxious as I switched on the motor-generator and pumped the telegraph key to indicate that 8DAN was calling. As I turned off the motor-generator and its whine gradually died down my stomach churned. I waited and waited. Finally, I heard the station come on but he was replying to someone else. He had not heard my call. My heart sank. I continued to tune. I heard another CQ and responded. Still no luck. I tuned around some more and answered another CQ. This time the station heard me and replied. I broke out in a cold sweat. My hand trembled as I penciled the message that our signals were R7 (strong and clear), that his location was in Pennsylvania and that the weather there was clear and cold. He stood by and I responded. After several exchanges we sent our 73's (best regards) and signed off. I slumped limply in the chair. I had made my first radio contact!

Gerry and the club members thought I was qualified for a license. I filled out the necessary forms and applied by mail for a temporary license which required no formal examination. Some weeks later I received a letter from the Radio Inspector enclosing my license. The call letters he had assigned my station were 8AFJ.

A station then, as now, consisted of a transmitter, a receiver, and an antenna. The transmitters were simple, consisting of a single vacuum tube oscillator and a high voltage power supply. The noisy and spectacular but less efficient spark transmitter had given way only a few years earlier to CW, or continuous wave, transmitters using vacuum tubes.

The attic of my home had two finished rooms, and I acquired one for my station. I designed my transmitter around a 210 tube, a type that was popular with amateurs. It was rated at a power of only a few watts but it could be overloaded to handle 10 or 15 watts or more if one was careful.

I stretched an antenna between the chimneys of my house and Whelan's house, next door, using a 30-foot extension ladder to climb to the roofs.

My first high voltage power supply for the transmitter consisted of several 45-volt batteries connected in series. However, these discharged rapidly and had to be replaced every few days. So I began constructing a chemical rectifier to provide the high-voltage direct current. It consisted of 48 pint-sized glass Mason jars of the kind my mother used for canning fruits and vegetables. I built a large rectangular wooden trough to hold the jars in 6 rows of 8 jars each. I purchased some sheets of aluminum and lead and cut them into strips about an inch wide by 4 inches long. I then bolted one end of an aluminum strip to the end of a lead strip and bent the pair to form a "U." Inverting the "U," I dropped it into two adjacent jars so that the aluminum part was in one jar and the lead part in the next jar. In this way I fitted every jar with both a lead and an aluminum electrode. Finally, I mixed a solution of borax and water and filled the jars. Ann Arbor city water had a high iron content which would spoil the rectifier action so I carried rain water from Whelan's cistern.

By connecting the jars to a high voltage transformer, the arrangement rectified or converted the alternating current from the transformer into direct current for my transmitter.

The Mason jar rectifier had taken many evenings to construct. At last, one evening I hooked the jars to my transmitter and turned on the power. Things seemed to be OK but as a final test I turned out the lights in the room and scrutinized each of the 48 jars in the tray on the floor under my transmitter. Most of the aluminum strips fluoresced brightly in the dark. This was a sign that they were working properly. But a few did not glow. So I turned off the power and removed the non-glowing strips from their jars. After drying them I cleaned the aluminum with fine sandpaper. This cleaning made the strips glow when

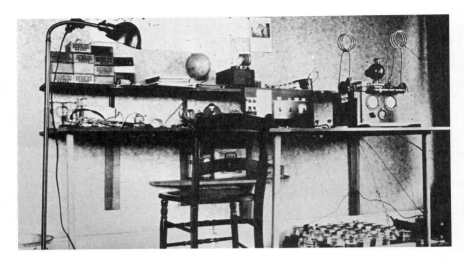

**1. "The 48 Mason jars were a messy nuisance but they worked."
They are under the table with transmitter on the table, at the right,
and receiver at the center, behind the top of the chair.**

they were put back. But it was not long before others failed to glow.
It was difficult to keep all 48 jars working properly all the time and I
often used the rectifier with a couple of non-functioning jars. It did
not seem to matter too much as long as most of them were working.

In the dark the glow from the 48 jars blinking on and off gave me
a satisfied feeling as I sent my dots and dashes. But with all the
maintenance that 48 jars required I looked upon them more and more as
a messy nuisance. I put up with them for a long time because they
provided the least expensive system available at the time and they
worked.*

The 48 jar rectifier involved high voltage but I was careful. It was
not a matter of learning this by experience because one might not get
a second chance.

At last I got 8AFJ on the air. I "worked" or communicated with
many amateur stations throughout the United States and quite a few
in Canada. Everything was in Morse code and my proficiency improved.

For a long time my ambition had been to work an "Aussie," that is,
to communicate with an Australian station, far away at the opposite end
of the earth. I had heard that the best time to work Australia was in
the early morning near dawn. So one Tuesday evening in mid March
(1927) I retired early and set my alarm clock for 4 A.M. Earlier that
evening I had carried a pail of rain water from Whelan's and topped
off the borax solution level in all 48 Mason jars. I also made adjustments
on the transmitter. Everything seemed to be in order.

When I awoke at four I was full of anticipation. To avoid waking
my parents I tiptoed to my attic radio room. It was dark outside and
as I turned on the receiver the tubes glowed brightly. Putting on ear-

---

*The principle of the Mason jar rectifier is widely used today in electrical equipment
except that small solid state diodes are used instead of the jars making the rectifier
exceedingly small and compact.

phones I tuned the receiver slowly back and forth across the 40 meter band. Everything was dead. There were no signals to be heard. Was something wrong? Was the antenna disconnected? I checked. Everything *seemed* to be OK. Finally near one end of the receiver dial I heard a weak signal from a station sending a series of "V's." I was relieved. At least the receiver wasn't dead and the band wasn't entirely dead. The signal was just outside the amateur band so I concluded it must be a commercial station. Frequently, commercials sent the letter "V" over and over when they had no messages to transmit.

So I continued to tune back and forth. Still no amateur signals. But I persisted. At last I heard the low-pitched musical chirping of a faint signal. It turned out to be a "6", that is, a California amateur station. Should I call him? I hesitated. Maybe the band was opening now and conditions would improve and even more distant stations would come through. So I continued to tune the receiver. It was now five o'clock and dawn was breaking. Then I heard a faint but clear high-pitched tone repeating

"Dah-dit-dah-dit dah-dah-dit-dah (CQ)" over and over, slowly and regularly. I thought

"Who is it? Why doesn't he sign?"

Then came a break followed by

"Dah-dah-dah dit-dah (OA) dit-dit-dit-dit-dit dah-dit-dit-dit dah-dit-dah-dah (5BY)."

It was an Aussie! "OA" was the abbreviation used by amateurs for Australia and "5BY" the station call letters. The "5" meant that the station was in South Australia. Finally, I heard

"Dah-dit-dah (K) meaning "Go ahead."

I was trembling as I switched on my transmitter and tapped out slowly on my telegraph key

"5BY 5BY 5BY..." many times to give the Aussie a chance to tune his receiver and find my signal. The Mason jars under the table blinked at me reassuringly. Finally I sent

"NU 8AFJ 8AFJ 8AFJ."

This meant that station 8AFJ in the United States (NU) was calling. Then I sent "K" (go ahead)", switched off my transmitter, pressed the headphones tight to my ears and strained listening. I heard nothing. Seconds passed. They seemed like minutes. Then there it was,

"8AFJ 8AFJ OA 5BY 5BY - GE OM UR SIGS R4 DC STDI IN ADELAIDE SOUTH AUSTRALIA....."

I could hardly believe my ears. It was like a dream. With only 10 watts into my transmitter the Aussie had heard my signals and was coming back to me! I was in contact with Australia 10,000 miles away!

He had sent "GE (good evening)." It was morning in Ann Arbor but evening in Adelaide. His "GE OM" meant

"Good evening, old man." Regardless of age, amateurs greeted each other as "old man."

"UR SIGS R4" meant that although my signals were not strong, they could be copied without difficulty. "DC STDI" meant that my signals had a "direct current" or smooth musical tone and were also "steady" or not fluctuating in pitch.

I felt transported right out of the attic across continents and oceans. I let out a whoop and stamped my feet on the floor. I heard muffled protests from the floor below; I had awakened my parents. I later apologized, but I had lost my senses.

The Adelaide operator told me his name was Doug Whitburn and that he would QSL, that is, send me a postcard confirming our QSO or communication. We exchanged our full addresses and after many more transmissions back and forth we sent our "73s" (best regards) and "SK" the sign-off symbol.

It was now after six o'clock and it was bright outside. I was walking on air when I went down to breakfast. Afterwards as I went outside into the cool, clear spring morning and looked up at my antenna above the roof tops it was no longer just a copper wire between two chimneys, it was one end of a bridge that stretched around the world!

My parents accepted my apology for having so rudely awakened them. They also accepted my story that I had worked Australia. But actually I had no proof or anything tangible to show.

Five weeks later a QSL card came in the mail from 5BY. This listed the date, time, and wavelength of our QSO. The card was confirmation of our contact and when I showed it to my parents they were duly impressed.

I had also sent 5BY a QSL card and on its receipt he responded with a several page letter written neatly in pen with a clear, bold hand. Doug Whitburn, 5BY, worked as a clerk and bookkeeper for a large flour mill in Adelaide. He told me much about himself and life in Australia. I responded with a letter about myself and Ann Arbor. We became pen pals and corresponded for several years even though we never contacted each other again by radio. Much of what I know now about Australia I learned first from Doug.

Of all the subjects I took in high school, physics was the one I liked the best. My teacher, Mahlon Buell, had a knack for making it interesting by relating it to many things in everyday life. Gerald Fox also made electricity and physics fascinating subjects. I had devoured "Makers of Science" by Hart, a book which related interesting facets of the lives of many scientists: Galileo, Isaac Newton, Michael Faraday, Lord Kelvin and others. I eagerly read stories about Thomas Edison, the Wright brothers and other inventors. To me science and especially physics was a great frontier and I wanted to help explore it.

I often tingled with excitement as I read stories of new discoveries or ideas in the latest *Popular Science Monthly*. There was one article which aroused my curiosity. It described a scheme for signalling the Martians with an array of huge mirrors placed in the Sahara desert to catch and reflect the sun's rays. Would it work and were there really any people there? I wondered.

CHAPTER 4

QUARTZ CRYSTALS

Baseball was my favorite sport and during my earlier years on Church Street I played it summers in vacant lots as often as I could assemble a gang of boys. My ambition was to become a major league baseball player.

Ann Arbor High School had a football and a basketball team but no baseball team so I persuaded a group of my high school pals from the Church Street area to form a baseball team and we played teams from other parts of the city. We used the regulation hardball but often the only diamond we had available was laid out for softball. The distance between bases was less on a softball diamond so scores were sometimes very high. I remember one game when our team scored 22 runs and lost!

Although I was fond of baseball I was aware that my ability left much to be desired so after entering the University of Michigan I gave no serious thought to going out for sports. My radio station 8AFJ was my principal extra-curricular activity while I was a freshman. During my sophomore year we moved from Church Street and for a while I did little with radio. In my senior year my interest returned. I went to the U.S. Radio Inspector's office in Detroit, passed the amateur license examination including the Morse code test, and was assigned new call letters, W8JK. I had requested these since JK were my initials. A "W" before the 8 was now also included in the call as the prefix for the United States.*

We now lived on Arlington Boulevard in the open country east of Ann Arbor. In June of 1930 I received my bachelors degree with major in physics and the following fall I entered graduate school. That year I built an entirely new and more elaborate transmitter. This one was crystal controlled. The technique of using a quartz crystal for frequency control was coming into vogue. It was remarkable that a quartz wafer the size of a postage stamp and only a little thicker could hold a transmitter steady on its wavelength more effectively than any other means.

Instead of purchasing manufactured quartz crystals I began to cut and grind my own. My dad had taught me a lot about minerals and encouraged me to do this.

My first job was to cut a wafer from a large quartz specimen. Quartz is very hard and easily scratches glass so it was necessary to use a

---

*An international agreement had been reached whereby prefixes were attached as an integral part of all amateur calls to indicate the country.

special type of motor-driven saw. Then came grinding by hand with fine carborundum powder to reduce the thickness of the wafer. It was vital to start with a thick wafer and grind it gradually thinner, with frequent checks of its thickness, until the desired wavelength was reached. If too much was ground off the wavelength would be too short with no way of going back. The quartz wafer would be ruined. It was nerve racking work.

After some weeks I began to master the art of making quartz crystals, and as the word got around to my amateur radio friends I received many orders to cut and grind crystals for particular wavelengths which they had selected. I soon found myself with a booming business making custom-ground quartz crystals. It consumed a great deal of time but financially it did not amount to much. My price was $3 for a crystal ground to the buyer's special frequency. I also made crystal holders which I sold for $1 each.

Although I improved the efficiency of the enterprise by adopting batch processing procedures I did not continue in the crystal business more than a year or two. But I did grind many quartz wafers and I also experimented some with tourmaline instead of quartz as the crystal.

CHAPTER 5

ULTRA-SHORT WAVES

Thomas Edison was my idol. I grew up with stories of his exploits and inventions. Later, I read about Michael Faraday. My high school physics teacher, Mahlon Buell, often spoke of him.

Faraday was born in 1791 over 50 years before Edison. Michael began at 20 as an apprentice washing retorts and cleaning apparatus in Sir Humphrey Davy's laboratory in the Royal Institution in London. Some ten years later he was performing original experiments. Although he died penniless, his work forms the basis for electromagnetics: the science of electricity and magnetism from which has come the telegraph, the telephone, radio, television, the generator, the motor and hosts of other inventions. Faraday, like Edison, was an experimentalist. Because of my practical bent they both appealed to me.

Physics and radio were my strong interests. As long as I can remember I also had a keen interest in aeronautics and during my first years in college my choice of a career had oscillated between radio and aeronautics. Should I build radio stations or should I design airplanes? I didn't know. Lindbergh's epic flight to Paris in 1927 boosted my interest in flight. I bought several text books on aircraft and their principles and studied them.

My first ride in an airplane was over Detroit and Windsor in a Ford tri-motor. I took my mother up with me; it was her first ride too. We took off from the Ford Airport in Dearborn. I still recall vividly the sensation of hanging motionless, except for the whirling propellors, high above Detroit while the ground beneath slid slowly by.

I joined the U of M glider club and had a chance to get the feel of flying. The club had almost a dozen members. All were fellows except one, Cornelia Burwell. The club met afternoons twice a week near the edge of town at a field with an abandoned barn in which we stored our training-class glider. There was a hill at one end of the field from which we launched the glider by means of two long rubber ropes, each about 2 inches in circumference and a couple hundred feet long. The two ropes were laid out down the hill with the glider held by a short rope from its tail by two men sitting on the ground, heels dug in. The long ropes were like the legs of a "V" with the glider at the apex. Four men held each rope at open ends of the V. At a signal from the pilot, the two teams of four fellows sprinted down the hill stretching the ropes. When the pull was about all the men on the tail could hold, they let go and the glider catapulted into the air as if from a sling-shot, flying between the four-man teams on the pull ropes.

On one occasion I was anchor man on one of the pull ropes, that is, I was the nearest of the four to the glider. At the shout of "pull" from the pilot we ran down the hill as fast as we could. The ropes grew tight, then suddenly slackened as the glider was released. While still running I turned my head enough to catch the glider out of the corner of my eye.

"Holy mackeral," I muttered, "he's coming right at me!"

I tried to run faster but he was gaining rapidly. Then I saw one wing go up as the glider flipped completely over and crashed upside down right where I had been running a half second before!

On our glider the pilot sat totally in the open with his back strapped against a vertical spar just below the leading edge of the wing. The crash had shoved the pilot along the spar so that with the glider now upside down his head was jammed against the ground. There he hung helplessly on his head, legs up and arms flailing the air. He was badly shaken up but otherwise unhurt. End of "Lesson 1."

The glider was damaged but was repaired in a few days.

Not long after "Lesson 1," I was again on a pull rope. We gave the glider a good pull and the pilot got it up beautifully and steered straight between my team and the one on the other rope. I watched him soar over us. My pullmates commented that it was a good flight. Then tentatively I thought maybe it was too good because he had so much speed and altitude that unless he make a turn he would run out of field. But he didn't turn; he flew straight into an oak tree at the end of the field. Fortunately, the tree buried itself into the wing a few inches to one side of where he was sitting. He was not hurt and was able to unbelt himself and climb down. We spent the rest of the afternoon dismantling the wrecked glider and carrying it back to the barn for repairs. End of "Lesson 2."

2. "He flew straight into an oak tree at the end of the field . . . and we spent the rest of the afternoon dismantling the wrecked glider and carrying it back to the barn for repairs."

There were many close calls but we took these mishaps lightheartedly as a matter of course. We should have realized that something more serious could happen and it did. One of my fellow club members tried to stretch his glide too far and stalled the glider. It crashed and he was killed.

His death had a sobering effect on the club and my enthusiasm was dampened. The accident was tragic and quite unnecessary if a few precautions had been taken. Perhaps that was "Lesson 3."

In 1929 I attended an air show at the Ford Airport. The Franklin brothers of Ann Arbor were there with several of their latest gliders. The older brother, R.E. Franklin, was a professor of engineering at the U of M. He had developed some of the highest performance sailplane gliders then in existence. Wally Franklin, the younger brother, was the pilot who flew them. I knew both quite well.

Wally had gained national prominence by flying a Franklin glider across the United States in the tow of a Waco biplane piloted by Milo Oliphant of Ann Arbor. The flight had been made in several hops over a period of days.

The glider belonging to the U of M glider club was of the simplest, primary type. The Franklin gliders were, in contrast, a much more advanced secondary type. The pilot was completely enclosed except where his head projected above the surface of the fuselage just forward of the wing. The glider was fully streamlined and had a long, narrow high-performance wing. In the air the glider's graceful lines were like those of a soaring gull or hawk.

At the air show Wally had been towed aloft to several thousand feet by an airplane and then cut loose. After soaring around for about an hour he came in for a landing.

Wally was a showman and, probably to demonstrate the long gliding range and low air speed of the Franklin glider, he came down very low west of the landing field until he was just skimming over the tops of hundreds of automobiles parked in a field a quarter of a mile from the edge of the airport. Someone shouted, "He's going to crash!"

A stampede started and people rushed toward the parked automobiles to see the crash at closer range. But the crowd was disappointed; Wally didn't crash. After floating slowly over the automobiles he pulled back on his control stick and climbed rapidly until he was several hundred feet in the air as he crossed the edge of the airport. He finally landed far out on the flying field. It was a first-class demonstration of the capabilities of the Franklin glider.

We soon had another demonstration. A second Franklin glider was to be pulled up by an automobile. This was a common means of launching a glider. The glider was attached by about 500 feet of slender steel cable to an automobile. As the automobile accelerated, the glider could climb to a few hundred feet and then cut loose. This method didn't get the glider up high enough to stay up long unless there were strong updrafts or thermals.

In this demonstration the glider was to be flown by Sam Bensky, a U of M engineering student. The glider was right at the edge of the flying field close to the viewing stands and hoards of people pressing against the airport fence. The tow car was at the end of the steel cable 500 feet farther out in the flying field. The car was to pull the glider out toward the center of the flying field and directly away from the crowd.

At a signal from Bensky the car began to move and Bensky's glider slid along the ground. Then as the car began to accelerate, Bensky began to climb at a very steep angle. It was breathtaking. He was up well over a hundred feet and climbing fast. Suddenly the glider veered to the left in a big arc and crashed nose first into the ground with a resounding "c-r-u-m-p", like a clap of thunder.

"My God," someone yelled, "Bensky's killed!" Hundreds of spectators began to climb over the airport fence and rush to the wrecked glider. But before anyone could get there, we could see the cowling over the cockpit fly off and Bensky emerge. Those who got there first said that Bensky's cursing scorched the grass for a hundred feet around. Miraculously, he wasn't even scratched. Soon the announcer on the public address system commented,

"The pilot's escape is a tribute to the strong tubular steel construction of the Franklin glider. He would not have been so lucky in another type of glider."

The cause of the accident was unclear but apparently resulted from a momentary reduction in pull as the automobile driver shifted gears at the very instant Bensky needed all the pull he could get to climb at such a steep angle.

During the late 1920's and early 1930's aircraft were evolving rapidly but they were still relatively primitive and crashes were not uncommon. For instance, the pilot who took my mother and me up on our first ride was killed a few years later when the wings of his small plane came off as he pulled out of a loop.

I hung around airports and learned about the many different types of airplanes, but by the time I graduated from college and entered graduate school, radio and physics had won out. So it was appropriate that I eventually did my Ph.D. dissertation on a study of the propagation of ultra-short waves, ones about 5 meters long.

The dissertation study required hundreds of field strength measurements for many miles around Ann Arbor from a transmitter on the roof of the Physics Building at the U of M. Radio was still new. Standard broadcasting was on wavelengths of 200 meters or more and 5 meters was, by comparison, a very short wavelength. Although these wavelengths later became jammed with television and FM stations there was absolutely no one using them in 1931 except an occasional amateur.

Later, radio astronomers found these 5-meter waves useful in surveying the sky. But in 1931 no one thought about this application.

*   *   *   *   *

Henry Muyskens was also working on his Ph.D. degree in physics. We had common interests and objectives. We met in an electrical engineering course and when Henry began talking about radio wave propagation as a dissertation topic he suggested the possibility of our doing it together.* We needed a transmitter, a receiver, a calibration system and a means of transporting the receiver to many measuring locations. The university had none of these so we would have to start from scratch. The scope of the problem was sufficient that the Graduate School approved our request to do a joint dissertation. Our Physics Department advisor

---

*Ultra-short waves don't propagate along the ground much beyond the horizon. However, there is some diffraction or bending beyond the horizon and it seemed important to make accurate measurements to determine how far a transmitter could reach in a practical situation.

was Professor Neil H. Williams,† whom I had assisted earlier in some of his laboratory courses on vacuum tubes. He was agreeable to a joint dissertation with our examinations held separately. It was a unique arrangement but Henry and I had the go-ahead to becoming a physical "pair-a-docs."

Henry was older, married with a year old son. He had been teaching physics and mathematics in secondary schools near Seattle, Washington. He wanted to get his degree and return to teaching. I, too, wanted to get on with the job so we wasted no time.

We hoped to make a 5-meter wavelength field strength survey and prepare a contour map. This had not been done before. There was no apparatus manufactured or available for measuring field strengths at a wavelength of 5 meters so we would need to devise our own. The Physics Department budget was enough to allow the purchase of a 5-meter receiver which we modified for field intensity measurements. We also developed a calibration system. We constructed a waterproof transmitter unit with antenna, mounting this on a wooden tower above the elevator house on the roof of the Physics Building, east of the Diagonal walk on the old central campus.

The receiver and associated equipment was mounted in the rear of a 1923 Studebaker touring car. Usually I drove and Henry sat in the back with the equipment. We rigged an aluminum tube antenna nearly 3 meters (8 feet) long above the car roof. This could be rotated from within the car from a horizontal position when moving to a vertical position when we stopped for a field strength measurement. We had selected many points in Ann Arbor and the surrounding countryside at which to take measurements, visiting some every day. The frequent appearances day after day of an old black Studebaker with side curtains and a strange moveable aluminum rod protruding from its top aroused both curiosity and suspicion and we were interrogated by many people including motorcycle policemen.

By the spring of 1933 Henry and I had completed our measurements and worked on reducing our data for the final draft of the dissertation. We drew one of the first field strength maps ever made at a wavelength of 5 meters. Its contours showed how the strength of the waves from the transmitter on the Physics Building decreased with distance over different types of terrain. With the advent in later years of TV and FM broadcasting at wavelengths of about 5 meters, similar maps became a standard requirement to determine the coverage of a station.

Early in May we sent a shortened version of the dissertation to the Institute of Radio Engineers in New York for publication in the *Proceedings*. Later that month Henry and I each passed our individually-held final oral examination and received our Ph.D. degrees at the June commencement exercises at Ferry Field. I was 22 years old at the time, although my 23rd birthday was later that month.

Gerald Ford, later to become the 38th President of the United States, was also attending the University of Michigan at that time. He was a star center on the football team. I knew about him then and although he did not know about me I like to think that at sometime we had passed near each other on the Diagonal walk.

Henry Muyskens returned to the state of Washington with his wife and son. Somewhat later I presented a talk on our 5 meter measurements

---

†Inventor of the screen-grid tube.

3. "The frequent appearances day after day of an old black Studebaker with side curtains and a strange, moveable aluminum rod protruding from its top aroused both curiosity and suspicion."

before the Detroit Section of the Institute of Radio Engineers of which I was an active member.

That fall our article with field strength map appeared in the September issue of the *Proceedings*. The lead article in the very next issue of the *Proceedings* was by Karl G. Jansky on "Electrical Disturbances Apparently of Extraterrestrial Origin." In this article Jansky indicated for the first time that the "steady hiss type static" he had noted only a year before appeared to come from a fixed direction in space, that is "the waves come from some source outside the solar system."

Two years later I heard Jansky present some further results at a National Convention of the Institute of Radio Engineers in Detroit. In this talk Jansky reported that the radio waves he had discovered were coming from our Milky Way galaxy and that he obtained the greatest response when his antenna pointed at the center of our galaxy. Jansky had made a giant step, but it attracted little attention. There were scarcely two dozen persons in Jansky's audience and I was personally responsible for bringing five of them.

* * * * *

Jansky was a radio engineer with the Bell Telephone Laboratories. He had been assigned the problem of studying the direction of arrival of thunderstorm static. Such information could be useful to the Bell system because, if a predominant direction were found, the beam antennas for the trans-Atlantic radio telephone might be arranged to discriminate against the static, thereby improving the quality of the telephone connection. In 1931, to investigate the problem, Jansky built a Bruce beam antenna a hundred some feet long at Holmdel, N.J. for operation on a wavelength of 15 meters. The antenna was mounted so that it could rotate and scan the horizon through 360° once every 20 minutes like a slow-motion merry-go-round. Jansky connected the antenna to a receiver and a pen-on-paper recorder. The following year (1932) he reported that he could identify three types of static: (1) from local thunderstorms, (2) from distant thunderstorms, most of which were in a southerly direction (this information would be useful in designing the trans-Atlantic beam antennas), and (3) "...a steady hiss type static of unknown origin." Jansky noted that the direction of the steady hiss-type static changed slowly, going almost completely around the compass in 24 hours.

In his October, 1933, article and 1935 convention talk Jansky went on to show that the steady hiss type static came from the Milky Way. I didn't realize it then and I don't think anyone else did but radio astronomy had been born!

* * * * *

The summer of 1933 while I was still working in the Physics Building, Arthur Adel, a fellow graduate student, came into the room.

"John, you know the one centimeter rig down the hall that Cleeton built for ammonia line absorption measurements?" he asked.

"Yes, Art," I replied, "what about it?"

"Well," he continued, "I have been thinking about the sun and sunspots and have an idea that there might be some radio emission from the spots, maybe strong enough at one centimeter wavelengths to detect with Cleeton's equipment."

"What makes you think so, Art?" I countered.

"Well, it's like this," Art replied. "Some pictures of sunspots show a swirling structure like that of a vortex. The sun has a magnetic field and if it is twisted around and charged particles are present, there might be radiation which would be greater than expected from an ordinary blackbody radiator, and maybe Cleeton's gear could pick it up. You're a radio man, John. Would you help me set it up?"

"Sure," I said. "It seems like a slim chance but that really would be something."

Only weeks before Claude Cleeton and his advisor, Professor Williams, had completed some measurements of the ammonia spectrum confirming a strong absorption line at 1.5 centimeters wavelength which had been predicted theoretically a year or so before. Cleeton designed and built a number of special vacuum tubes called magnetrons to generate the centimeter waves. It was the first time such short waves had been generated with a vacuum tube oscillator. The tube elements were so small that Cleeton had to assemble them under a binocular microscope. He placed a tube in the field of a strong electromagnet situated at the focus of a 36-inch diameter World War I parabolic searchlight mirror. Nearby he mounted an identical searchlight mirror to intercept the beam from the first mirror. The second mirror was fitted with an iron-pyrite phosphor-bronze crystal and galvanometer indicator. This combination acted as the receiving system. Between the two mirrors he suspended a yard square rubber bag filled with ammonia gas. The amount of signal received through the gas bag as the wavelength was changed gave data for the ammonia absorption spectrum.

The equipment was beautifully conceived and built. Professor Williams waxed ecstatic over Cleeton's abilities and was very excited about the results. We were not aware of it then but Cleeton and William's experiment was one of great historical significance, being the first microwave spectroscopy measurement. It ushered in the new field of molecular microwave spectroscopy or the radio spectral measurement of molecules.

Cleeton and Williams agreed to let Art Adel and me use their centimeter wavelength receiver for the sun test. It was easy for us to arrange the equipment for the test and make the observations. Our results were negative; there was no sign at all of any radio emission from the sun.

Why weren't we successful? Because the receiver was too insensitive. Nowadays radio emission from the sun is routinely observed at centimeter wavelengths but receivers a million times more sensitive are available. Strong emission is often observed from regions around sunspots. So Art Adel's idea that sunspots might be a source of radio emission was correct. But this type of radiation from the sun is strongest at meter wavelengths instead of centimeter wavelengths. In 1933 when we made our sun test, radio receivers were available at meter wavelengths with much higher sensitivity than the centimeter receiver we used. In retrospect it would have been better if Art and I had tried using the 5-meter receiver Henry Muyskens and I employed for the field strength survey around Ann Arbor. If we had built a beam antenna and connected it to the 5-meter receiver we would have improved our chances of detecting solar radio emission. But, then again, we might not have been successful because late in 1933 sunspots were at a minimum. Had we tried, however, about 5 years later in 1938 when sunspots were a maximum our chances of success would have been excellent.

Lesson: To succeed you need to be in the right place, with the right equipment, doing the right experiment, at the right time.

Ours was a radio astronomy experiment and Art and I were "radio astronomers" for a moment in the year 1933. Although our results were negative we were on the right track. The important thing is not that we failed but that we tried; because at that time no one knew whether the sun emitted any radio waves at all.

CHAPTER 6

A LITER OF BENZENE

"Excuse me please. Are you Fraulein Hoffmeister?" I asked in my best German.

"No," she replied with a friendly smile, "but won't I do?"

She was an attractive young brunette wearing a black hat and a close-fitting bright green coat with a broad tightly-drawn red belt. It was nine o'clock at night. We were standing at the Kurfurstendamm street entrance to the Berlin U-bahn (Untergrund-bahn) or subway.

It was to be a blind date. Ursula Hoffmeister's name had been given to me by a friend who said that she could speak English and wanted to meet Americans for practice in English conversation. In return, I was told, she might help me with my German. The previous evening I had reached Ursula by telephone and in a mixture of German and English we had agreed to meet at the Kurfurstendamm station at nine. She would be easy to recognize, she said, because she had dark hair and would be wearing a black hat and a green coat.

I had arrived by subway a little before nine and as I came up the stairs to the Kurfurstendamm street entrance I was startled to see no less than three brunettes standing there all wearing black hats and coats with some green of one shade or another. They all watched me intently but none made a move. So I walked over to the one with the red belt and asked if she were Fraulein Hoffmeister. Her answer was typical of the ones I got from the other two.

The significance of their remarks failed to register. I was so incredibly naive that it was only later when the full realization struck. I had been talking to some of Berlin's ubiquitous "ladies of the night."

I stood at the top of the stairway from the subway and watched the people coming up. After a while a young woman with green coat and black hat trudged up slowly. She paused at the top and looked around. I went over and asked if she were Fraulein Hoffmeister. No, she wasn't. So I continued to wait. Presently another girl came up who fitted Ursula's description but the answer was no again. It was now almost ten o'clock. Had I misunderstood? With Ursula alternating between German and English over the telephone and my replying partly in one language and then the other there was a good chance for a mixup. Could it be the wrong day, or the wrong time, or was there a different subway entrance I should be at?

I was debating these possibilities when I heard another subway train rumbling to a stop below. Then a crowd began to surge up the stairs.

Near the bottom of the stairs my eye caught a beautiful, slender, dark-haired girl weaving through the crowd and flying up the stairs two steps at a time. She was wearing a bluish-green coat and a black hat! Could this be Ursula? When she reached the top she looked around. She spied me and came toward me directly.

"Are you Fraulein Hoffmeister?", I asked almost automatically.

"Yes," she beamed, "and you must be John!"

She was out of breath and seemed nervous but before I could say another word she grabbed my hand and tugged me off with her into the night.

*   *   *   *   *

It was February 1934. I was living at the Amerikanische Kirche (American Church) on Motzstrasse at Nollendorf Platz in Berlin with my brother-in-law Dr. Edward Ramsdell. He was an ordained Methodist minister and was preaching at the church, which was attended by many of the Americans living in Berlin. We lived in an apartment connected to the church.

In 1931 Edward had married my sister Margaret who was 7 years older than I. After the wedding in Ann Arbor they went to live in Boston where Edward was working on his doctors degree. Less than a year later Margaret was killed when their apartment building exploded. A gas main leading into the basement had broken and explosive fumes had filled the building. Edward and Margaret were the only persons in the building at the time. They smelled the fumes, called the gas company, and went outside. They were on the sidewalk outside standing hand-in-hand when the building blew up and buried them under tons of bricks and debris. Miraculously Edward was spared.

Edward and Margaret were deeply in love and intensely devoted. Their marriage was full of promise. Then Margaret was gone. The blow to Edward was devastating. With a heavy heart he completed his degree requirements and took the pulpit of a church in Michigan. But he was restless.

In earlier years Edward had acted as a tour guide throughout Europe. He could speak French and German. Late in 1933 he received an invitation to fill the pulpit of the American Church in Berlin during the winter and spring of 1934. He accepted eagerly and invited me to go with him. I had just gotten my doctors degree and a trip to Berlin was an exciting prospect.

We crossed the stormy winter Atlantic on the newly commissioned S.S. *Washington* of the United States Lines. The U.S. had just recognized the Soviet Union and the newly appointed U.S. Ambassador William C. Bullitt was also aboard. Landing at Hamburg, we put up at a small hotel.

After supper, Edward stayed at the hotel but I went for a walk, heading in the cool night toward the center of town. I had not gone far before I came to a street blocked with people. Pushing my way through the crowd I saw that a torch light parade was in progress. Men in brown uniforms, each carrying a blazing torch, were marching in formation singing and chanting "Heil Hitler" and "Seig Heil, Seig Heil" (Hail to the Victor). Loud oom-pah oom-pah bands marched by. A group of men carrying large flags, one the German tricolor and another with a swastika passed.

Suddenly I heard angry shouting and a torrent of German behind me. Turning around I was confronted by a huge man in a brown shirt with swastika arm band. Slowly I became aware that he was addressing me.

What had I done? Why had he singled me out of this huge crowd? I had no idea. He bellowed and ranted. My German was at the level of slow, simple conversation. I was not prepared to cope with a rampaging, rapid-fire flood but I caught an occasional word. It gradually penetrated my consciousness that I had been picked as his verbal target because I hadn't saluted the swastika flag as it went by. I stood silent. He shouted louder and louder. Suddenly he stopped, turned on his heel, and strode off. He probably thought I was a "dummkopf" but he wanted to make an object lesson of me for the rest of the crowd.

After the parade had passed and the crowd began to disperse I observed that whenever a brown shirt met another brown shirt their right arms snapped up in the horizontal arm, hand open, palms down salute of the Nazis accompanied by "Heil Hitler!" shouted almost in unison.

Although Paul von Hindenburg was still officially President of Germany, he was old and ailing. Hitler had maneuvered his way into the Chancellorship and had become a virtual dictator. The National Socialist (Nazi) party was in power. Hitler's pictures were everywhere: on street posters, in store windows, on walls of homes. And wherever you went you heard the words "Heil Hitler," the new German greeting which took the place of "Hello," "Good Morning," "Good Day," and "Good Evening." I was learning rapidly that we had entered a mad, sick, tormented Germany where Adolph Hitler was God.

   *   *   *   *   *

Ursula and I walked some distance from the subway station without speaking. Finally she said,

"Are you angry?"

"What about?", I replied.

"I was late. I should be scolded," she said.

"No," I laughed, "I am just glad that you finally came. Where are we going?"

"To 'Die Insel'," she explained. "In English that means 'The Island.' It's a night club. All the young people in Berlin go there."

We walked several more blocks before we arrived at Die Insel. Although it was jammed we finally managed to get a table for two. Eating "eis" (ice or frozen flavored water somewhat like sherbet) and sipping beer we talked far into the night. German, English, German, English; our conversation alternated languages several times an hour. The effort to remember the German words and learn new ones left my brain numb and reeling.

Ursula told me something about herself. She lived at home with her mother and a sister. Her father had been killed on the Western Front in World War I. Both she and her mother worked. Ursula did typing and bookkeeping. I told her a little about myself.

It was very late. We walked back to the subway station. She went her way. I went mine.

In the weeks that followed I saw Ursula a number of times. As she got to know me better and felt reassured that I wasn't a Nazi agent she spoke more freely about herself.

"I am an atheist," she said, "and a communist and I hate the Nazis with a passion. Before Hitler came to power the communists had almost 5 million supporters in Germany but now all of us have gone underground."

The words "atheist" and "communist" jolted me. In an instant I realized that our philosophies were poles apart. We were from different worlds.

Ann Arbor was a stronghold of the Republican party. My father was an active Republican and had been an alternate delegate to the National Republican Convention in support of Herbert Hoover. My political beliefs were conservative. Communism seemed distant and irrelevant and communists as remote as Mars. Yet here was a beautiful, intelligent girl who said she was one. Ursula and I argued idealogies. She made no headway with me. I made no progress with her.

I believed in God, not so much because I had grown up in a very religious, Methodist atmosphere, but because I was deeply impressed with the mysteries of nature and the universe and could not believe that it all had just happened. I saw little connection between organized religion and God but to Ursula the church represented God and she had no use for the church. She found it hard to believe that with my scientific background I could live at a church. My answer was that there was no conflict between science and religion; both were seeking Ultimate Truth but by different routes.

One day I persuaded Ursula to stop by the American Church to meet Edward. To her surprise she found him to be friendly, warm and personable. While Edward talked, Ursula just stood there with her mouth open and said nothing. Edward was not what she had expected to meet; he was not a malevolent monster. She remarked about this many times afterwards.

My days were busy. I attended a course at the University of Berlin designed to help foreigners improve their German but now it included a nauseating amount of thinly disguised Nazi propaganda. The instructor lectured like a little Hitler about the glories of the Dritte Reich (Third Reich) and Germany's place in the scheme of things.

I visited with engineers and research workers at many radio and electrical factories and I talked with physicists at the Technische Hochschule (Technical Institute) and the Heinrich Hertz Institut für Schwingungsforschung. Heinrich Hertz was the first person to produce and measure radio waves (in 1888) and the institute named for him was devoted to wave research (Schwingungsforschung).

I visited transmitter sites at Tegal, Nauen, Zeesen, and Königswusterhausen where Germany's most powerful long and short wave radio stations were situated. Two of the transmitters, one on 357 meters and the other on 1571 meters operated with 300,000 watts of power. At Königswusterhausen there were 21 short wave stations and acres upon acres of huge antenna arrays filling the sky and beamed for all parts of the world. With so many miles of copper festooning the sky it hardly seemed like a "wireless" station.

On a Sunday afternoon I witnessed an airshow at Berlin's huge Tempelhofer Aerodrome. The most spectacular performance was a screaming dive from many thousands of feet straight down toward the earth by Ernst Udet, German ace, in an American-built Curtiss Hawk. I held my breath expecting him to crash, but at the last instant he pulled out of the dive and skimmed across the field only a few feet above the grass. Then he pulled back up into a vertical climb while spinning his wings like the blades of a helicopter until he rose so high his plane became a tiny speck in the sky. His maneuver traced out a gigantic standing "U" reaching a mile into the sky, U for Udet. It was a daring stunt which thrilled and delighted the crowd. Udet repeated it several times.

One evening Edward and I saw a performance of Wagner's "Tannhauser" at the Berlin Opera House. Sitting not far from us in a box was Hermann Goering, Hitler's corpulent air minister, resplendent in a medal-bedecked all-white uniform.

*   *   *   *   *

The Berlin amateurs invited me to address a monthly meeting of their radio club. I agreed and worked diligently preparing a talk on "Der Radioamateur in Amerika" for delivery in German. The meeting was held at night in a large beer hall in downtown Berlin. Hundreds of amateurs sitting at long wooden tables crowded the hall. It seemed that everyone was smoking enormous cigars. The air was blue with tobacco smoke and sitting at the speaker's table I seemed enveloped in fog. Out of the nicotine mists there appeared blond, big bosomed, dirndl-attired waitresses with beer mug laden trays. All evening they circulated, replacing empty mugs with full ones. These visions of Brunhilda were very friendly and when they found I was from the United States, they hung around me asking many questions about "Amerika."

A brown-shirted Nazi trooper with swastika arm band sat next to me at the speaker's table. I had learned that an official representative of the Nazi party had to be in attendance at every meeting held in Germany. There even was one in a front row of the American Church each Sunday when Edward preached. A copy of my talk had been given in advance to the Nazi representative. Apparently the talk was "satisfactory" because I was not asked to make any changes.

The brown-shirted trooper opened the meeting with a Nazi propaganda talk which ended with everyone chanting "Heil Hitler" and "Seig Heil, Seig Heil" in a thunderous roar while all stood like statues with arms outstretched in the Nazi salute. There were some items of business brought up by the club secretary. They needed money for a new tube in the club transmitter. They wanted volunteers to help with a club display at the Berlin Exposition. More beer was served. The smoke grew thicker. My sinuses begged for mercy. My eyes smarted. Finally the club chairman introduced me as "W8JK aus Amerika" (W8JK from America") and I began to read my talk in German. I was often complimented while in Germany on my pronounciation which had a trace of Bavarian accent. My grandfather Kraus came from Bavaria and my father had studied there while getting his doctors degree in mineralogy. I had carefully prepared the text with huge piles of verbs at the ends of sentences in proper German fashion. I hoped that my remarks would be understood.

The talk was strictly factual, with statistics about the number of amateurs, wavelengths, and power permitted and types of transmitters, receivers, and antennas used in the U.S. They seemed impressed that U.S. amateurs were allowed 1000 watts power. In Germany they were limited to 50 watts. I was in the middle of a sentence when tables rattled, the floor shook, and the whole building seemed to reverberate. I stopped and waited for the noise to subside. Had there been an earthquake? I didn't know. Slowly I connected the commotion with something I had said but I didn't understand what it was.

After the meeting one of the amateurs explained that I had been talking about wavelength allocations for amateurs in the U.S. and said that no phone transmission was permitted in the 40-meter band. This was what had brought the response because in Germany no phone was permitted on 40-meters either, but in France it was, and this was a matter of much annoyance to the German amateurs. The floor-shaking thunder was applause, German-style, done by stamping on the floor.

In a wooden-floored beer hall hundreds of stomping feet made quite a racket.

Several more times my talk was interrupted by foot stamping and at the end I got an especially loud "foot" from the amateurs. The chairman thanked me and asked me to convey their "Grüssen" (greetings) to the amateurs in America.

*   *   *   *   *

The Germans I met could be divided into three main groups: those enthusiastically supporting Hitler, those following the lines of least resistance and going along with him, and finally those opposed. There must have been many in the last group but they were very guarded in their statements and did not indicate their feelings unless they were certain they weren't talking with a Nazi or a Nazi agent. So how many were really opposed is hard to say. But some who did speak to me or Edward predicted that Germany was heading for disaster. How could a modern, intelligent people be led so astray? How could they pursue such an incredibly barbaric policy as Hitler's anti-Semitic persecution?

Those supporting Hitler said that he was reversing the bad effects of the ruinous inflation and depressed feelings following World War I. They cited statistics about increased production and income. Many such persons had rocketed from obscurity to power along with Hitler. An assistant's assistant in a large business corporation would become an ardent Nazi and overnight he would be dominant in the corporation. If the policies he suggested were not implemented at once he would report this to his party organization with dire consequences for his fellow corporation members. It was a dangerous game but the stakes were high and many played at it.

Many Americans were leaving Berlin. Attendance at the American Church services dwindled. The uniformed Nazi in a front row monitoring his sermons irked Edward. He felt he could do little good staying at the church so he gave notice that he was leaving in May. He suggested that we travel for a month in Russia. He had been all over Europe but never in Russia and now that the U.S. had established diplomatic relations we could go by making arrangements with the official USSR travel agency called Intourist.

We would leave the first week in May. But we were still in Berlin on May first and on this day the Nazis planned a gigantic celebration at Tempelhofer Aerodrome. In Russia May Day (May first) was the occasion of a huge communist celebration and the Nazis chose the same day for their own "Nationalen Feiertag" or national festival. We were told that the festival had been planned by Paul Goebbels, Hitler's Minister of Propaganda and Public Enlightenment.

Felix Cremers had taken me to the aerodrome a couple of days before the celebration to show me the public address system. Cremers was an engineer for Telefunken, the company installing the system. It was the most elaborate I had ever seen. Hundreds of loudspeakers atop 30-foot poles had been placed at regular intervals over an area of hundreds of acres. Cremers explained that each loudspeaker deflected the sound downward covering the area immediately below and around it and at most locations you were so close to one loud speaker as compared to the others that you effectively heard only one loud speaker, making echo or time delay effects negligible. Few outdoor public address systems even today are this well designed. Telefunken had gone to great expense to build a system that would project Hitler's voice with clarity and without echoes to a vast multitude.

On May first nearly two million brown-shirted Nazi storm troopers marched onto the field. I had arrived before noon and stood in an area reserved for spectators close to the speaker's platform. The troopers came from all over Germany and it took hours for them to parade in. Some groups carried short handled spades over their shoulders rifle-style but most carried nothing. A detachment of about 200 black-clad steel-helmeted soldiers goose-stepped to a position immediately in front of the speaker's platform. These were SS (Schutz Staffel) troops with rifles, great coats, and full combat equipment. They drew up at rigid attention. The Versailles Treaty restricted the German army or Reichswehr to 100,000 men, but the SS troops were not part of the army. They belonged to Hitler's private security guard.

Although the two million brown shirts were unarmed, the implications were obvious. They were disciplined like soldiers. All they needed was a rifle apiece and, presto, there would be an army of two million.

It was a warm, cloudless day. Hours passed as more troopers streamed onto the field. All stood at attention in straight evenly spaced rows. Suddenly one of the steel helmeted SS troopers fell to the ground like a toppled tree. He was carried off to a waiting ambulance. Then another fell. The heat was taking its toll.

The field was now filled with brown-shirted troopers. And among them I could now and then discern a prostrate trooper being carried off. The cry "Sanitäter" (first aid man) could be heard frequently. Some of the spectators near me passed out.

It was now mid-afternoon. No more storm troopers were arriving. Row on row of brown shirts reached to the horizon. Never before or since have I seen two million people in the same place at the same time.

Someone said that Hitler was coming. We all turned toward the nearest entrance to the field but the automobile approaching had only a driver. More brown-shirted troopers fainted, another SS trooper toppled over. Again there were rumors that Hitler was arriving but they proved false. Time dragged. I had been standing without food or drink under the blazing sun for four hours. Many had been there longer. The crowd grew impatient. Shadows were lengthening. But there was still no sign of Hitler or any dignitary.

Finally after what seemed like ages — it was about four o'clock — a string of open-topped Mercedes cars rolled through the entrance to the field. Although there had been music off and on all day over the public address system, now it was suddenly louder and more blatant. There was a resounding fanfare of trumpets and as the cars came closer I could see Hitler standing next to the driver of the second car. He was saluting in response to the crowd whose roar became deafening.

Although the troopers stood at attention they were extremely vocal. Hitler's Mercedes moved slowly across the field and stopped in front of the speaker's platform. He stepped out and moved with long measured strides to the platform and up the steps. Gigantic German flags a hundred feet high hung as a backdrop to the platform.

Hitler wore an unadorned military uniform with a Sam Browne style broad leather belt and narrow shoulder strap. Bareheaded, he was accompanied by Paul Goebbels, his wizened Propaganda Minister. While Hitler and Goebbels stood at attention, the strains of "Deutschland Über Alles" came over the loudspeakers and in a gigantic, sentorian chorus of two million voices, the troopers began to sing. After this they joined in the Nazi's "Horst Wessel" song, a second national anthem.

Then Goebbels went to the podium. The crowd grew silent. Goebbel's introduction consisted of three words,

"Der Führer spricht!" (The Leader speaks!)

Hitler then strode to the podium. A gigantic "Heil Hitler, Sieg Heil," rose from the crowd. Beginning his talk with the words,

"Meine Genossen und Genosserinen" ("My comrades" — both genders), Hitler spoke slowly and deliberately. Gradually, but very gradually, his tempo increased. The Telefunken public address system functioned flawlessly. There was no echo or distortion. Hitler's every word and guttural nuance were clear and distinct. Slowly he grew more impassioned and his words came faster; his head shook in emphasis. A lock of black hair fell across his eyes and he brushed it back with his hand. Now his words came in staccato bursts, faster and yet faster. He gestured dramatically; like a sorcerer he was bringing the crowd under his spell. Loud cheers from the crowd punctuated his sentences. He told a persuasive tale of Nazi accomplishments — how the Nazis were righting past wrongs, increasing production and leading Germany and her "master race" to a glorious future. He reeled off long lists of production figures on raw material tonnages, agricultural yields, and manufactured goods to support his claims.

The suspense and timing of the festival, the content of Hitler's talk and his method of delivery showed careful preparation by a master of mob psychology. He continued for nearly an hour. He reached crescendo heights and in a voice choked with emotion ended his talk. "Heil Hitlers" and "Seig Heils" rent the sky. Hitler stepped down from the platform, entered his car and, saluting the crowd, sped off. The troopers began to file out rapidly with military precision. Within an hour the aerodrome was nearly deserted. I headed for the nearest subway station and back to the church.

A few days later Edward and I left by train for Russia. We travelled across Poland to East Prussia. We stopped at Konigsberg visiting the birthplace and abodes of the great German philosopher Immanuel Kant. We recalled some of his words,

"The starry heavens above and the moral law within inspire the greatest awe."

Knowing what we know today about the heavens and the universe Kant's statement is as true now as when he wrote it.

We went on into Latvia and then on to Leningrad where we were met by an Intourist representative. In Russia we were no longer on our own. With Intourist interpreters as our guides, we followed a largely prearranged itinerary. The first night we saw Tschaikovsky's "Swan Lake" performed by the Russian State Ballet at the Leningrad Opera House. The next day we were taken on a round of museums, Houses of Culture, Czars' palaces, and the university.

Intourist had provided a woman interpreter, an open Lincoln touring car and a driver. After we all were in the car the driver got out and pushed. He jumped back in as we started to roll, engaging the gears to start the engine. I presumed the battery was dead but the reason was not apparent until we had driven some distance through the city. We were almost the only automobile to be seen and the driver tooted the horn continuously to clear a path through the throngs of people wandering in the street. There were so few motor vehicles that pedestrians had to be reminded of their occasional presence. Maybe the driver overdid it a bit but driving a car was a prestige symbol. With the horn going all the time the battery did not have a chance to recharge adequately and after nearly every stop the driver had to get out and push. Sometimes Edward, the interpreter and I pushed. We grew to accept this as a regular routine with the Intourist Lincolns.

Neither Edward nor I spoke Russian. We had, however, studied the Russian alphabet diligently and found that many of the words we saw became intelligible if we pronounced them. But we were happy to have an interpreter, usually a personable, intelligent young woman with an excellent command of English. She would continually slip in bits of communist propaganda. If we tried to argue a point or correct her, it was to no avail. So we let these pass but we played a game. Each night back at the hotel Edward and I vied with each other to see who could recall the most absurd propaganda story we had heard that day.

Although amateur radio had been permitted in the Soviet Union for some time it was only within the past year that communication had been allowed with amateurs outside Russia. Through Intourist I arranged to meet a number of Leningrad amateurs and visited some of their stations. After talking awhile to the amateurs through the interpreter I tried whistling the Morse code. This code and a host of concise abbreviations form an international language used by amateurs over the air. It worked. The amateurs grinned and whistled back. Now it was the interpreter who didn't know what was being said! But the Morse code was slow so our whistling was somewhat restricted in its scope. It was fun, though, and I used it elsewhere with amateurs I met in Russia.

We went on to Moscow, arriving six hours late. We learned that in Russia you were on time if you got there the same day as scheduled.

In Moscow I visited the studios of the Central Bureau of Short-Wave Broadcasting on Ilinka Karuninskaja Place. I had wanted to see a transmitting station and this was finally arranged. When some of the Moscow amateurs heard that I was going to visit one of the big radio stations they asked to come along; they had never been there either.

There were six Russian amateurs, our attractive interpreter Valentina, the driver and myself in the Intourist open Lincoln touring car. We were going to Mutusche about 30 kilometers north of Moscow where several stations were situated. One was RV49 operating on 748 meters with almost one-half million watts input. Another was RNE operating on 25 and 50 meters with almost 100 000 watts input. The countryside leaving Moscow was flat and monotonous and the dirt road leading to Mutusche was very rough. It was full of chuck holes and bumps and we bounced and jolted as we crawled along.

When we finally got to Mutusche we were escorted around by Boris Vitkevitch, the engineer in charge. It was mid afternoon and the big long wave half-million watt station RV49 was off the air. Although it transmitted only evenings, Boris turned it on for us. The transmitter occupied one end of a large building and when it came on it looked like Christmas. Colored lights and huge vacuum tubes glowed. Accompanying this was the sound of rushing water like a hundred commodes going all at once in a royal flush. The water was for cooling the tubes.

Then Boris showed us the short wave transmitters which were in a large spacious basement. Some of them had been built in America by RCA. Afterward we went outside and he explained the antenna systems. The big long wave station RV49 had a "flat-top" quarter-wave vertical antenna supported between two gigantic wooden towers 500 feet high. The antennas for the short wave stations were on smaller towers and were directed for Asia and North America.

On the way back to Moscow the amateurs and Valentina began to sing Russian songs with a slow beat almost in time with the bumps in the road.

From Moscow, Edward and I went to Gorki where we boarded a river boat for an 800 mile trip down the Volga. The boat was a 300-foot oil-fired, twin-screw steamer.

Two of the passengers wore green uniforms. They were Red Army colonels. One was tall and slender, the other short and overweight. We were told that they were on holiday leave. The first day out, while Edward and I were on deck, the tall colonel approached us with a checker board and box of chess men. By sign language he indicated that he would like to play chess. Edward was much better at the game than I, so he went with the colonel to a table in the forward observation cabin. They played for hours. Afterwards Edward said,

"He is the best chess player I have ever met. He beats me every time but it's a challenge to slow him down all I can."

Every day for the rest of the trip, Edward and the colonel were at the chess table for hours at a time. They had no spoken language in common, but to play chess they didn't need one.

The short, corpulent colonel bunked in the stateroom next to ours and often kept me awake at night. He snored a lot and whenever he rolled over in his bunk he made the paper-thin wall between his bunk and mine bulge out several inches. I fully expected to see him burst through the wall into my bunk at any moment.

One day while on deck I could see far ahead downstream a long multiple-span railroad bridge across the river. Two of the spans were down in the water resting at crazy angles. A ship's officer ordered me and the other passengers on deck to go inside and stay there until the boat had passed well below the bridge. We were told that it had been sabotage. We heard this word often; foul-ups or delays in the Five Year Plan were blamed matter-of-factly by our guides on sabotage.

We made stops at the Asiatic appearing cities of Kaza. and Samara. We also went ashore at Saratov. Four days after boarding at Gorki we left the boat at Stalingrad.

We were met at the dock by Tanya, our pretty Intourist guide. When she saw the heavy suitcases Edward and I were carrying she decided it might be too much for us to tote them the four miles to our hotel. She explained that Intourist had no Lincoln in Stalingrad but that if we would follow her she might be able to find a taxi. So lugging our suitcases, we followed her several blocks into the city, stopping in front of a rundown building. An old battered Fiat sedan stood at the curb. I wondered if this was our taxi. It was the only motor vehicle to be seen. We later learned that it was Stalingrad's only taxi although it bore no exterior lettering of any kind.

Edward and I waited by the Fiat while Tanya disappeared into the building. Eventually she reappeared with a young man in soiled work clothes. He looked at us and our suitcases. He talked and gestured to Tanya. Then he disappeared. Minutes later he returned smiling with a liter (quart) of benzene which he carefully poured into the Fiat's gas tank. Tanya explained that this should be enough fuel to take us to our hotel so we all got in the Fiat with the young man as our "taxi" driver. After several attempts to start the car the old Fiat coughed and wheezed alive and we lurched into motion.

We had not gone far when our driver slowed to a crawl. We were approaching some men standing in the street with a fire hose. The hose was connected to a hydrant and I could see that the water was turned on because a little water, but only a trickle, was coming out of the nozzle. The man holding the nozzle was trying to wash down the street and as we came closer I could see what the other 7 or 8 men were doing. Each was holding a cloth "bandage" around the hose at a place where it was leaking. In spite of these heroic measures a lot more water poured out through the holes than from the nozzle. To me this fire hose was symbolic of the Russia we saw, a country of vast potential with but a trickle to show for it.

The next day Edward and I were met at the hotel by Tanya with Fiat "taxi" and driver. They took us to the Stalingrad tractor factory. The factory representative who showed us around could speak German so we didn't need Tanya although she accompanied us. When we got inside the huge factory I thought I was back in the United States. Everywhere I looked I saw lathes, milling machines, stamping presses and drill presses with names in big letters like Cincinnati, Milwaukee, Eire, Bucyrus, Cleveland, Buffalo, Detroit, Chicago, Rockford. They were making 150 "Volga" diesel-engine farm tractors per day. They were using all American machinery and methods.*

Wherever we went in Russia there were always crowds of ragged people milling around the railroad stations or boat landings. They carried cloth sacks over their shoulders or at their sides. They looked gaunt and hungry. If I had a left over hard-boiled egg or cookie in the box lunch Intourist had provided, they accepted them eagerly. They used every possible pretext to board the train or boat. They would shove crumpled pieces of paper, any paper, at the conductor in the hopes that he would let them aboard. Sometimes a train started with many still trying to get on only to fall off or to squeeze inside just before we reached a narrow bridge.

We didn't know it at the time but Russia was experiencing a great famine in connection with their farm collectivization program and many people seemed convinced that no place could possibly be worse than where they were. Even though we Intourist visitors lived off the fat of the land it was slim fare. I was thin when I entered Russia and I lost 20 pounds there in one month. When I left Russia I was grateful that I had suspenders; no belt could have kept my trousers up.

From Stalingrad, Edward and I went to Rostov on the Sea of Azov. It took 23 hours to cover the 360 miles at an average speed of less than 16 miles per hour. And this in spite of the fact that part of the way we had two locomotives, one in front facing backwards but pulling forwards and one behind pushing. From Rostov we went to Kharkov and Kiev, to Lvov in Poland, through Czechoslovakia to Vienna, and finally to Munich, Germany.

From Munich we headed by bus for the quaint, colorful village of Oberammergau nestling in a scenic valley of the Bavarian Alps. We were there several days and saw the Passion Play enacted by the townspeople of Oberammergau in fulfillment of a vow made in 1633. The play was presented twice a week and nearly all of the villagers participated as members of the cast, orchestra, or stage crew. The first Passion Play had been given in 1634 and the year of our visit was the 300th anniversary. Edward and I lived at the home of Anni Rutz (Roo-ts)

---

*Eight years later, in and around this same tractor factory, the Red Army stemmed the advance of the Nazi war machine.

who was playing the part of the Virgin Mary. We ate our meals with her, her parents and two sisters in their kitchen at a plain bare wooden table. Anni was an extraordinarily beautiful, vivacious, personable brunette in her early twenties, the oldest of the Rutz daughters. She had taken the role of Mary only a short while before because the girl who had played it was pregnant, reportedly by a Nazi trooper. I wondered if the pregnancy was part of a Nazi plot to discredit the play.

We conversed with Anni often. She told us that the Nazis were exerting great pressure on the townspeople of Oberammergau to abandon the Passion Play. The fiercely independent villagers refused but were being compelled to shorten it. Late one afternoon Anni came out of the Rutz living room in tears. She had been in there behind closed doors almost all day with three uniformed Nazis who cut the play from six hours down to two.

From Oberammergau Edward and I went to Garmische Partenkirchen in the Bavarian Alps where we saw preparations for the winter Olympics. From there Edward went back to Berlin. I returned to Munich. There I stopped at the house on Nordendstrasse where my father had lived while he attended the University of Munich three decades earlier. It appeared just like he had described it.

From Munich I motored to Wurzburg where I visited the university laboratory in which Wilhelm Roentgen had discovered x-rays in 1895. Looking at the equipment he had used I tried in my mind to recreate the scene. Then at Mainz I boarded a steamer which floated down the Rhine past scores of towering, massive castles in a setting right out of the Middle Ages. In Hamburg I met Edward where we boarded the S.S. *Washington* for our return to America. We had visited eleven European countries and had travelled 3000 miles in the Soviet Union. We had been in Europe for six months and we looked forward to getting home.

After we landed in New York Edward went on to Michigan while I stayed for a week in and around New York. I visited many scientific laboratories and radio factories. I also travelled down the Atlantic coast of New Jersey to visit Bell Telephone Laboratory field stations where short wave experiments, such as Jansky's pioneering cosmic noise measurements, were in progress.

Some weeks after returning to Ann Arbor I drove with some other radio engineers to the WLW transmitter site near Hamilton, north of Cincinnati, Ohio. At that time WLW was transmitting with one-half million watts input on an experimental basis. Standing near the base of the huge antenna tower, it was possible to draw sparks by touching the person beside you. If the spark could be maintained you could hear the music or speech being transmitted. The WLW engineers told us about other strange effects produced by the super high power. In nearby farm houses lights often shone brighter when the wall switch was turned off than when turned on and one farmer's wife toasted bread in a toaster connected to their receiving antenna. Some time later WLW reduced power back to 50 000 watts which is the standard maximum allowed in the U.S.

In the space of a few months I had visited the transmitting sites of WLW in the U.S., RV-49 in Russia, and DJA and DJB in Germany, all with powers approaching or equal to one-half million watts. They were at that time the world's most powerful broadcasting stations. If some of their many watts escaped the earth, how far would they travel and who, out there, might hear them?

CHAPTER 7

SULPHUR DIOXIDE

Ernie Abbott was a specialist on noise-reduction in machinery and would have been a good teacher but he worked full time on research.

Stockily built, young and energetic, his philosophy in attacking a problem was to break it down into component parts, the more and the smaller the better, and then to deal with these both individually and collectively.

When I received my doctorate in 1933 during the great depression, jobs were very scarce. After returning from Europe I felt lucky that I was hired to work on the "Norge Project" in the University of Michigan Physics Department under Ernie's supervision. The Norge Corporation in Detroit manufactured refrigerators using a unique rotary-type compressor pump with sulphur dioxide as the coolant. The compressor was highly efficient, but had an objectionable knock. The Norge people had engaged the university to study the problem and suggest ways of making it quieter.

Ernie Abbott and I worked in close consultation with Floyd Firestone, an assistant professor in the Physics Department. Floyd was young, slender, strikingly handsome, good humored and artistic. His specialty was acoustics and I had studied it with him a few years earlier.

My work on the Norge project began by setting up a Norge refrigeration compressor unit in operating condition in a basement room of the Physics Building. A microphone and sound level meter were placed near by to measure the compressor noise. To find out how the knocking was related to pressure changes in the pump, I designed a piezo-electric pressure-sensing unit for the pump chamber. For this I cut and ground a small wafer of quartz for which my experience in grinding quartz crystals came in handy. Weeks went into getting the system to work properly, but at last I got consistent noise measurements and could display gas pressure variations over a complete cycle on an oscilloscope screen.

Firestone suggested cutting small passages in the wall of the pump chamber to reduce the pressure fluctuations. I tried a number of variations of his idea. Some were ineffective; others were encouraging. Each change meant taking the compressor pump apart, modifying a component, putting all the parts back together, filling up with sulphur dioxide and running more measurements, over and over again.

Enough residual gas was absorbed in the lubricating oil that every time I took a compressor pump apart the room filled with the pungent, penetrating stench of sulphur dioxide gas. I gradually became accustomed to the smell and must have developed a considerable tolerance, because visitors entering the room often stopped and gasped. Then, in panic, they rushed out slamming the door behind. Looking up from my work on the compressor, I usually was startled and puzzled until I realized that the sulphur dioxide fumes must be quite strong.

4. Measuring the noise of the Norge compressor amid the pungent vapors of sulphur dioxide.

Sometimes during tests a leak occurred and huge amounts of gas escaped. I kept a big jug of liquid ammonia handy for such emergencies and sloshed it around to partially neutralize the sulphur dioxide. But even so, a great deal of the gas escaped into the ventilating system and was pumped throughout the Physics Building. Irate professors and students from all parts of the building stormed into the room and converged on me with watering, smarting eyes. Coughing and wheezing, they demanded that the project be stopped. Ignoring their threats, I opened the windows and left the room, closing the door behind me to wait for the fumes to dissipate. I did promise to be more careful and fortunately such occurrences were rare. (Present day environmental protection agencies impose stiff penalties against factories whose smokestacks belch even a little sulphur dioxide. It's really not good for either animals or plants.)

Eventually Firestone's ideas began to pay off, and we found that the introduction of a small relief passage near the exhaust port of the compressor pump was effective. It resulted in a gradual, as contrasted to a sudden, equalization of pressures in the pump chambers providing for smoother, quieter operation. At the same time there was no noticeable reduction in efficiency. The Norge people liked the idea, and soon new, quieter models were in production incorporating the modification.

CHAPTER 8

THE ATOM SMASHER

"Hello W-6-I-T-H, Berkeley, California. This is W-8-J-K, Ann Arbor, Michigan, calling you on schedule." I was speaking into the microphone of a 500 watt transmitter in my bedroom. I sat at a desk loaded with equipment. Bob Thornton was sprawled across my bed while Ernest Lawrence and Jim Cork were sitting on one side. The big Eimac tubes of the transmitter glowed red and white. The pointers on the front panel meters danced as I spoke. There were wires and cables everywhere. Two wires from the transmitter disappeared through holes drilled in a glass window pane, running to a field south of the house where I had erected a Bruce beam antenna.

It was seconds after midnight on the sixteenth of July 1936. The beam antenna was not visible in the darkness outside but I had connected small flashlight bulbs to the antenna and these could be seen blinking on and off with every word I spoke. I continued calling to give W6ITH a chance to tune me in,

"Hello W6ITH. This is W8JK calling. Do you read me Reg? Come in please."

I threw a switch which turned the transmitter off and the receiver on. The loudspeaker boomed,

"Hello W8JK. This is W6ITH replying. Good evening, John. You're Q5 R9 (amateur jargon for loud and clear) here in Berkeley. Don Cooksey and Ed McMillan from the lab are here. How do you receive me?"

"W6ITH from W8JK," I replied. "You're Q5 R9 also here in Ann Arbor, Reg, and good morning to you, Don, and Ed. Ernest Lawrence, Jim Cork and Bob Thornton are here and I'm going to turn the mike over to Ernest now."

I gave the microphone to Ernest who said,

"Hello Don, Ed and Reg. Maybe I should say good morning because it's after midnight here. It's a new experience and a real thrill to talk to you by radio. We should do it regularly. The big news here is that we got a beam on the Michigan cyclotron. It's about 50 microamps at 4 million volts but we haven't shimmed the magnet carefully yet so I know we can go higher. My lectures at the Physics Colloquium are going well. The students and others here are a stimulating group and I'm enjoying it all. I'm keeping up on my tennis and doing some swimming too. Please tell Molly. (Molly was Ernest's wife.)

"What's the status on the new tank (acceleration chamber), Don?" Ernest continued. "Is it assembled yet? I'm anxious to know. I'm giving he mike back to John."

I took the microphone and said,

"This is W8JK standing by for W6ITH. Come in please."

Reg answered, "All OK John and Ernest. Very good. Here's Don Cooksey." Taking the microphone Don said,

"Hello Ernest, Jim, Bob and John. Congratulations on the Michigan cyclotron. That's very exciting. It's great to hear your voice, Ernest. It's just like you're right here in the room. Good news on the tank. It went together yesterday and we have gotten most of the welding done. If we don't have any unforseen problems we should be able to seal it and put it on the pumps tomorrow to check for leaks. The new aluminum parts look beautiful, Ernest, and the machining is about done on the new oscillator tubes. Do you have any suggestions about the mounting for the target? We haven't decided yet exactly how we're going to install it. Now back to you."

Ernest took the microphone again and continued his dialogue with Don Cooksey. Back and forth it went. First Ann Arbor. Then Berkeley. It was not possible to switch fast enough between transmitting and receiving to converse as in an ordinary dialogue so the conversation was really like a series of monologues.

Ernest and Don continued to discuss the new components being built to increase the capability of the Berkeley cyclotron or "atom smasher" with its 85 ton magnet. On some transmissions from Berkeley, Ed McMillan took the microphone while Bob Thornton and Jim Cook took their turns at the "mike" in Ann Arbor. The Ann Arbor-Berkeley conversation continued past one in the morning Ann Arbor time when I signed off with W6ITH.

*   *   *   *   *

In 1936, Ernest Lawrence was America's most famous native-born physicist. His cyclotron was making headlines. He was being showered with medals and honorary degrees. His picture soon appeared on the cover of *Time* magazine and three years later he received the Nobel prize. Ernest later remarked to me, "Once the honors started coming, it was like a row of dominoes going down."

From his home in South Dakota, young Ernest had gone via the University of Minnesota and the University of Chicago to Yale where he earned his Ph.D. and taught physics. In 1928 he sped west in a Reo Flying Cloud coupe to the University of California to accept an associate professorship in physics. Two years later at the age of 29 he was promoted to full professor, in spite of strong opposition by some who said that he was too young. During the next few years he invented the cyclotron and with a team of co-workers developed it into an instrument capable of disintegrating almost any element placed in the path of its deuteron beam. By 1936 his cyclotron was producing a 100 microampere beam of deuterons at the unprecedented energy of 5 million electron volts.

Lawrence's cyclotron was ushering in the new age of high energy or nuclear physics and subordinating the older atomic physics. Atomic physics dealt with the electron shells around the atom. To strip these electrons from the atom did not require very high energies. The new high-energy physics dealt with the disintegration of the tiny inner nucleus or core of the atom and this required atomic projectiles with energies of millions of electron volts. Only particles of such high energy could penetrate the small, hard nucleus of the atom and disintegrate it causing its transmutation, or the creation of new elements and isotopes. Lawrence's cyclotron was the first machine able to do this on a grand scale.

Lawrence's work moved the focal point of high-energy physics from Europe to California. He attracted a group of about a dozen talented physicists and engineers to work with him on the cyclotron in his Radiation Laboratory. Don Cooksey and Ed McMillan were two of the lab members. Cooksey was a 44 year old bachelor millionaire physicist from Yale. He became Lawrence's expediter and business manager. Ed McMillan came to the Radiation Lab from Princeton and busied himself with improvements in the measuring equipment and the cyclotron itself. The group at the Radiation Laboratory was unique in that there was no formal organization, and no paperwork, just a group of people working together. Each did what he saw needed doing.

Life at the lab pulsed with excitement. New radioactive elements and isotopes were created almost daily. The ancient alchemists' dream of transmuting the elements became commonplace. There was a constant effort to upgrade the cyclotron performance and a sense of big things ahead.

Lawrence had come to Ann Arbor to lecture in the summer Physics Colloquium. One evening he was scheduled to give a special lecture at seven thirty. A large crowd packed the Physics auditorium but at seven thirty there was no Lawrence. We waited and waited. Finally, Lawrence trotted in breathlessly forty five minutes late and apologized. Bob Thornton had taken him to the Dearborn Inn 25 miles east of Ann Arbor for supper. Discussing isotopes, barrier potentials and beam energies while they ate, they had lost track of time. Lawrence was unperturbed and plunged immediately into his lecture. It was stimulating and exciting, and well worth waiting for.

Bob Thornton had gone from McGill in Montreal to work with Lawrence at the Radiation Laboratory. In 1935, when Jim Cork, professor of physics at Michigan and his department chairman, Harrison M. Randall, were formulating plans to build a 100 ton cyclotron, they hired Thornton. They felt his experience with the Berkeley cyclotron would be of great value. The Michigan cyclotron with its 100 ton magnet would be the largest in the world and among the first of many cyclotrons to spring up outside of Berkeley.

Soon after Thornton came, I was also hired to work on the new cyclotron. I found more than enough to do installing the maze of electrical wiring and control circuits and the powerful radio frequency oscillator. The cyclotron lab was at the opposite end of the basement in the Physics building from the lab where I had worked on the Norge refrigerator compressor and inhaled more than my share of sulphur dioxide. In a sense I jumped from the frying pan into the fire because after the cyclotron began running I was drenched daily with gamma rays and beams of the new and mysterious neutrons. But more about this later.

During the summer of 1936 we finished assembly of the cyclotron including the wiring for all of the control circuits. Lawrence had been in and out of the cyclotron lab every day talking with Thornton, Cork and me about details and was on hand when everything was finally ready to go. The motor generator supplying the current for the huge magnet coils whined a steady high-C to the background sound of rushing water used to cool the big oscillator tubes. Sitting at the control console at the opposite end of the room from the cyclotron, Lawrence fiddled with knobs and checked indicators as he nursed the cyclotron into life. We watched the galvanometer, indicating the beam current, gradually increase. Like an organist working up to a crescendo, Ernest drove the current higher and higher. It leveled off around 50 microamperes. There was cheering, shouting, backslapping and dancing. The Michigan cyclotron was in operation! Magnetic resonance could be achieved in Ann Arbor as well as Berkeley!

Lawrence was enthusiastic. He always was. He had boundless energy, mental and physical. He was tall, handsome, athletic. He played tennis every day and liked to roller skate when he had the chance. Late one hot July afternoon he bounded into the cyclotron lab clad only in swim trunks and low shoes to talk to Jim Cork and me about an improvement we might make. He talked almost on the run because Bob Thornton was waiting for him outside in his Ford roadster to take him for a swim at Whitmore Lake.

One day Ernest mentioned to me that it had been many days since he had gotten a letter from the boys at the Radiation Laboratory and he wondered how they were doing. I told him that I might be able to help because I had an amateur short wave radio station and if I could set up a schedule with a Berkeley ham, then he could talk to the boys from the lab. He was so pleased with the prospect that I proceeded at once with arrangements.

I had heard of Reg Tibbetts, W6ITH. Radio was both his hobby and profession. He had attained national prominence in radio circles by providing radio communication between the construction barges, foundation sites, and shore installations of the San Francisco-Oakland Bay Bridge then being erected. It was said to be the first time efficient, reliable radio voice communication had been provided for a big construction job. His communication system proved to be of immense value in getting the right concrete barge to the right location at the right time. Tibbetts used 5-meter waves! As Henry Muyskens and I had found, these waves were admirably suited for line-of-sight communication.

I telegraphed Tibbetts requesting a schedule for midnight on the morning of July 16 and, as already related, it was very successful.

Because Ernest was eager to have more Ann Arbor-Berkeley radio talks Reg and I set up a schedule for about once a week. We had them regularly through that summer and fall and into the winter months. Ernest was at my station several times. After he returned to Berkeley later in the summer, he was a frequent visitor at W6ITH and sometimes he brought Molly along. Don Cooksey was at W6ITH regularly and, at one time or another, nearly all of the Radiation Laboratory workers, including Luis Alvarez, Franz Kurie, and John Livingood, came for the talks with Ann Arbor. Both Bob Thornton and Jim Cork were almost always at the Ann Arbor end and other Michigan physicists, including Harrison M. Randall and Dick Crane, came on occasion.

On the night of October 1, 1936, Robert Oppenheimer of the University of California physics department was on hand at the Berkeley end. Oppenheimer was the theoretical physicist whose advice Lawrence sought on problems with the cyclotron and its products. Oppenheimer had a brilliant, penetrating mind that made him one of the giants of theoretical physics.

    *   *   *   *   *

I was not aware of it then, but at that very time in October 1936 Robert Oppenheimer had begun to work on the problem of what would happen to a star when it stopped burning. He deduced that without internal heating the star would collapse under its own gravity into a cold superdense neutron core. For example, his studies suggested that if the sun's fires eventually go out it will collapse from its nearly million mile diameter to a diameter of only a few miles and the rotation will speed up from one revolution per month to many revolutions per second. Its density will be so high that a cubic inch would weigh as much as a cubic mile of lead. With one of his graduate students, G.M. Volkoff, he published his study in 1939.

Oppenheimer went even further and suggested that continued gravitational contraction could cause the star to collapse to an even denser state, like the earth crushed to the size of a pea. It would be such a small ultra-dense core as to be invisible. Its gravitational field would be so strong that not even light could escape. Oppenheimer published his work on these invisible objects later the same year with another graduate student, H. Snyder.

In their article they stated,

"When all thermonuclear sources of energy are exhausted a sufficiently heavy star will collapse . . . and this contraction will continue indefinitely. Light can escape only over a progressively narrower range of angles."

By implication the star becomes invisible.

Although there had been speculation that neutron stars (or neutron cores) might occur, Oppenheimer and Volkoff were the first to analyze the problem quantitatively.

Nearly 30 years passed. Then in 1967 the astonishing pulsars were discovered at the Cambridge, England, radio observatory and these turned out to be Oppenheimer's neutron stars. Unfortunately, Oppenheimer did not live to see his predictions fulfilled. He died only a few months before the pulsars were discovered.*

The invisible, ultra-dense cores that Oppenheimer and Snyder proposed are now referred to as "black holes." Currently there is much interest in them because in 1974 a few peculiar stars were found which behave as though they may be accompanied by a black hole. A black hole can not be observed directly but its presence may be inferred from its gravitational effects on a companion star. It may be only a matter of time before astronomers can say with complete assurance,

"Yes, there are black holes in the sky."

And they may be very common.

Oppenheimer's brain-children, the pulsars and black holes, are so fantastically esoteric as to make the most outlandish science fiction seem tame by comparison.† To paraphrase J.B.S. Haldane,

"Nature is not only more fantastic than man imagines but it is more fantastic than man *can* imagine."

Fact outstrips fancy!

*   *   *   *   *

The Ann Arbor-Berkeley talks were like a seminar on the latest high-energy physics but they had the informal, jocular atmosphere of a corner table in a club or bar. Words like beam current, target, isotope, deuteron

---

*In 1974 Antony Hewish of Cambridge University was awarded a Nobel prize for his discovery of pulsars.

†During World War II Oppenheimer was Director of the Los Alamos Laboratory and with Ernest Lawrence became a principal architect of the atomic bomb. After the war Oppenheimer was appointed Director of the Institute for Advanced Study at Princeton.

and neutron were in every sentence. We heard of recent articles in scientific journals and news of visitors. But sprinkled throughout were personal anecdotes, many humorous, about life at Berkeley and Ann Arbor.

Other famous physicists who visited my station, but not necessarily to talk to Berkeley, were Werner Heisenberg, Enrico Fermi and his wife Laura, Wolfgang Pauli, and Nils and Mrs. Bohr. Pauli had broken his shoulder while diving at Whitmore Lake and went around all one summer with his arm held straight out by a brace in what looked like a caricature of a Nazi salute.

There was lots of activity in the Physics Building during the summer. The Physics Colloquium, with its roster of world-renowned scientists, including many Nobel laureates, attracted many graduate students. Many physics professors from other institutions also came to learn. But all that went on was not cold, impersonal science.

Only a few of the visitors had automobiles. Being young and helpful I often assisted with transportation. On one occasion I called for a visiting physicist lecturing at the Colloquium. A handsome, likeable, distinguished-looking man well past middle age, he asked me to drive to a rooming house to pick up a graduate student who had been attending his lectures. She was a bubbling, smiling, laughing beauty with sensuous, wavy chestnut hair tumbling down over her shoulders. They made a dashing twosome — happy, animated, carefree. You might have thought he was a doting father out on a lark with his lovely daughter. I drove them to the bus station; they were leaving for Lake Michigan and a week-end cruise on a Great Lakes steamer. I don't know if the girl got an A in the course but I presume she did.

Initially, my job on the cyclotron had to do with electrical circuitry and construction. After the cyclotron was in operation I helped keep it running and also did research with it.

Jim Cork had suggested that we bombard palladium, a silver-like element, with deuterons in the cyclotron. We placed a sample of shiny palladium foil in the target box of the cyclotron, and after about an hour's bombardment we removed the foil and took it to another room where we placed it on an electroscope, like a Geiger counter, to measure the radioactivity which had been produced. We measured the sample every few minutes for several hours and then every few hours for the next week. The manner in which the radioactivity decayed gave clues as to transformations which had occurred. To study the energy of the electrons emitted from the samples, we took hundreds of photographs of their tracks with a Wilson cloud chamber. I laboriously measured the curvature of each of the tracks and plotted graphs and histograms of their energies.

Jim Cork and I presented our findings at the spring 1937 meeting of the American Physical Society in Washington, D.C., and we published a more complete discussion of our work in the *Physical Review*.

We reported that bombardment of palladium by six million electron volt deuterons in our cyclotron produced several radioactive isotopes of both palladium and silver. We had actually transmuted some of the palladium into silver. We had succeeded in doing what the ancient alchemists had tried in vain to do.

Unless shut down for repairs or improvements, the cyclotron ran day and night. Radioactive materials were produced for many different experiments like the one Jim Cork and I did on palladium. We also made radioactive phosphorous for university botanists so they could study how this element was taken from the soil and diffused through the plant structure. Techniques using radioactive elements as tracers were just emerging. They were among the many by-products of the cyclotron.

Our cyclotron had been designed as an experimental research instrument but we continually pushed it to the limits of its productivity and it often broke down, giving notice of the fact even at a distance.

The tank or acceleration chamber of the cyclotron was kept evacuated by large oil diffusion pumps which ran continuously. Sometimes, however, air leaked into the chamber faster than the pumps could remove it. This caused internal sparking, overloading the powerful radio transmitter and automatically shutting it off. By waiting a moment for the pumps to evacuate the chamber, the cyclotron operator could turn the transmitter on again and sometimes the cyclotron might run smoothly for a while. But if more sparking occurred, the transmitter would go off again. If, after many trials, it was not possible to keep the transmitter on continuously, the operator usually elected to shut down the cyclotron and search for the leak or other trouble.

The transmitter operated on 26 meters wavelength with more power than most broadcasting stations. However, the power was fed to the acceleration chamber instead of being radiated into space by an antenna. But, in a sense, whenever the cyclotron was running it was "on the air" because a small fraction of the power leaked out and was radiated. If I listened on my short-wave receiver at my home, about 3 miles away, it was easy to hear the cyclotron signal with its guttural tone whenever the machine was in operation. If the signal was steady and continuous I knew things were going OK but if the signal was off and on repeatedly it spelled trouble and I might rush to the campus to see if I could help.

Radio waves weren't the only thing the cyclotron was leaking. It produced prodigious amounts of neutrons and these permeated the whole laboratory. Their effect was strong even many paces from the machine. As a demonstration I would stand a few minutes at the control console, which was nearly 50 feet (15 meters) from the cyclotron, then walk away and down a long corridor to the room containing the electroscopes and counters used for measuring radioactivity. Removing a silver coin from my pocket and putting it on an electroscope, its pointer zoomed off scale! A few minutes in the cyclotron room had been enough for the silver piece to become highly radioactive and although the radioactivity decreased rapidly after I left, it was still very strong when I got to the electroscope.

If the neutron radiation did that much to a silver coin what was it doing to us who worked with the cyclotron? Were we servants to a monster? There was concern that we might be getting zapped. The effect of the neutron radiation was unknown. There had been a horrible toll among the first x-ray workers before the dangers of x-rays were realized and adequate precautions taken. We did not want to repeat that sorry tale.

So weekly blood tests were instituted for all members of the cyclotron team soon after the machine went into operation. The team now included Cork, Thornton, myself and a number of students. The Simpson Memorial Institute of the university was entirely devoted to blood studies. World-famous Dr. Raphael Isaacs was the director and he personally supervised the blood studies on the cyclotron team. Certain blood cells were known to be affected by x-rays. In particular, white cells, or leukocytes, would proliferate to the stage of leukemia. Isaacs wanted to monitor the count of the many types of white cells, the polymorpho nuclear neutrophiles, the lymphocytes, large and small, the monocytes, basophiles and eosinophiles, as well as the red cells. Perhaps the neutrons would be highly selective, affecting one cell type more than others. He wanted to find out.

A technician from the Simpson Institute became a familiar figure around the cyclotron laboratory. Carrying a tray of test tubes, glass plates, needles, sterile gauze, cotton and alcohol she cornered one cyclotron worker after another in order to draw blood samples. Skillfully, she would pierce an ear lobe, remove a drop of blood onto a small glass slide, cover it with another slide, then quickly draw the two slides apart, waving them to hasten drying, finally dropping them into special slots in her tray. She made several sets of slides and also drew more blood into a test tube from each individual on weekly visits. As a token of parting she placed a small piece of gauze or cotton on our ear lobes which we wore proudly as a badge of our profession.

Isaacs pointed out that cell counts vary widely among normal individuals and also from week to week for the same individual so it might take a long time, months or years, to establish any meaningful trends due to the neutrons.

"What I really need," he said, "are some post-mortems on your group. These could be quite informative."

In the rush to build the cyclotron no thought had been given to shielding or means of keeping the neutron radiation confined. Should we wait for the post-mortems or should we do something now? I favored doing something now, to build some kind of shield but this posed a real problem. To shield against x-rays or gamma rays a wall of lead bricks would suffice. But the neutron was a sly culprit, which had the mass of a proton but possessed no charge. The lack of a charge meant that the lead shielding would be ineffective; the neutron would go right through. The best means of stopping the neutrons appeared to be by absorbing their energy with large amounts of light elements. Water, enough of it, could do the trick but this would require the construction of large tanks.

I was the only one in the cyclotron group much interested in doing something about shielding. I talked to Jim Cork about it. He was nominally in charge. Although he agreed that something should be done he didn't give shielding a high priority. Michigan had the world's biggest cyclotron in operation. It was producing results. We could not afford to stop or slow down while we put in shielding. Besides we didn't have the money for shielding. Jim's attitude reminded me a bit of Admiral Farragut entering Mobile Bay during the Civil War. When told that the bay was heavily protected by torpedoes (mines) Farragut exclaimed,

"Damn the torpedoes, full speed ahead!" In the same way, Jim dared the neutrons to do their darndest.

I didn't give up. Maybe there was a cheaper way to get some shielding and one that wouldn't require a long shut down. Big steel water tanks would be too expensive and too difficult to install. I considered many alternatives short of flooding the laboratory and working in a diver's suit. Finally, a simple inexpensive arrangement evolved. Why not build a double wooden wall with a 3-foot space between and fill this space with damp or wet saw dust? It would meet the requirements of light element content, hydrogen, oxygen and carbon from both water and wood, and it would be relatively inexpensive. Furthermore, the walls would not need to be water tight, only damp proof.

I thought the scheme had merit but others either ridiculed it or were apathetic. The scheme generated all kinds of counter arguments, most of questionable validity like the ones people give now for not wearing seat belts. A frequent "argument" was that the saw dust would attract rats and mice and these could not be tolerated. Or where would we get so much saw dust? (They had never been to a saw mill.) Weeks and months dragged on. I was growing discouraged.

One day while I was seated at the control console operating the cyclotron, Ernie Abbott walked into the laboratory. He came over to me and began talking. The research organization, called the Physicists Research Company, which he had set up after leaving the university a short while before, was doing well. He had just gotten a contract with the Beloit (Wisconsin) Iron Works to quiet some of their machines. Beloit built huge paper making machines. The Kimberly-Clark Corporation had bought some of these for making kleenex tissues at their Neenah, Wisconsin, plant. These machines ran very fast, producing a continuous ear-splitting scream. The sound was so loud you no longer heard it, you *felt* it — like a knife in your ear! Even a short exposure to it could make you permanently deaf.* Kimberly-Clark had complained to Beloit that it was impossible to keep the machines properly adjusted because the operating crew refused to approach the machines when they were running. Beloit felt that it was imperative to do something.

Abbott had told the Beloit engineers he could provide them with a solution although at the time he had no idea how to do it. He simply had confidence in the research method and that through it a solution could be found. I listened to Ernie with interest while I kept my eye on the cyclotron gauges and meters, occasionally making an adjustment. Ernie then came to the real purpose of his visit. Would I come and work for him on the paper machine project? I said that I would like to think about it and call him. I then told him a little about the cyclotron and our research with it. I explained the shielding problem.

I casually mentioned that during the time he had been talking to me the silver coins in his pocket had become strongly radioactive. Ernie's eyes popped. His jaw dropped. Ernie had more respect for neutrons than Jim and he beat a hasty retreat for the door, calling as he went,

"Think it over, John, and call me soon."

Should I stay and split atoms or should I try to silence a screaming banshee with Abbott? It was a difficult decision but in a few days I called Abbott and told him I would come in two months, which was as soon as I could manage to leave.

I am glad to say that sometime after I left, shielding was installed but only after Berkeley had done it first!

While I was with the cyclotron my amateur radio activity involved much more than my schedules with Reg Tibbetts in Berkeley. It introduced me to the realm of antennas, leading to a deep involvement with them. So before I describe my experience with "The Kleenex Machine" let me go back a few years and relate my antenna tale.

---

*The noise was as loud as from the modern super-sonic Concorde on take off except that it was a scream instead of a roar.

CHAPTER 9

BEAMS FOR AFRICA

My antennas were simple and worked almost equally well for stations at all points of the compass. I was satisfied. After all, I had no preferred direction in which I wished to communicate.

Then one day in November 1933 I made contact with station ON4CSL in the Belgian Congo (now Zaire) in central Africa. The operator, Carroll Stegall, was an American missionary who had lived in the Congo for 20 years. Stegall hailed from Georgia and had a daughter, Sarah, in college in North Carolina. A letter from her took two months to reach him coming the last 20 miles on foot. Stegall sent me several messages, one for his daughter and some for other relatives. Stegall transmitted in Morse code while I replied with voice. His transmitter was very simple with power supplied by a generator which a native cranked by hand. His receiver ran off batteries.

During the following weeks I talked with him nearly every day, sending and receiving many messages thus reducing the round trip time for his correspondence from four months to a few days. We set up a regular schedule. Many days signals were strong and it was easy to communicate. But on other days signals were weak and communication was slow and tedious. Sometimes interference from other stations was a problem.

As time passed I began to think about the possibility of a beam antenna for my station, one which would concentrate my station's radiation in a preferred direction. If I constructed a beam antenna aimed at central Africa it would not only boost the strength of my signals there but would make Stegall louder at my end. It would also discriminate against stations in other directions and thus reduce interference. But a beam antenna would require more space than the simple types I had been using.

Our house on Arlington Boulevard was on a three acre lot with no near neighbors. The open fields were an invitation to experiment with beam antennas. What I wanted was one that would be effective but not too large and which could be supported between two poles no more than 40 feet high. But to locate the poles properly I needed to know the direction of the Congo and which way that was with respect to reference points in the field.

Ordinary maps were of no use for determing the direction. On a regular Mercator world map Calcutta is south east from Ann Arbor whereas its true direction is almost due north over the pole as can be determined by stretching a string on a globe. The string might be good enough for a rough idea but a more accurate value can be calculated with trigonometry so I pulled from the shelf a trig book I had used in college. What had been a casual interest in spherical trigonometry when I was a freshman now became an obsession.

After figuring out the direction, I next needed to relate it to points in the field for the two poles. I asked Professor Ed Young of the U of M civil engineering department, who was also a ham, to "lay down" Polaris (the north star) with his surveyor's transit and then swing off the direction I had calculated for Stegall's location.

5. In February 1935 "I constructed a folded antenna called a Bruce type which was identical to the one Karl Jansky used when he discovered radio waves of extraterrestrial origin except that Jansky's rotated while mine was fixed."

With poles erected I next constructed a folded antenna called a "Bruce type," named after the inventor, Edmond Bruce, an engineer at the Bell Telephone Laboratories. This antenna was identical to the one Karl Jansky used when he discovered radio waves of extraterrestrial origin (Chapter 5), except that Jansky's rotated while mine was fixed. Although the antenna had nearly 300 feet of wire, it was folded reducing the overall length to only 135 feet. I pulled it up between the poles set for my Africa beam.

On my next contact with Stegall he reported that the Bruce beam antenna gave "vastly better signals" compared to the simple antenna I used as a comparison. This was encouraging.

I wrote up my experiments on the Bruce antenna and some other types I had tried during the previous months and sent the material to a West Coast amateur magazine called *R/9* which published it in June 1935.

6. Talking with Carroll Stegall, ON4CSL, on his visit to my station, W8JK.

Maybe I wasn't entirely aware of it but antennas were really beginning to excite my interest. The idea that by bending a wire or arranging several wires near each other, radiation could be concentrated or beamed in a preferred direction held a real fascination. Even simple beam antennas could increase the radiation in a desired direction as much as a 5-fold increase in transmitter power. To raise the transmitter power that much was a lot more expensive than the wire, insulators and rope needed for the beam antenna. The beams from an antenna might not be as sharp as a searchlight beam but beams they were nevertheless.

The Bruce antenna was bi-directional with a beam eastward to Africa and one westward to Australia. My next step was to place more beam antennas for other directions. So I erected more poles in the field for other Bruce beam antennas aimed at Europe, Asia and South America. With more poles and more antennas the field began to take on the appearance of a forest of wires. I installed switches to quickly connect any one of the beams to my transmitter. The results began to show in the stations I was able to work.

By late 1935 and during 1936 I had communicated with many stations in Australia, Asia, Indonesia, New Zealand, Africa, South America and Europe. Nearly all were on voice from my station and either voice or Morse code from the foreign station. The Australian cities I worked read like a page from an atlas.

All the while I was also carrying on contacts with the Radiation Laboratory personnel at Berkeley through Reg Tibbett's station and maintaining a regular schedule once or twice a week with Carroll Stegall in the Congo. My experimenting and radio communications were done evenings and weekends while I was working days at the university.

Wherever there were amateur stations that I heard, I could work them. After putting out a CQ call on the Australian beam, I could hear my call letters (W8JK) in strong Australian accents from many stations as I tuned across the band.

"Allo, double-you eye-t jah-ee kah-ee" the voices intoned.

Entries in my logbook show that my signal was reported by some Australian stations as "the strongest American" or "the loudest phone." One Aussie told me that my signal was so loud it "paralyzed" his ear and another said, "You Yanks certainly know how to throw out a signal!"

I had the world at my finger tips and my knowledge of geography grew by leaps and bounds. The world was my oyster.

Then one day in January 1937 I received my copy of the *Proceedings* of the Institute of Radio Engineers. An article by George H. Brown of RCA entitled "Directional Antennas" caught my eye.* It was a long article loaded with mathematical equations, figures and graphs.

Brown took an important new step. He considered the power input to the antenna as constant and demonstrated that smaller spacings between wires could be used effectively than had previously been employed. One graph which caught my eye indicated that two wires one half-wavelength long and spaced one-eighth wavelength apart could produce a gain or improvement equivalent to a 2.5 fold increase in power. At 20 meters wavelength, one-eighth wavelength was only 2.5 meters or about 8 feet. This was a small, convenient spacing. †

Immediately I began to visualize how it might be possible to deploy such an array for 20 meters. The wires could be hung horizontally between

---

*A beam antenna is a directional antenna but with the implication of more directionality or concentrated radiation than conveyed by the words "directional antenna." Thus, a beam antenna may be thought of as a special kind of directional antenna.

†Although even closer spacing appeared at first to be practical, I was later able to demonstrate mathematically that losses in the antenna would seriously limit the gain at too small a spacing. Curiously, it turned out that the one-eighth wavelength spacing which I used in the first flat-top beam antenna was the optimum value!

two poles with an 8-foot wooden spreader at each end to separate them. The half-wavelength wires would be about 10 meters or 30 feet long. If two such sets of wires were rigged end-to-end I calculated the gain would go up another factor of 2 for a total improvement equivalent to a five-fold increase in power. So much gain with an array only 60 feet long by 8 feet wide was an exciting prospect.

Could it be that such a compact antenna with wires spaced so closely would really work? I wanted to build one and test it. But first I needed to figure out a way to feed the array, that is, how to connect the wires properly so that the power would be equally distributed. I decided to bring the transmission line from the transmitter up to the middle of the array and connect it there.

I calculated all the dimensions carefully and gathered the wire, insulators, wood and rope I needed. The last Saturday in January I braved the freezing weather to assemble the antenna and pull it up between two poles in place of one of the Bruce antennas. It was just a week from the time I had opened the January issue of the *Proceedings* with Brown's article.

7. The first "flat-top beam" antenna at W8JK. "It looked like something old but it was really something entirely new and different."

When I hauled the antenna up into place its general appearance reminded me of the "flat-top" or "T" type antennas used by some broadcasting stations, like RV-49, the big one I had visited in Russia. It had the horizontal wires or flat-top and a vertical downlead (feeders) from the center like the vertical bar of the "T." At a casual glance it looked like something old but it was really something entirely new and different. It was horizontally polarized, not vertical, and it was a beam antenna, not omnidirectional.

It took several hours to adjust the transmission line which fed the antenna. When this was done I set up my field strength measuring unit several hundred feet away. I turned on the transmitter, went outside and took a field strength reading. Then I turned the transmitter off, let down the flat-top beam antenna and pulled up in its place a simple comparison antenna and with the same transmitter power as before I made a field strength measurement. It was less than for the flat-top beam antenna by a considerable amount! Although the measurements were not precise they indicated that the flat-top beam antenna was functioning properly and giving something like the expected improvement. So I put the flat-top beam antenna back up. It was now ready for tests over the air with other amateur stations.

The antenna was in a field a hundred paces from the house. The transmitter and station were in my bedroom on the second floor. In rigging and adjusting the antennas I made hundreds of trips back and forth, often jogging to save time. In very cold weather I wore a heavy jacket but often froze my fingers because gloves or mittens were too clumsy. Not removing the jacket when inside to save time, I often got overheated, only to get chilled when I went out again.

Although the flat-top beam antenna had ideally no more gain than the Bruce antenna I had been using, the new antenna had two advantages: (1) it had the wires horizontal and if the height were proper this might give a significant improvement over the Bruce antenna with its vertical radiating wires and (2) it was half as long as the Bruce antenna. This compactness was an asset.

During the evening and early morning hours of the next few days I worked stations in England, Egypt, India, and elsewhere. The reports of my signal strength were good. The antenna really worked!

I wanted to pass along the benefits of close-spacing to other amateurs so for the next several evenings I prepared a short article about the antenna. I mailed it to *RADIO,* a new monthly west coast amateur radio journal, which was the successor to *R/9.* Three weeks later the article appeared in the March 1937 issue.

On a Sunday afternoon only a few days afterwards, I tuned my receiver to the 20 meter band. I was amazed. Many amateurs were discussing the flat-top beam antenna. Only most of them referred to it as the "W8JK antenna" after my call letters or simply the "8JK antenna." Several amateurs, who were booming in with very strong signals, said that they were using one of the antennas, having just put it up. I was overwhelmed by all the talk. I felt too embarrassed to turn on my transmitter to call someone or put out a CQ. So I just sat there and eavesdropped.

Then in a few more days I began to receive letters. First a few, then a flood. Life was never the same afterwards.

Typical of early letters was one from H.L. Graham, a medical student in Los Angeles, and an avid amateur. He said,

"You have created quite a sensation out here in the West with your 'Small but Effective Flat-Top Beam' as described in RADIO. Most every time I tune in to the 20 meter band I hear the boys talking about it in glowing terms. Many have made and installed the beam, myself included." He went on to ask a question about exact dimensions.

And Henry Gilbert of New Hampshire wrote,

"Everyone I work is running an 8JK so I simply had to have one."

The article in the March issue of *RADIO* had focussed on a flat-top beam antenna for the 20 meter band. Many of the inquiries I received concerned the dimensions for other wavelengths. There were also questions about other transmission line or feeding arrangements. To answer these and other questions I prepared a more comprehensive article which was published in the June issue of *RADIO*.

The new article did not stem the tide of letters which continued to pour in unabated. One from G.M. Wilford in Birmingham, England, started this way,

"There is no doubt in my own mind that your antenna is the finest I've ever used. I'd hate to say how many feet of wire I've wasted in past years experimenting with every known type of antenna. I can now work anything I can hear and that's saying a good deal for any sky wire."

Stanley Parker, in Guayaquil, Ecuador, wrote,

"We have found the flat-top beam by far exceeds any other which we have had in operation here at this station."

Amateurs weren't the only ones interested as indicated by this letter from Otis Hill of Hilo, Hawaii,

"I have just finished reading your article in *RADIO* on the flat-top beam antenna. To me this radiator seems to be just the thing not only for hams but equally as good for commercials. Can you furnish me with formulas for figuring out the proper dimensions for an antenna of this type to be used on 5375 and 6610 kilocycles (both commercial frequencies)?"

I began to feel like a newspaper columnist to whom you wrote with your problems. Instead of writing to "Dear Abby" with questions about your personal life, you wrote to "Dear John" about your antenna problems.

Some letters came addressed to "Ann Harbor" and one to "Hen's Harbour." Many came special delivery with self-addressed special delivery envelopes enclosed. I typed my replies, often two pages long, evenings and weekends, but I apologized if I was as much as ten days late in answering. My files bulged. I hardly got on the air anymore except for my schedules with Stegall in the Congo and Tibbetts in Berkeley.

I felt obliged to answer every letter. The 8JK beam antenna was a new concept. The design was unprecedented. It was the first of a new breed of antennas with close spacing. Most everything about it was entirely different from older, more conventional antennas and these differences raised questions.

Thousands of 8JK antennas had been built and put up all over the world. It was staggering to contemplate the miles of wire and rope, the tons of insulators, and the thousands of man-hours which had been required! My name had probably been both blessed and cursed in every corner of the globe.

And now I began to get many visitors, not just from around Ann Arbor but from everywhere. Whenever an amateur journeyed near Ann Arbor he would detour and drop in to see my station and antennas and at all hours. My station became a sort of Mecca where amateurs could do homage to an antenna.

My next project was an ambitious one, the construction of a flat-top beam antenna 60 feet long mounted on top of a 50-foot pole with a motor for rotating it to point in any direction. This antenna would replace the many fixed beams I had put up in the field.

8. "It looked like a graceful, lacy, open gondola . . . perched atop a pole."

The project was more mechanical than electrical involving a long light framework of wood slats and bamboo poles supporting the antenna wires, with drive gears, pulleys, struts and guys. When I got the monster up in August (1937) it looked like a graceful, lacy, open gondola 60 feet long perched atop a pole. I tested the antenna for a number of weeks all the while building a smaller 30-foot single section version to replace it. The 60 footer was a good antenna but was more than most amateurs would want to tackle. I thought that a 30-foot model would be more practical. I got this model up in place of the bigger one by October and kept it up for a long time. I put together a lengthy article with many diagrams and photographs describing the two rotary antennas and it appeared in the December 1937 issue of *RADIO*.

9. "Alongside the 60-foot gondola . . . immersed in a sea of Queen Anne's lace."

In November I had been on the west coast and had paid a visit to the office of *RADIO* in Los Angeles. I met many of the staff: Ray Dawley, Margaret Lloyd, and Bernie Ontiveros. My article on the rotary flat-top beam antennas had been received and was being readied for publication. Margaret had majored in English at Southern Cal and was working as managing editor of *RADIO* to acquire practical experience. She was personable, vivacious, intelligent and beautiful. In discussing my article she said that one of the photographs was an artistic masterpiece. I didn't understand. She explained that it was the one showing me standing alongside the completed 60-foot "gondola" and immersed in a sea of Queen Anne's lace. These are a very common field flower in Michigan. They were so ubiquitous and familiar I had hardly noticed them.

I had met Woody Smith, the editor, a few days earlier in Chicago where he was correcting proof at the printers on a new edition of the *RADIO* Handbook. E.H. "Bill" Conklin, an associate editor of *RADIO* had invited Woody and me to dinner at his home in Wheaton, Illinois, a block or so from Grote Reber's house with 30-foot diameter dish-type antenna he had built in his back yard and about which we will hear more later.

While in California I visited the high voltage laboratory at Cal Tech and met Bill Fowler, Lewis Delsasso and Charles Lauritsen all famous for their nuclear research work. I also stopped in at the shop where the 200-inch mirror for the Mount Palomar telescope was being ground. And in downtown Los Angeles I talked with Chuck Perrine, a technical consultant to *RADIO* who, the next summer, flew with Howard Hughes as his radio operator on his record-breaking 91 hour round-the-world flight.

After Los Angeles I visited San Francisco and the bay area. I went to the Radiation Laboratory at Berkeley to see the cyclotron and talk with members of the staff. Ernest Lawrence was away on one of his many trips. While in Berkeley I also paid a visit to Reg Tibbetts at his station W6ITH.

From San Francisco I traveled north and spent a few days with Henry Muyskens, my Ph.D. colleague, at his home in Port Orchard, Washington, and from there I returned to Ann Arbor.

*   *   *   *   *

A year or so earlier I was at the cyclotron lab at the U of M one afternoon when a Dr. George Westcott walked in and introduced himself. He said that he was a native of Ypsilanti (a town just east of Ann Arbor) and that he had gotten his medical degree at the University of Michigan. Then he interned in Pennsylvania and followed this by two years studying tropical medicine in Belgium. After that he sailed for the Belgian Congo where he had established a hospital. He was back on his first furlough after eight years in the Congo. On the steamer coming back from Africa he met some other missionaries returning from Africa who had told him about Carroll Stegall and his radio contacts with my station. Dr. Westcott wondered if I would help him acquire equipment for an amateur radio station which he could take back to Africa when he returned that fall (1936). I agreed.

In the weeks that followed I designed a 75-watt radiophone transmitter and ordered the necessary parts. I helped George with the layout and some of the work but intentionally had him do much of the construction and all of the wiring so that he would be personally familiar with the details of the equipment. This would make it easier for him to repair it should that be necessary. By August 1936 the transmitter was complete and George brought it to my station for tests. I used it on the air with an antenna and found that it performed satisfactorily. George then packed and shipped it to Africa along with a short-wave receiver he had purchased.

When George left for Africa in September he told me that he hoped to get on the air soon after he arrived there but months went by with no word. Several times a week I called and listened for him on the wavelength we had chosen but I heard nothing. George's dad, who was 80, although he looked and acted 50, phoned me from Ypsilanti several times, expressing concern.

On the fifteenth of February 1937 I again called George and as soon as I switched over to listen my loudspeaker boomed,

"Hello W8JK, hello W8JK, this is ON4CGW at Tondo in the Belgian Congo calling you. I am receiving you first rate, John. Do you receive me? Come in please."

I was elated.

"Hello ON4CGW, this is W8JK replying; OK George, fine business; you have a good signal," I answered. "We're very, very pleased to hear you. How are you? Come in please."

George answered that both he and his wife, Ellen, were fine. There had been so much work to do at the hospital when he got back that he hadn't been able to connect up his radio equipment until just a few days before. We talked for most of an hour and as soon as we signed off I called George's dad in Ypsilanti who was delighted to get the good news.

I had arranged a schedule with George for the next evening at ten thirty. Dr. Wallace Teed, a classmate of George's in the U of M medical school, came and brought George's dad. Three Ann Arbor amateurs, Roy Purchase, Stocker Sturgeon, and Bob Schumacher also came. Conditions were apparently not good at ten thirty because George did not answer my call. I continued to call every few minutes until nearly eleven when George finally responded. His signals were good and our contact lasted over an hour with the visitors all taking turns at the microphone. I suspect that George's dad had been a bit skeptical about the possibility of talking by radio to his son in the Congo but he wasn't anymore. He was beaming.

During the weeks and months which followed, a continual stream of people visited my station to talk to George. Both George's father and mother came several times and one night in February 1938 I called them on the telephone so they could hear George's two day old daughter (their granddaughter) cry into the microphone.

By August 1937 George had replaced his antenna with a flat-top beam and his signals improved noticeably.

When Dr. "Wally" Teed was at my station George often consulted with him and through him or me with other doctors on the U of M medical faculty concerning some of his more difficult or unusual cases. Carroll Stegall on occasion also sought medical advice to assist the doctor at his mission. Sometimes the advice and information from Ann Arbor was crucial in saving a life.

One such instance involved Ngalula (Nah-lou-lah) a seven year old Mbagani girl who had been orphaned at two and brought up by the Stegalls. On my regular schedule with Carroll one evening, three doctors were at my station and Carroll sought their advice concerning Ngalula who was deathly ill. The mission doctor was away so Carroll described her case history and symptoms in detail. The Ann Arbor doctors were Bob Cummings, my boyhood chum of the backyard telegraph and now an M.D. living in Texas but back in Ann Arbor on a visit, his father, Dr. Howard Cummings, and Wally Teed.

The three discussed the case among themselves and asked questions of Stegall leading to more information. They finally concluded that Ngalula was suffering from a virulent infection and that a new drug, sulphanilamide, might be used to advantage. Stegall responded that they had just recently received some of the drug and that he would start giving it immediately according to the dosage the doctors prescribed.

A week later Carroll reported that Ngalula had shown steady improvement. In a couple of weeks she was completely recovered and one morning in Africa (evening in Ann Arbor) she spoke to me from Carroll's station.

I continued regular schedules with both George Westcott and Carroll Stegall until the fall of 1939 when the Belgian government ordered all of its amateur stations to shut down due to the war in Europe.

George and his family, now increased to three children, returned to the U.S. during the war and George began a medical practice at Ypsilanti which he continued until retiring in 1972. A widower and with children grown, he went back alone to Zaire where he now commutes by private plane between four hospitals which he serves. George speaks several native dialects plus French and English. George's father lived to be 104 and George hopes that he himself can continue to serve productively for many years.

To many persons a hospital in central Africa evokes the image of Albert Schweitzer, often called the conscience of the civilized world.

I like to think that a culture which has produced an Albert Schweitzer can't be all bad, and a doctor like George Westcott, carrying on in the Schweitzer tradition, is surely another entry on the credit side of the ledger of our society.

*   *   *   *   *

I gave talks before large amateur gatherings — at regional and national conventions and I talked to many smaller groups both in and out-of-state. But all the while I kept on experimenting.

Hooking up to a flat-top beam antenna usually required a number of adjustments on the transmission line from the transmitter. To eliminate these adjustments I had begun to experiment with multi-wire dipoles and I published many articles about them. My most elaborate application of the idea was a three-band rotary antenna supported by two new towers with an elevated walkway between for rigging and servicing the antenna.

10. Adjusting the 3-band rotary beam antenna at W8JK from the elevated walkway.

One day it occurred to me that a novel arrangement for an antenna would be a reflector of two flat sheets intersecting to form a corner. The "corner reflector" antenna could be easily analyzed by an extension of the method I had used on the flat-top beam antenna. Calculations showed that a square-corner reflector was capable of a 10-fold power gain or improvement over a single dipole antenna! This was impressive.

In the middle of the winter I assembled a square-corner reflector of parallel wires and set it up in the field south of the house. Measurements with a field strength meter showed that the antenna performed nearly as well as the calculations predicted it should. I put together an article and rushed it off to *RADIO*.

Next I constructed an improved model working at a shorter wavelength and using window screen for the reflectors.

Finally, I built reflectors of a row of equally spaced parallel metal rods, like the slats in a picket fence, and through a long systematic series of tests determined what spacing between the rods made them equivalent to a solid metal sheet reflector. I arrived at an optimum design consisting of a dozen rods for the reflector and, with a bow-tie shaped dipole, this combination subsequently became very popular. I summarized my results in an article published in the IRE *Proceedings*.

In the years since, millions of corner reflector antennas have been

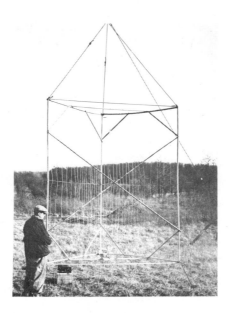

11. The first corner reflector in the field outside my house. This one worked at 5 meters wavelength.

12. Smaller corner with window screen reflectors operating at 1-meter wavelength and mounted on turntable for field pattern measurements.

manufactured and sold, particularly as ultra-high frequency (UHF) television receiving antennas, sprouting from rooftops all across the country, especially in fringe areas where the extra gain is needed.

13. The corner reflector "consisting of a dozen rods with a bow-tie shaped dipole became very popular and millions have been manufactured and sold as ultra-high frequency (UHF) television antennas, sprouting from rooftops all across the country."

*　　　*　　　*　　　*　　　*

George Westcott's classmate, Dr. Wallace Teed had an ear, nose, and throat practice in Ann Arbor. He had become interested in the use of ultra-short waves for treating severe colds involving sinus congestion. He asked if I would build a diathermy machine for him which he could use in treatments of his patients. There were a number of machines on the market but none incorporated a method for measuring the power dosage to the patient. The physician using the machine could only guess at the dose.

Dosage measurement is important because we humans have heat sensitive receptors only in the skin. Ultra-short waves penetrate deeply and it is possible for a patient to get badly burned internally while feeling only a slight amount of heating. Wally believed that in the interests of safety and sound therapeutic practice one should be able to measure the dosage accurately and he wanted a machine with this capability. I undertook the job.

Most diathermy machines at that time were inefficient because they radiated a good deal of power into space instead of getting it all into the patient. This caused interference with radio stations not only nearby but often at great distances. I didn't want our machine to have this fault. So I applied my experience with antennas, whose function *is* to radiate, in a reverse sense to produce a machine which did *not* radiate or radiated as little as possible. To measure the dosage I adapted a new method which had just been published.

After constructing the machine I had to calibrate it, that is, fix it so that when the meter read 10 watts it meant that the patient was actually receiving a 10 watt dose. The patient sat with his head between two electrodes projecting from the machine with one electrode close to each cheek. This appeared to be the best way to get heat to the sinus regions. For the calibration work I needed an artificial human head. I made a thin-wall wooden cubical box about eight inches on a side and filled it with water. Then placing the box between the electrodes I turned on our diathermy machine and watched a thermometer in the water. Knowing the volume of water, the temperature rise, and the time it took, the heat absorbed and the power dosage could be easily calculated.

14. **The diathermy machine with the doctor, Wally Teed, as the patient. The needle on the meter above his head reads a dosage of 15 watts, giving a safe, comfortable warmth.**

But I couldn't get the water to heat. I also noticed that the machine did not react the same with the box as it did with a real patient. It became apparent that plain water was not enough. I experimented with a number of mixtures but nothing seemed to work. In desperation I bought a big loaf of white bread, broke it up into small pieces and stirred and mixed it into the water until it was of uniform consistency, like a pulpy ooze. To my delight it worked beautifully, reacting with the machine just like a real patient. The machine couldn't tell the difference between a wooden block filled with bread dough and a real human head! This was perfect for the calibration work and I soon had the indicators on the machine calibrated so that the power dosage to the patient could be read directly in watts.

Wally and I first used the machine experimentally on ourselves and then he began to use it on his patients. Barely perceptible heating occurred when the dose was about 10 watts, definite warmth at about 20 watts, intensive warmth at 30 watts, and intolerable heat at 40 watts. Wally found that 15 to 20 watts for a period of 15 to 20 minutes was a safe and effective dose for the majority of patients.

Wally and I collaborated on two articles about the machine and our results with it and in June, 1940 I presented a paper on it at the national convention of the Institute of Radio Engineers in Boston. Dr. Frederick E. Terman of Stanford University presided at the meeting and following my presentation remarked that he was glad to see a diathermy machine designed so as to reduce radiation and prevent interference. Most diathermy machines, he said, were like short-wave broadcast stations operating without a license. (You needed a license for a short-wave broadcast station but not for a diathermy machine.)

Between 1933 and 1940 I had published 26 articles. From about 1 article per year during the years 1933 to 1936 my publication rate had increased to 4 articles in 1937, 5 in 1938, 6 in 1939, and 8 in 1940. The topics ranged from the transmutation of palladium and ultra-high frequency propogation to otolaryngological applications of diathermy but most of the articles were on antennas.

Leaving the atoms spinning in the cyclotron and the beams dancing on the antennas, I next turned my attention to the kleenex machine.

CHAPTER 10

THE KLEENEX MACHINE

The Beloit Iron Works had contracted with Ernie Abbott to quiet the huge machines they sold to paper companies for producing light tissues such as kleenex. Ernie put me in charge of the project.

Two rooms over a bakery and a butcher shop on Ann Arbor's south Main Street — this was the Physicists Research Company. By the time I came in the spring of 1938 Ernie had also rented an old automobile repair garage on the alley behind our building. The garage was very spacious and we planned to construct and install a small-scale version of the paper machine there for our work.

In the manufacture of paper, wood or other fibrous material is ground up and mixed with water until it forms a pulpy suspension. The mixture is then poured out onto a large felt or blanket. From there on the process of making the paper centers on removing the water from the mixture so that only the intertwined pulp fibers remain as a thin layer or sheet. To facilitate this process on high speed machines, a moving belt-like blanket or felt is employed which passes over a large rotating cylindrical drum perforated with holes. By applying suction to the inside of the drum, water is sucked out of the felt, drying the pulp. A typical kleenex maker might have a felt 10 to 15 feet wide moving several thousand feet per minute with a perforated rotating drum of the same width and two feet in diameter. The entire machine might be over 100 feet long.

Beloit's machines were very successful but paper companies using them complained bitterly about the noise. To produce the suction in the drum a motor of several hundred horse power was needed. Acoustically this was like having a siren with a 200 horse power engine driving it. The noise was so great no operator would stay around the machine. They had tried ear plugs but they didn't always work.

Beloit's engineers had thought of building a sound-proof enclosure around the drum part of the machine. However, this would be expensive, very cumbersome, and would prevent easy inspection and maintenance on a vital part of the machine. Wasn't there some way to reduce the sound at the source? Abbott really didn't know but he had convinced Beloit that it would be worth-while letting him try.

For our test model, Beloit sent us a two-foot long section of the big perforated drum. We added rollers and installed the parts in a steel frame about 10 feet long. It had a real felt, like an endless belt, which ran over rollers and the perforated drum. The felt was two feet wide to match the drum. We installed a powerful motor and vacuum pump to provide the suction and a variable speed motor to drive the belt. We even had a water sprayer to wet down the belt. Everything was the same as on an actual machine except that the drum was not as wide and we didn't have any wood pulp on the belt. We didn't think that these differences would have much effect on the noise and we were right.

15. The Kleenex machine which "produced an ear-piercing, nerve-shattering scream fully as loud as that of its giant brothers in Wisconsin."

When we turned the machine on for our first tests it produced an ear-piercing, nerve-shattering, high-pitched scream fully as loud as that from its giant brothers in Wisconsin. Ernie and I wore rubber eraser-tips as ear plugs so we weren't in any pain but the butcher and the baker were upset with our kleenex maker. Although the walls between us and their shops had reduced the noise, it penetrated their inner ears like rapier thrusts. We explained that it was an experimental machine and that we hoped to reduce the noise so the loud screeching would be over before too long, but they weren't impressed.

Our next step was to run a series of tests where we measured the noise under carefully controlled conditions at various felt speeds, suctions, and wetness conditions. The noise was intense and remarkably constant over a very wide range of conditions. Although my ears were fairly well protected by the ear plugs, I noticed that after working for an hour or so my sinuses became very congested as though I had a cold, only I didn't. The noise had gone up my nose and had agitated my sinuses. I thought that maybe I should clip a clothespin over my nose as protection, but I never did. Maybe the sound got through and addled my brains. Who knows?

Next we began a thorough step-by-step analysis of exactly what happened in the suction drum to produce the noise. As the wet felt passed over the drum, water was sucked into the perforations and a partial vacuum introduced next to the slug of water. When the drum perforation passed the edge of the suction box inside the drum, the partially evacuated perforation was suddenly exposed to the atmosphere. The air rushing in to fill the hole caused the noise, or so we thought, and to quiet the machine what we needed to do was make the transition more gradual instead of so abrupt. This all sounds very simple and straight-forward but we did a lot of work and made extended calculations before coming to this conclusion. I got my first in-depth experience with dif-ferential equations applied to a practical problem as we matched the coefficients of an equation with the parameters of the machine. We ground out solutions and plotted curves and graphs.

Knowing what we thought should be done, the next step was to do it. I designed a moveable trailing edge or lip for the suction box which could be electromagnetically controlled so that the edge of the lip rode either tightly against the inside of the drum (standard position) or was dropped a millimeter or two away from the inside of the drum. I installed the new arrangement and prepared for a test. I started the machine and as it began to pick up speed motors whined, water spray wet the felt and dampened the air, and the machine screamed as potently as ever.

Half trembling I reached for the switch to activate the electromagnets and drop the lip. Would it work? I threw the switch and instantly the noise was gone! Everything else seemed to be normal but the noise was not there, at least it was so much less that I took out my ear plugs and didn't mind it at all. I ran around checking gauges and meters to be sure we still had the proper speed and suction.

I called Ernie on the office phone and he rushed out. So did Sam Bousky, another staff member who had helped on the project. I repeated the demonstration. Ernie was ecstatic. He telephoned Beloit and a few days later their top engineers Hornbostel and Ostertag were on hand for another demonstration. They were much impressed and greatly de-lighted. They said excitedly that it would require only a simple modification of existing machines to utilize the quieting scheme.

Although the end of the project was now in sight, we still had many weeks of work ahead preparing the final report and specifying exact dimensions for the new feature on an actual machine.

Our research led to the construction of quieter paper-making machines. Later, after I left Abbott's company, Ernie used what we had learned on the paper-making machine in reverse to design louder and more efficient diesel locomotive horns and air raid sirens! So maybe in spite of our quieting job the total noise pollution in the world remained constant or perhaps, heaven forbid, even increased.

CHAPTER 11

DEGAUSS WITH KRAUS

It was dark and cold with fog so thick I could barely see the lights at the bow and stern of our small open whaleboat. A sailor at the bow cupped a hand to his ear. A sailor at the stern, one hand on the rudder and the other on the throttle, had reduced the engine speed so we were almost dead in the water. The three of us strained listening. The sailor in the bow turned and shouted,

"I hear her coming!"

Sure enough, off to starboard, I could hear the splashing of something cutting swiftly through the water to the faint pulsing accompaniment of deep-throated diesel engines.

"Where is she?" the sailor in the stern asked anxiously.

"I can't be sure," the bow sailor replied, "but I think she's coming right at us!"

"Jesus Christ!" the other sailor burst out with as he jammed the throttle full speed ahead. We leaped through the water and none too soon, for cutting across our wake, only feet astern, the dimly-lit, ghostlike outline of the huge Cape Charles-Norfolk ferry-boat whooshed by with the roar of a tidal wave.

"God, that was close!" the bow sailor exclaimed. "Those bastards barrel along like they owned the whole bay! Don't they slow down for fog or anything?"

It was January 1941. We were in the middle of Chesapeake Bay. For two days I had been doing experiments on the huge aircraft carrier *Wasp* and less than an hour before had climbed down a 35-foot rope ladder from the *Wasp's* main deck to the whaleboat bobbing below. As dusk closed in, the two sailors were groping their way across the bay to take me to Cape Charles to catch the night boat back to Washington, D.C., and the Naval Ordnance Laboratory (NOL) where I worked.

Before describing my NOL experiences let me back-up a bit.

      *   *   *   *   *

The diathermy machine I had designed and built for Wally Teed had many novel features. There was the possibility that other M.D.'s would want ones like it so I might get orders for more. A manufacturing company in Detroit wanted me to design antennas for them to be sold to the amateur and commercial market. There was the possibility of doing additional antenna consulting work for pay. All these developments influenced me to leave Abbott's company and set up in business for myself.

I also thought about teaching. When I wrote an article describing how an antenna was built and how it worked, I was teaching and I enjoyed doing that. So by the spring of 1940, when orders for more diathermy machines did not materialize and the Detroit company's business did not flourish, I wrote to the physics and electrical engineering departments of several dozen universities in the east and midwest applying for a teaching job.

I received two replies. One was from the physics department of an eastern school indicating some interest but nothing further developed. The other was from none other than Gerry Fox, my former high school radio club advisor who had become a physics professor at Iowa State at Ames. He invited me to come out for a visit and interview which I did. I was well impressed with Iowa State but I don't think they were with me because I didn't receive any offer. Maybe the chairman thought that my background had too much engineering and not enough physics or that my activities as a radio amateur were not compatible with a good professional attitude.

Out of the several dozen inquiries I sent out, no electrical engineering department had responded. Could it be that the engineers thought I was too much of a physicist? I didn't know. But some people are that way. If your background is unconventional, if you don't fit completely in a slot, they have trouble sizing you up. My background bridged physics *and* electrical engineering. Physicists could call me an engineer while engineers could call me a physicist. Didn't it occur to anyone that I might be both?

Spring passed into summer. I was busy designing and testing antennas and writing articles about them. World War II was intensifying in Europe. Dunkirk had been evacuated. The U.S. was not yet directly involved but there was growing concern that we might be and the U.S. Navy was confronted with some serious problems on which it needed all the help it could get. So it was that in September 1940 Ralph Bennett hired me to work at the Naval Ordnance Laboratory (NOL), Washington, D.C., as a contract civilian scientist at $14 per day. I agreed to come for 3 months. One week later I reported to the Mine Experiment Building at the Navy Yard on the Anacostia River in Washington.

The NOL was a small, new group when I joined it. None of us had much of an idea about the nature of the problem we were to work on until after we arrived. Then we learned that it had to do with magnetic mines and the protection of our ships against them. It was all hush-hush; no publicity had been given it, but the Germans had developed a new type of mine which was devastatingly destructive and against which the U.S. and Allied navies and merchant marines had no defense.

A conventional mine consisted of a bouyant spherical steel container a yard or so in diameter containing explosives and held a few feet below the surface by a vertical cable attached to an anchor. The strategy was to place these at intervals across the channels of rivers or harbors so that the ships were likely to strike them, whereupon the mines exploded sinking the ships. A number of schemes had been devised to deal with these. One used a shallow draft vessel which deployed two small underwater "craft" called paravanes towed to either side of the vessel by underwater cables in the manner of submerged kites. The cable carried cutting teeth which severed any vertical cables attached to mines that it encountered. The free mines then popped up to the surface where they could be harmlessly exploded from a distance by gunfire. In this way a ship channel could be swept clear of mines. Appropriately, the vessel doing the job was called a "mine sweeper."

But the new mine developed by the Germans was of another breed. It could be sown from the air by parachute, usually at night, and had been dropped in many British rivers and harbors. After hitting the water, the parachute detached, and being heavier than water, the mine sank to the bottom where it might settle in under several feet of mud. Typically it was cylindrical in shape, about 10 feet long by several feet in diameter, weighing upwards of one ton.

Not needing to float, it could be almost completely filled with explosives. When a ship passed over, the vessel's magnetic field triggered the mine. The explosion produced an immensely powerful jet of water rising above the mine like a gigantic underwater piston, so strong that it could lift a ship bodily out of the water and break it in two. Many deaths and injuries occurred because the impact of the jet was so great that sailors had their thigh bones driven up into their lungs, instantly shortening them to half their height, or they were thrown up against the overheads or ceilings, fracturing their skulls, or both. This man-compacting, skull-smashing, ship-shattering mine was effective even in deep channels where the ship's bottom passed many feet above the mine. It was a fiendishly clever device, controlled by a veritable witch's brew of intricate clockwork and sensitive magnetic relays against which we had no defense. Our job was to develop one. Without it all our shipping could be sunk or bottled up. Fortunately for us the British had been at work on the problem and we could benefit from their experience.

Our "laboratory" was a large barren room where each of us had a desk. There were about a dozen of us in October when I came. But our ranks gradually increased as more of Bennett's "recruits" began to arrive. As more and more desks were crowded in for newcomers, my desk and those of the other "old timers" were shoved closer and closer together so tightly that we could hardly squeeze between them. Fortunately, we all weren't at our desks at the same time. I was away a good deal on trips to the Navy Department buildings on Constitution Avenue (forerunners of the Pentagon) and to Chesapeake Bay where we were setting up field measurements and testing facilities.

In spite of the daily shuffling around to accommodate new arrivals, the lab was well organized and we made progress. We were all civilian scientists, coming from all over the country with a wide range of backgrounds. It was electrifying to watch the group become welded together and attack the problem. There was dead seriousness and real determination. We were the brain cells of a nation coping with a new and mysterious enemy.

The line of attack or countermeasure by NOL centered around methods of reducing a ship's magnetic field. Containing thousands of tons of steel, a ship is like a huge magnet. Some of the magnetization is permanent, having been pounded into it by riveting hammers while under construction in a shipyard. The rest of the magnetization is of an induced or variable kind which depends at any instant on the earth's magnetic field and the ship's heading. If the total magnetization, due to either one or both kinds, can be reduced sufficiently the ship might pass over a magnetic mine without triggering it.

To reduce the ship's magnetic field we wrapped several tons of very heavy insulated copper wires around the ship. By sending an electric current through these wires in the proper direction a magnetic field was created which opposed or counteracted the ship's own field so as to partially or wholly nullify it.

The unit of magnetic field (or flux density) is the "gauss" after Karl Friedrich Gauss, a German physicist. The process of reducing the magnetization of a ship was called "degaussing" and my colleagues and I became known as "degaussers." The wires we coiled around a ship were called the "degaussing coil," the "degaussing belt" or the "degaussing girdle."

In theory the idea was simple but applying it in practice was anything but simple. A ship is a complex assemblage of steel plates, beams and rivets and a single coil was only partially successful. Additional coils encircling specific parts of the ship were needed to reduce the magnetic field further. Each coil required the proper amount of current and this needed to be changed on a moment-to-moment basis if the ship were changing direction. A detailed schedule of currents needed to be worked out for all the different headings. If the schedule was not followed correctly, the ship's field might be inadvertently increased instead of decreased and the ship rendered more vulnerable to the magnetic mines instead of less so.

On new ships coils could be installed during construction in the shipyard. But ships already afloat had to put into port and be ripped apart to get the coils installed. It was a big job. The wires in each coil might make a bundle as big as a man's wrist. Tons of copper were used on every ship and degaussing coils became number one in our country's use of copper.

Once the coils were in and connected to special generators it was vital that the whole system be tested. For doing this a measuring range was set up in Chesapeake Bay. It was in deep water miles from shore. Magnetic measuring instruments called magnetometers were placed on the bottom and connected by cable to instruments in the *Hannibal*, a ship anchored nearby. First, the ship under test passed over the magnetometers with no current in its degaussing coils. This gave the ship's undegaussed or "normal" magnetic "signature." On following passes different amounts of current were put through the coils to check the effectiveness of the degaussing system and to determine if the current-heading schedule was correct or needed modification.

All day, every day naval ships paraded by the *Hannibal* for their degaussing check. There were all kinds from battleships to destroyers. The ships came by close, only a hundred yards away, and then after going a distance, they turned in a big circle to come back by the *Hannibal* headed in the opposite direction. This went on for as many passes as needed to complete the tests. The smaller, more maneuverable ships might complete the tests in an hour or so but the bigger ones might take half a day. Sometimes several ships were on the range at once, following each other around in single file like so many ducklings in a pond.

The *Hannibal* was a tub. She was a relic out of the past. Built originally as a collier or coal-hauling ship, I was told that she had accompanied Admiral Dewey's fleet into Manila Bay in 1898. Her top speed was so slow that, although it was a well guarded secret, one might infer what it was from her claim-to-fame as the only ship to pass Cape Henry three times in a day all on the same heading. Rounding Cape Henry into Chesapeake Bay, strong headwinds had driven her backwards by the Cape where she barely held her own until, with wind subsiding, she again made it by the Cape. She had been resurrected and outfitted by the Navy for the measurement job.

One of our biggest problems was good communication between the *Hannibal* and the other ships which were rarely more than a mile away. Because of the short range the Navy procedure was to send messages in Morse code by blinker lights. When visibility was good and a ship was passing near the *Hannibal* the system was at its best but it was slow and messages were rarely completed before the ship turned and the signalman's light disappeared. The signalman then had to run around the deck to a blinker light on the other side of the ship to resume the message. This caused delays and in rough weather and poor visibility the system failed almost completely.

On the *Hannibal* one windy day we had been measuring a big cruiser, as long as a battleship but lighter and faster. Jim Moore and I were in the instrument room with the chart recorders which hung from gimbals. Jim was the civilian scientist in charge of the measurements on the *Hannibal*. As we watched the "signatures" of the cruiser appear on the charts we decided that the cruiser should try a new set of degaussing coil currents not on the original schedule so we sent a message to the cruiser. After a few more passes it became obvious that something was wrong because the new signatures didn't make sense. We sent another message. The cruiser made more passes but still without improvement. So we sent yet another message. Just then Captain Bell, the commanding officer of the *Hannibal,* burst into the room to find out why the cruiser hadn't finished up its tests and gone on its way. We explained that the cruiser was apparently not setting the currents correctly in spite of several messages we had sent. Bell said,

"Kraus, I think you better get over there and find out what in hell's going on."

So he ordered two sailors into the whaleboat kept tied alongside the *Hannibal* and I jumped in with them. The sea was rough and as we bounced toward the cruiser every wave hitting us sent a sheet of spray over the boat drenching the three of us. The cruiser slowed almost to a stop as we came alongside. At one instant we were in the trough of a wave 10 feet below the main deck and the next instant on the crest of one level with the deck. We bounced up and down a few times until I got the timing and then as we rose to a crest I lunged for the deck while outstretched hands grabbed me and hauled me aboard. I went forward and climbed up several decks to the bridge (the forward position where the ship is controlled) and there I met with the captain, the engineering officer and the navigator. They had not yet received the last message we sent before I left the *Hannibal!* While we were talking, a signalman popped in breathlessly and handed the message over. The captain read it aloud. I was puzzled so he showed it to me. It was garbled!

"This is incredible," I thought, "the sheriff in Podunk, Kansas, has better communication with his deputy out in his patrol car!"

Not only were the messages taking ages but they had mistakes. No wonder the tests with the cruiser were all fouled up.

The mixup was soon straightened out and I returned to the *Hannibal*. The cruiser finished its tests and steamed out of sight but the communications problem nagged me. We were wasting a lot of time. Maybe these big ships with crews of a thousand men or more had nothing better to do than cut capers in Chesapeake Bay but I thought that they did. And later on I had a chance to do something about it.

Interspersed with my stays on the *Hannibal* I spent several days on the enormous aircraft carrier *Wasp* (CV-7) and a week on the huge battleship *Arkansas* (BB-33) while we made extended tests at the *Hannibal* measuring range. The tests on these ships were not the usual routine ones and many more current combinations were tried than there was usually time for.

Life on shipboard was a world apart. I soon got used to the bosun's (boatswain's) whistle with its piping tone and descending pitch echoing from the public address system before announcements like this one every morning before dawn,

"Now hear this! Special sea detail. Clean sweep-down fore and aft. All hands hit the deck!"

I learned the sailor's three "don'ts": Don't stand in a bight, don't bump your head on hatchways, and don't spit to the windward.

I also got accustomed to finding fresh paint everywhere. To keep all the men on the big ships busy, painting went on continuously. When the paint on any part got too thick, sailors were set to work chipping it off with hammers and chisels so that painting could begin all over again. This went on in an unending cycle. Often I would be awakened before dawn by the deafening clatter of chipping hammers pounding on a deck or bulkhead just above or outside my room.

Bunking next to the ammunition magazine or torpedo room took longer to get used to. If an accident occurred it could blow you and half the ship to Kindgom Come; not the most comforting thought when trying to get to sleep.

On windy, sunny days the seascape could be breathtakingly beautiful as we churned up and down the bay. In the troughs of the waves the water was dark, emerald green while the crests were capped in dazzling white foam. The contrast of green and white was spectacular. The effect was heightened when the ship went into a sharp turn, churning up a tremendous wake astern.

All of the ships (except the *Hannibal*) were oil fired and the pungent oil smoke made my eyes smart and nostrils sting. The effect was so strong that even today when I get a good whiff of oil smoke, I can, by closing my eyes, imagine myself standing on the deck of a gray navy ship ploughing ahead at full speed.

In my capacity as a civilian I was in a unique position to observe the Navy as few people could. One day I might be discussing ship construction with an Admiral at the Navy Department building on Constitution Avenue and the next day I might be working alongside the lowest ranked sailor or seaman installing or testing equipment on a ship in Chesapeake Bay, while a week later, wearing a hard hat, I might be crawling around inside a half-finished cruiser in a shipbuilding yard in Wilmington, Delaware. I dealt with all ranks of sailors and officers, with other civilian employees of the Navy, and with manufacturers and shipbuilders. I was aboard every kind of ship the Navy had afloat or on the ways: battleships, cruisers, light and heavy, destroyers, destroyer escorts, submarines, aircraft carriers, PT (patrol torpedo) boats, repair ships, tenders and supply ships.

While the officers' speech was often colorful it was rarely obscene. In contrast, many seamen spoke a language of expletives. The four letter word for sexual intercourse was in every sentence as a verb, noun, adjective or adverb. Often it was the whole sentence. It was the ----ing Navy, the ----ing ship, the ----ing this and the ----ing that. It was the Navy's most popular word. It was spoken a million times a day. Yet it wasn't in the dictionary!

All who would listen were regaled boastfully of sexual exploits in lurid, clinical detail. The seamen made it plain that they existed aboard ship to live it up ashore. I was informed that the girls were currently charging $2 but it was rumored that in some east coast ports the price was going up to $3. The concensus was that such an increase would be a blow to the Navy and Congress should act at once to prevent it.

Although the *Hannibal* spent most of her time at anchor far out in Chesapeake Bay, she had a vicious roll that more than made up for her lack of travel. She was the Navy's only coal burner and could hold enough black fuel to stay out a month or more at a time. However, about every other Saturday morning an "emergency" conveniently developed, like a leaking valve or a bad generator commutator, which required that we return to port at once. So Saturday noon we would up anchor and chug off to Portsmouth, Virginia. It was usually dark by the time we got there.

The first time we made it in, I went ashore as did most of the crew and took the ferry across to Norfolk to see the sights. It was after ten o'clock when I started walking back from downtown Norfolk. Unconsciously, I followed some sailors until I came on a puzzling scene. There ahead for some distance were hundreds of sailors milling around in the street which was lined with shabby store fronts two or three stories high, interspersed with an occasional old house standing back from the sidewalk. Sailors were going into and coming out of the houses. They were also entering and leaving doorways between the stores that revealed stairs leading up to what I presumed might be living quarters above. It soon got through to me that I had walked into the "red light" district of Norfolk, except there weren't any red lights. All of the establishments lining the street for several blocks had numbers prominently displayed in large black figures on white illuminated globes hanging from gooseneck brackets over the doorways.

Through many doorways an occasional sailor entered or left but there were some doorways where several sailors stood waiting. Most noticeable were doors before which many sailors were queued up like in a bread line and in front of some of the old houses there were sailors on the porch, down the steps and along the walk to the street, maybe two or three dozen, standing and waiting. Was it the number of girls in the house that caused the waiting line outside or did one of them have something special to offer? There were no girls on the street. Apparently they were in their rooms with all the business they could handle. From what I had read and heard I had imagined that one might find places of such wholesale, wide-open prostitution in far off cities like Singapore, Hong Kong or Calcutta but not in America.

In sharp contrast to the sailors on leave roaming the street in their plain blue uniforms, were the sailors on patrol duty. Arm bands with big letters "SP" advertized that they were the Navy's Shore Patrol or police whose duty it was to break up fights and brawls and to see to it that the sailors didn't get into too much trouble. Natily dressed in white and blue uniforms with laced-up leggings, Sam Browne belts and swinging billy clubs from their hips they paraded up and down the street like animated mechanical dolls. They marched in pairs, pacing quickly in synchronized military precision side-by-side, as inseparable as Siamese twins.

I was standing transfixed by the incredible scene, when I noticed in the very midst of this vast realm of whoredom an illuminated store with the words "Salvation Army Mission" in big letters across the front. I moved closer. A store had been converted into a meeting room. There were rows of chairs with a hymn book on each and a lectern to one side with a large open Bible. A trumpet, accordian and large bass drum rested on chairs near the doorway. The mission was empty except for two men and two women in Salvation Army uniforms standing at the open door and gazing out at the sailor-laden street. One of the women was a buxom matron. The other was an attractive, demure girl.

The mission was pathetic and forlorn, engulfed in a sea of sailors hell-bent on a Saturday night of pleasuring. The setting was right out of "Guys and Dolls" with the girl, perhaps, another Sargent Sarah Brown. Here was a mission at the ready, poised to dispense salvation to any errant sailor who might stumble in. But none did; there were no Sky Mastersons among them. They didn't want salvation, at least right then.

I moved on and caught a ferry back to Portsmouth and found my way through the dimly-lit city streets to the Navy Yard and the old *Hannibal*. Aside from an officer and a few sailors on watch, the *Hannibal* was deserted.

Sunday the *Hannibal's* crew returned and we chugged out and up the bay to our position where we dropped anchor and made preparations to measure the signatures of the fleet of ships that would show up starting on Monday.

I was on the *Hannibal* almost as much as at the lab in Washington during the fall and winter of 1940. I was aboard for a week or more at a time, alternated with like periods at the lab to relate the theoretical work at the lab with the actual results we got on the ships. Theory and practice became well blended.

Arrangements had been made for a special series of degaussing tests on a new destroyer, the *Walke*, DD416, which had just been commissioned. I was one of a dozen scientists from the lab scheduled to go. We were to take tons of equipment including magnetometers which would allow us to measure the ship's magnetic field while we were at anchor. We would supplement these stationary measurements with runs over the *Hannibal* range. We all boarded the *Walke* at Portsmouth and put out into the bay.

Whereas battleships were weighted down with foot-thick armor plate, destroyers had none. They were aptly called "tin cans" and sailors on them quipped that the steel hulls were only thick enough to keep out the water and smaller fish. Although the *Walke* displaced only 1500 tons, it was propelled by engines as powerful as those on the largest ocean liner, making it a very fast ship. As we steamed up the bay Captain Saunders revved her up for a while. We raced through the water sending out huge foaming bow waves to the sides and creating a mountainous wave astern that seemed to dwarf the ship. A few hours later we slowed down and put into a sheltered inlet where we dropped anchor.

The tests ran for several weeks and required close cooperation between the officers and crew of 200 with our group of a dozen civilian scientists. We tried innumerable arrangements for degaussing the ship using temporary coils of wire laid out on the decks, through companionways or slung over the sides.

In the middle of the tests some technical problems came up that necessitated my going back to the lab in Washington for a day. When I returned to Chesapeake Bay the next night it was almost midnight. George Farrell, a co-worker from the lab, who drove me down in his car, pulled onto a beach where we could see the lights of the *Walke* riding at anchor a mile or so out. It was important for me to get back to the *Walke* as soon as possible but how could I let the ship know I was there? I asked George to turn his car so its headlights pointed directly at the *Walke*. We then got out and while George stood with his back against one headlight to block it off, I took off my hat and moved it systematically back and forth in front of the other headlight to spell out the *Walke's* number "DD-416" in Morse code flashes. Soon a powerful searchlight beam from the *Walke* sliced upward, piercing the sky.

"Who are you?" it blinked. I blinked back who I was and what I wanted. The ship replied,

"Sending boat." The ship also asked whether the car which had brought me was going right back to Washington. I answered that it was.

We kept the headlights on and in about 15 minutes a whaleboat with two sailors came in to shore right where we were parked. With them was one of the *Walke's* crew who had gotten emergency shore leave to return home because of serious illness in his family. He needed the ride back to Washington. He hopped out of the boat and I jumped in and went back for another week on the *Walke*. Blinker communication might leave a lot to be desired on the *Hannibal* range but here it had proved its mettle.

As the months passed, the lab began to make substantial progress but the magnitude of the problem was gigantic. It was necessary to design coils, specifying the number of turns and exact locations where they should be installed on hundreds of ships and to determine how many amperes of current would be needed in each coil for all possible headings. To expedite this task I was put in charge of building accurate scale models or miniature replicas about 5 feet long of each type of ship, installing coils in many different locations on each model and then measuring the effectiveness of each coil. It was a formidable task but I had a staff of about 100 scientists and engineers, half with Ph.D.s, to do the job.

We started construction on a number of temporary all-wood buildings, each the size of a big two-car garage, in which to do the measurements. We had just gotten these under way when Captain Jackson, the commanding officer of the Navy Yard, threatened to stop the whole operation.

Captain Jackson was an irascible, ruddy-cheeked, stocky old sailor. He hadn't made Admiral which had soured him and, stuck with a shore job, he radiated bitterness and resentment. To him the NOL was a confounded nuisance. Command of a ship carried a God-like authority not found in a shore assignment and, like many a navy-man, Captain Jackson, ashore, was a fish out of water.

I was at the building site one afternoon as the floor timbers were being placed when Captain Jackson strode up under a full head of steam.

"What the hell do you think you're doing?" he yelled and pointing to the buildings he screamed, "Stop those workmen!"

"We are constructing some test facilities for our degaussing work, sir," I replied as calmly as I could.

"Why can't you do your god-damned testing somewhere else instead of in my Navy Yard?" he bellowed. "And who the hell gave you permission to put those buildings up?"

"Well sir, it's like this," I replied, explaining the situation as best I could. Our dialogue continued and as the minutes dragged by old Captain Jackson slowly began to cool down in spite of the fact that none of the carpenters had missed a single hammer blow.

An hour later we were still talking. By now Lynn Rumbaugh from the lab had joined us and alternated with me in marshalling arguments in our defense. Finally, Captain Jackson blurted out,

"Well, don't let it happen again!"

He shook his head and stomped off muttering,

"I don't know what in hell the Navy's coming to with all you god-damned scientists running loose."

Having withstood Captain Jackson's salvos of broadsides, the buildings, or "shacks" as we called them, were completed in a matter of days and we moved in with our equipment and ship models. But we had so many models and so many measurements to make on each that work was organized around the clock. I set up three shifts of scientists so that the work went on continuously in each of the shacks. It took careful scheduling to make the work run smoothly and it was necessary for me to overlap all three shifts. I arrived about seven in the morning so as to have most of an hour to talk with the night shift groups as they were completing their work. During the day I had plenty of opportunity to discuss things with the day shift. I then stayed around until eight or nine to check out progress and procedures with the groups on the evening shift.

I was even roused out of bed on occasion by frantic phone calls from my "boys" on the night shift. Once at 3 A.M. I was breathlessly informed that "the admiral" had just come by and asked a lot of questions. The next morning at the lab I found that "the admiral" had really been an ensign on night duty. My caller was embarrassed, but I said,

"That's OK, to the uninitiated all officers are admirals and all ships are battleships."

As my responsibilities increased at the lab during 1941 I began to spend most of my time in Washington and very little on Chesapeake Bay. When I first came to Washington the previous fall I had moved into a rooming house on Kalorama Road Northwest with a number of other lab scientists. I had a small room in the basement which had been the coal bin before the furnace had been converted to gas. It was satisfactory except that the lab was in southeast Washington and to get there from our house in northwest Washington we had to travel right through the center of town. I enjoyed the trip through what was to me one of the world's most scenic, historic and beautiful cities, but it took 30 to 40 minutes each way. So during the summer I moved to the residence of a Mr. and Mrs. Gilbert on Pennsylvania Avenue Southeast where I had a small second floor room. With a bed, chair and chest of drawers there was barely enough room to turn around. It was a quiet location near the edge of the city and best of all only 10 minues by car from the lab. The address fascinated me because it was the same as that of the White House but at the opposite end of town. My new address was 1600 Pennsylvania Avenue Southeast while the White House was 1600 Pennsylvania Avenue Northwest.

Not long afterward, two bachelor Ph.D.s at the lab hinted about a proposition they wanted to make. They had rented an apartment in a brand new development nearby. Would I come over to see the apartment and have supper? Yes, I said, I would. When I got there I discovered that a good looking young woman was also there. She had prepared the dinner which was delicious. She taught chemistry at a high school in Baltimore but on weekends came down to Washington to stay with the boys. The proposition was that I move in and share expenses and also the girl on weekends. I expressed appreciation for the offer but declined. I had other ideas in mind which I thought were better.

In Ann Arbor during the fall of 1939 I was attracted to a beautiful, vivacious blond, Alice Linnea Maria Nelson, who was doing graduate work at the U of M in bacteriology while on leave from Colby Junior College in New Hampshire, where she had organized and taught courses for medical technologists. She had come to Michigan specifically to study with none other than Professor Isaacs, the famous hematologist who had directed the blood studies on our cyclotron team.

Alice was level headed, personable, forthright and very intelligent. Although she had majored in science at Simmons College in Boston she had many interests. She was a very good violinist with years of orchestra experience. I feigned an interest in music and took her to concerts such as the Ann Arbor May Festival. I helped her translate German medical journals for her language requirement and she taught me Swedish. In June 1940 Alice received her masters degree from Michigan and returned to Colby. I travelled to New England to visit her and meet her Swedish-born parents.

Alice was industrious. She could sew and was a superb cook. Her smorgasbords were fantastic. And I was very much in love, so what in Heaven's name was I waiting for?

In the fall of 1941 I invited her to meet me for a weekend in New York and late one night I proposed to her in the observation tower at the very top of the Empire State Building, then and for decades after, the tallest man-made structure in the world. At that dizzying height she had no alternative but to accept. We set the date of our wedding for the twentieth of December (1941) during the Colby Christmas vacation.

After the Japanese attack on Pearl Harbor on December 7, it looked like I might have difficulty getting so much as a day off to be married. The lab went to a nine-hour day, six days a week, plus eight hours on alternate Sundays. This didn't make much difference to me because with my three shifts working around the clock I had been putting in 14 hours a day at the lab anyway.

I managed to wangle a weekend off and we were married on Saturday, December 20, in the Immanuel Episcopal Church of Bellows Falls, Vermont, by the Reverend John Currier. It was a simple, small ceremony. The Reverend Currier did something I have never seen at any wedding before or since. He tied a knot, literally! After Alice and I had exchanged our marriage vows, he drew one end of his stole from around his neck and, as Alice and I clasped hands, he wrapped it firmly around them and, tying a tight knot, he pronounced us man and wife. We were deeply in love, a pleasant condition which all the years since have not changed.

Alice and I returned to Washington and my small room at the Gilberts. Two weeks later Alice returned to Colby Junior College to complete her teaching for the semester which ended late in January (1942). In the meantime I rented a small apartment and we moved in there when Alice came back. In mid October she gave birth to a son, John D., Junior, whom we called Jack, and when he was a few months old, he was baptized by Peter Marshall.

When I first came to Washington in 1940, I attended a number of different churches on those Sundays when I was not out on Chesapeake Bay. The one I liked best, and came to attend as regularly as possible, was the New York Avenue Presbyterian Church. The preacher, Peter Marshall, was sincere, unpretentious, yet forceful. He spoke simply but meaningfully and his words seemed to spring directly from his heart in a way that completely captivated me. He was big, young, virile, handsome and his speech was spiced with a delightful Scottish burr. After Alice came to Washington, we went to hear him as often as we could and after Jack arrived we asked Peter Marshall to baptize him. I could say more about Peter Marshall but his story is better told in the book "A Man Called Peter" by his wife, Catherine.

We were working under terrific pressure. I moved further up in the lab to succeed a man who had left because he couldn't take the strain. Added to this I was a member of the Board of Editors of the Institute of Radio Engineers. This meant that I had highly technical manuscripts to review in such odd moments as I could find.

One day at the lab a sign appeared on my desk which read,

"Degauss with Kraus"

It seemed appropriate and I kept it.

The NOL staff included Ellis Johnson and Francis Bitter of M.I.T., both authorities on magnetism. There was also John Bardeen, who in later years was co-inventor of the transistor and received not just one, but two Nobel prizes. Interestingly, he had attended Physics Colloquia at the U of M while I was working on the cyclotron there and decades earlier my dad had known John's father. We also had outside consultants, one of whom was Albert Einstein at Princeton.

Another lab member was Grote Reber, an electrical engineer from Wheaton, Illinois, who had made pioneering observations with a backyard radio telescope, a parabolic dish antenna 30 feet in diameter of a design which anticipated the modern radio telescope. Reber was the first person after Jansky to make radio astronomical observations or as he put it, to listen to "cosmic static." For almost a decade he was the world's *only* active radio astronomer.

Reber had already published a couple of articles on his work before he joined NOL in 1941. For a while Reber roomed at the Kalorama Road house while I was staying there. He described his equipment and observations of the Milky Way to me with a contagious enthusiasm and if we had not been at war I think that I would have started building a radio telescope then. But it was not until 10 years later at the Ohio State University that I had a chance to do it.

Our degaussing efforts saved many ships but it was accomplished at great cost in time and materials. The U.S. used more copper for degaussing coils than any other application. The need for copper was so great that the government was compelled to substitute steel for copper in pennies. The effort required huge amounts of manpower to design, manufacture, install and operate the degaussing systems. So even if the Germans failed to sink all the ships they hoped to, they diverted a vast amount of the Allies' resources.

I had not forgotten about the poor communication problem at the *Hannibal* range. It was a waste of both time and money and I felt something should be done about it. I had in mind employing ultra-short waves even shorter than Henry Muyskens and I had used on our dissertation experiments. In testing corner reflectors I had built some one meter wavelength equipment and found that even with a power of only one or two watts, it worked extremely well for distances of several miles.

I wanted to use two-way voice communication. The Navy had no intership telephones. It had no radiophones at all, all radio communication being by Morse code.

I thought that my scheme had merit but when I mentioned the word radio to any navy man I ran into a stone wall. To him radio meant something that could transmit hundreds or thousands of miles. You wouldn't want to inform half the world about your degaussing coil currents.

"Blinker lights are what you use when you are within visual range of other ships," I was told. "Radio isn't practical."

Offsetting this skeptical and generally discouraging attitude, my friend Bill Conklin of Wheaton, Illinois, and now a Lieutenant in the Navy at the Bureau of Ships in Washington, was sympathetic. He recognized the potential of my proposal and was helpful and encouraging.

So I put two of the men in my section, Ron Smith and Mike Hammer, to work on a simple system to do the job. It would be a small, portable battery-powered radio telephone unit that could be put aboard the ship under test. Within a few months we had built several prototype units weighing a few pounds each.

We tested the units between the lab and men on foot, on bicycles, in automobiles and in aircraft. We tested them between ship and shore on Chesapeake Bay and for their intended use between ships. They performed beautifully and exceeded our expectations. They provided loud, clear voice communication for distances up to 5 or 10 miles, more than we needed. With one unit in the chart room of the *Hannibal* and the other in the degaussing control room of the ship under test, the ship's degaussing engineer could talk *directly* to the scientist-in-charge on the *Hannibal*.

As an added demonstration we would place one of the units on the desk of an officer deep in the interior of one of large Navy buildings on Constitution Avenue, while one of us with another unit remained outside of the building at a distance. When the officer found he could talk to someone outside the building, the usual reaction was one of disbelief. His experience had told him that an all-steel building acted as a shield to radio waves, cutting them off, so how could this radio work inside the building? We explained that with a wavelength as short as one meter, the waves could enter the building through windows and doors and travel down corridors, acting as waveguides, to all parts of the building.

It finally got through to some of the older Navy personnel that the one-meter wavelength made this radio quite different from those they had been accustomed to and the unit's value was at long last recognized. The unit was given an official Navy type designation and a quantity was authorized for manufacture.

The units were years ahead of their time. With all of the walkie-talkies made since, there have been few produced working at one meter wavelength which provide the reliability, range, and flexibility of the ones we developed for the Navy while we were almost 100 percent occupied with other aspects of the degaussing problem.

By 1943 most of the basic degaussing problems had been solved or were, at least, well understood. Ships afloat were equipped with degaussing systems. Those under construction were being equipped with systems designed from our model measurements. The work was becoming less critical and more routine. Some personnel began leaving NOL to enter other phases of the war effort. The exodus was accelerated by a bureaucratic move to put all of the lab personnel on civil service. They had almost all been recruited, like I was, on a per diem contract. By fall all employees had to go on civil service.

By late summer I had the unusual distinction of being one of the two remaining NOL scientists retained on contract. The other was Albert Einstein.

Although my background was more in radio than magnetism, I had, I thought, been able to contribute to the degaussing work and my radio interests had been responsible for developing some useful one-meter equipment. But my work in radio and particularly antennas was well known. Shortly after joining NOL I met a senior scientist from the Naval Research Laboratory (NRL) at a party a friend had in his home. When I was introduced as "John Kraus from NOL" the scientist puffed up like a toad, grunted "Harrumph," and walked away. Much later I learned why.

To him I was an antenna man. NRL had developed radar and radars needed antennas. So, he concluded, if NOL had hired me that meant that NOL was working on radar too! The secrecy surrounding radar and degaussing was very tight, so tight the people in different laboratories of the Navy or different parts of the same laboratory didn't know what the others were doing. The NRL scientist had suspected, incorrectly, that NOL had begun work on radar which would undercut his program at NRL; hence, his rudeness.

Lesson: Don't jump to conclusions.

Then late in the summer of 1943 I received an invitation to work at the Radio Research Laboratory (RRL) just established at Harvard University under Professor Frederick E. Terman to do some type of radio work. I agreed to come. Maybe at RRL my radio and antenna experience would be useful.

I reported to RRL in October almost three years to the day from the time I started at NOL. The three months I had agreed with Ralph Bennett to come to NOL had stretched to an eventful, work-packed three years.

CHAPTER 12

STALKING RADARS

The U.S. and Britain as well as Germany had radars going early in the war. The radar on the German battleship *Bismark* was credited with sinking the British battle cruiser *H.M.S. Hood* on its first salvo. The Germans also had an effective radar, called the "Wurtzburg," for controlling anti-aircraft guns. RRL's job was to develop systems for locating radars, determining their characteristics, and making them ineffective by jamming or other radio techniques.

"Radar" is an acronym. It stands for "**RA**dio **D**irection **A**nd **R**ange." (It is also a palindrome: spelled the same forwards or backwards). A radar works like this: A transmitter sends out a series of short pulse signals in a beam from an antenna. An obstacle in the path of the beam reflects an echo back which is detected by a sensitive receiver. The time required for the echo to return indicates the distance or *range* of the obstacle and turning the antenna (and beam) for maximum echo reveals its *direction*. Ultra-short wavelengths, like the 5-meter waves Henry Muyskens and I had used or the 1-meter waves I had employed on my corner reflector tests or in the *Hannibal* range radiotelephone, were an asset. The shorter the wavelength, the sharper the beam could be for a given-sized antenna and the sharper the beam the more accurately the direction could be determined. So there had been a push by radar developers to go to shorter and shorter wavelengths.

By 1943 when I joined RRL, radar systems were already developed for wavelengths as long as 10 meters to as short as 3 centimeters. It was up to RRL to develop receivers, antennas, and jamming systems capable of operating over this entire range of wavelengths and to do it quickly. We described our job as one of radar counter-measures (RCM).

Perhaps the most remarkable thing about RRL was not *what* the lab did but *how* it did it. The lab was organized and operated with the objective of providing an atmosphere conducive of maximum productivity with a minimum of red tape. The goal was to transform an idea into a practical, tested, mass-produced device in a minimum of time.

Each scientist and engineer had the technicians, machinists, and secretaries needed in a spacious building on the Harvard campus. There was a large machine shop, plastics shop, wood working and pattern shop. Facilities were also available where prototype units could be given shake tests and subjected to salt spray to determine if they worked satisfactorily under conditions of severe vibration and high humidity. And at many places throughout the lab were small shops where the scientist or engineer could use a lathe or other tools to fashion a device without making any drawings beforehand. Everything was planned to get the job done as quickly as possible. Paper-work was a minimum and if there were any bureaucrats they kept a very low profile.

Not that everything at RRL was wholly without faults or imperfections. On one occasion I had dictated material for a memorandum describing an antenna we had developed, and had mentioned that in constructing the mounting bracket I had employed four pieces of "cold rolled steel." I was startled to read later that I had used four pieces of "cold roast veal!"

I was assigned to a group on the top floor of the lab. Our main job was to develop antennas. Andrew Alford, the group leader, had worked for the International Telephone and Telegraph Company (ITT) and had been responsible for developing a number of important devices including a blind landing system for aircraft.

Alford was fortyish, reserved and less than average height and weight. He had a penetrating mind and sharp wit. But above all he was unconventional. Born in Russia he had escaped during the revolution.

I found Alford's unconventionality refreshing and stimulating. He looked at problems from entirely different viewpoints than I had been accustomed to. I thought, "Alford is to antennas what Sikorsky is to aircraft."

After hours, with the lab largely deserted, Alford often lectured to me about antennas. Thinking aloud, he paced back and forth before the closed door of his office. Holding a Parliment cigarette and gesturing with his hands, he sketched imaginary drawings of antennas on the door paneling while I sat spellbound.

The basic countermeasures principle was simple. A ship or aircraft carried a special rapidly-tunable receiver which could scan the wavelength bands in which enemy radars might be operating. If one was detected its strength and characteristics gave clues as to the dangers involved and what the next tactic should be. If the operator was flying over enemy territory he could switch on a jammer, a powerful transmitter which would overload the radar receiver rendering it ineffective. Or he could dump bales of aluminum "chaff" from the airplane, or he could dump and jam.

Chaff consisted of thin strips of aluminum cut to the wavelength of the radar. As the bales opened, millions of aluminum strips fluttered through the air, like real straw or chaff, forming a huge cloud. Usually the radar echo from this cloud was so strong that the echo from the aircraft was hidden. The first time a German "Wurtzburg" operator at the controls of his radar witnessed a chaff drop he is said to have exclaimed,

"The bombers are reproducing!'

He had seen three American aircraft approaching on his radar scope when suddenly there appeared to be 50 more "aircraft," making him lose track of the actual ones.

An unanticipated side effect of the chaff drops was that thousands of German cows died from eating the aluminum strips along with grass as they grazed in the fields over which the bombers had flown. The aluminum strips were very light and, depending on the height of the drop, might stay up nearly an hour. But eventually they came down. If there was much wind they might land many miles from the point over which they were released.

To the operator in the aircraft it was important to know that there was a radar in the vicinity. His countermeasures receiver could tell him that. But it was almost as important to know *where* the radar was. Was it dead ahead, to the right, to the left or at some other angle? For this he needed a direction-finding system.

My work at RRL soon became concentrated on the development of direction-finding antennas and I had a small but highly competent group to work with me. We were charged with developing direction-finding antennas for both aircraft and ships. The general principles were the same for both but the aircraft units generally had to be smaller and lighter than the shipborne versions and also had to be streamlined.

We developed a series of antennas which spun rapidly inside fiberglass enclosures or "radomes." The corner reflector antenna, which I had invented just before the war, was incorporated as one of the rotating antennas.

After developing the antennas and testing them in the laboratories we made field tests. For the flight tests we went to an Army airfield at Bedford where the lab had a hanger with several aircraft. One of the workhorses we used for our tests was a big 4-engine B-17 bomber from which machine guns and other armament had been removed. We flew over Cambridge and the Boston area observing any and all radars that were running. RRL had transmitters and radars we turned on for these tests. The Radiation Laboratory at MIT was a radar development organization and usually many radars were also operating there.

The Army Airforce maintained a pool of pilots to fly our planes. One was Captain Dryden, whom we called the "old woman," really a complimentary nick-name. It meant that he was careful and particular; in fact, downright fussy. He wouldn't take off unless the plane and its four engines were all working just right. When I asked him to fly in circles so I could test our direction-finding antenna at all compass points, he only agreed to do so if he could circle to the left. This was because he sat in the left-hand pilot's seat which afforded him good vision ahead and to the left but not to the right. Although he had a copilot seated on the right side, he never entrusted anything to him except in emergencies. All of the lab members wanted to fly with Dryden whenever possible, and, on occasion, I flew with him.

But other times I flew with other pilots. One, not so popular with the lab personnel, was the "cowboy," who was the exact opposite of the "old woman." He was of the "baling wire and chewing gum" school and would fly anything that would flap in the breeze. He had been awarded a Distinguished Flying Cross for sinking a Japanese battleship in the South Pacific.

"Just plain luck," he said. "There I was on a night bomb run over the Jap fleet. I was dodging flak when my bombardier reported that our bomb release mechanism was jammed. So I pulled up as hard as I could to get the hell out of there when, whamo, all the bombs came loose and scored direct hits on a battleship I didn't even know was there!"

One day I went up with the "cowboy" at the controls of our B-17. I was aware that our takeoff had been somewhat unorthodox but, inside the plane and busy with my equipment, I did not realize how close the "cowboy" had shaved it until we got back. The pilots had gone when "Chris," the lab's airfield expediter, came over to me shaking his head.

"Wowie," he said, "we really held our breath as we watched your takeoff! He had hardly gotten his wheels off the ground when he made an awfully sharp left bank like a crazy god-damn fool! I'm telling you, John, the left wing tip was actually clipping the dandlions and timothy tops! If that wing had hit the ground the plane would've cartwheeled and crashed making French fries of you all!"

Without a load of bombs, the "cowboy" probably thought that the big bomber was so light he could perform any maneuver with it. I'm just glad he didn't try a loop.

On another flight that I made from Bedford airport with another pilot, we had just leveled off at about 3000 feet preparatory to some test runs when clouds of yellow-brown smoke began to billow from the direction-finding receiver unit in front of my seat. Fires can be bad anywhere but in an airplane flying 300 miles per hour at 3000 feet they are a very serious matter. I tripped the mechanical safety release and pulled the receiver out of the rack holding it. This automatically shut off the electric power to the unit and gradually the smoke dimished. Coughing and wheezing I debated what to do. I could call the pilot on the airplane interphone and request that he return to Bedford airport or I could see if I could fix the receiver. It often took weeks of work and planning to arrange for a test flight and once up on one I didn't want to abort it if it could be helped.

Inspection showed that the smoke had been coming from a large resistor. Why this trouble hadn't shown up on all of the previous tests I never knew. A short circuit must have developed. I could detect no significant damage so I pushed the receiver back into the rack and, holding my breath, turned the power on again. There was no smoke this time and the receiver seemed to function normally. Before I could make another move the pilot called me on the interphone to inquire if I was ready for him to start on the test runs or was there some problem. I told him to go ahead saying, "Yes, there was a problem. But it's OK now." Even so, I kept my fingers crossed for the rest of the flight!

For tests on ships we went to Navy Yards at Boston and elsewhere. In the middle of the winter I went to the Brooklyn Navy Yard to accompany the new destroyer escort *Sturtevant* (DE239), on some sea trials of our system. The direction-finding antenna in its fiberglass enclosure or "radome" weighing several hundred pounds had been installed on a steel arm extending forward from the main mast at a point high up on the mast. To balance it the captain should have added a couple tons of ballast close to the keel of the ship but he didn't bother. He believed that the ship had enough stability.

This question came up regularly on many ships as more radar, counter-measure, and other antennas were added on the mast. Their weight could make the ship unstable unless it was compensated by ballast added below decks in the ship's hold. It had been reported that some Navy ships out-fitted with more than the usual complement of antennas had actually turned over in a typhoon in the Pacific.

We put out to sea on the *Sturtevant* and proceeded up the New England coast testing our direction-finding system. Things went fine until the second day when we ran into a vicious nor'easter. Waves began to break right over the top of the flying bridge, the highest deck on the ship. The ship bounced and kicked like a bucking bronco. Everytime a huge wave lifted the bow of the ship up at a crazy angle, the whole ship shuddered as we came crashing down. But the roll was worst of all. Sometimes we rolled over so far I wondered whether we would ever come back. I thought about our antenna and its extra weight up there on the mast. Would it pull us over on the next roll?

The captain had reduced speed so we were just holding our heading into the wind but we still bounced and rolled. Water was coming in from the upper decks and toilets had reversed and were backing up. In the chief's quarters where I had been bunking, everything came loose and spilled out onto the floor. There were pots and pans, knives, forks, spoons, plates and cups, chairs and tables all sliding across the floor in a huge crashing, banging, tinkling heap first against one wall (or bulkhead) and a half minute later against the opposite wall.

Almost everyone aboard became sea sick, retching everywhere, any-where. I had sailed a lot and been in a number of storms and had never been sea sick. I felt smug. I wasn't sea sick at all. But then it got to me too.

A day later the storm subsided and we had ample opportunity to test our direction-finding system, which performed admirably. The officers of the *Sturtevant* were delighted with the new addition. The *Sturtevant* was scheduled to escort a convoy of ships leaving for England in a few days and was the best equipped radar countermeasures ship in the convoy.

Another test was arranged for a Navy ship based at Fort Lauderdale, Florida. I booked a flight down on the Eastern Airlines leaving Boston early one hot summer afternoon. From Boston to New York at 5000 feet our DC-3 wound through dazzling white canyons of cumulo-nimbus thunder-head clouds that towered miles above us on all sides like gargantuan, never-ending cauliflowers.

On the New York to Miami leg, Captain Davis, our pilot got little help from the copilot, who spent most of his time in the rear of the plane talking with the stewardess. When it was time for our supper he helped her fill the trays while she served the passengers. I have never before or since had such fast service and I wondered about his motives. After we arrived late that night at Miami I talked with the copilot and the stewardess. They were both radiant and beaming from ear to ear. I didn't ask but I guessed that on the flight down he had proposed and she had accepted.

I was shaken a day later to read in the Miami paper that on Captain Davis' return flight north, his DC-3 had been struck in mid-air over Florida by an Army fighter plane. Captain Davis had made a skillful wheels-up landing in a corn field with his damaged DC-3. Two of his passengers, sitting where the fighter plane had struck the fuselage, had been killed but he, his crew, and the rest of the passengers were unharmed. The fighter pilot had parachuted to safety.

Our tests at sea on the destroyer provided much information. I was able to evaluate the performance of our direction-finding system as to ease of identifying radars, accuracy of bearings and distance over which radars could be detected.

I returned north on a National Airlines Lockheed Loadstar piloted by Captain Wedge. At supper time he came back and sat next to me while we ate. We discussed the mid-air collision of the DC-3. Wedge said that fighter pilots frequently stunted around passenger planes. A favorite trick, he said, was for the fighter pilot to come in from behind and above the passenger plane. Then diving below it to gather more speed, the pilot would pull up in a vertical climb in front of the passenger plane. Wedge said,

"It's really startling to have a plane flash suddenly out of nowhere going straight up just feet in front of you!"

The passenger plane pilots had complained, but the Airforce had its oddballs, and crashes like the one a few days before didn't seem to faze them.

Back at the lab things were normal until one noon when fire broke out on the roof. A high-power jammer being tested at the lab was putting out so much power that its big wood and wire antenna on the roof burst into flames. It could be seen from all over the Harvard campus and someone in another building turned in the alarm. The Cambridge fire department arrived in force but the security guards at RRL would not let them in because the firemen didn't have security clearances.

It made for a strange picture. Engines and firemen were there but they stood helplessly outside while fire raged on the roof above the reach of their ladders. Meanwhile a hurried conference was called in the building to deal with the situation. Presently the firemen were admitted one at a time with one security guard assigned to each fireman, trailing him all the way to the roof and standing by while the fireman joined the others using portable extinguishers and hoses pulled to the roof from fire stations on the top floor. The fire was soon brought under control but the antenna was wrecked.

Some of the radar jammers developed at RRL had enormous power. One had been under test at the Bedford airfield on a cold, windy day when I was there installing a direction-finding antenna on a B-17. The jammer was connected to an antenna radiating a beam across the field. The antenna was nearly a quarter of a mile away and, even though the beam was invisible, I could guess its direction from the way its antenna was pointed. I had only to walk a hundred paces out onto the field to get into the beam. I had been shivering but suddenly I felt warm all over as I entered the beam. It was a pleasant sensation, like going from Boston to Miami in a single step, but I didn't stay long. From my experience with the diathermy machine which I built for Wally Teed I knew that there were hazards. The RRL jammer was like a giant diathermy machine or electronic oven which could cook you a half mile away!

At an Institute of Radio Engineers meeting in New York I had seen Grote Reber. He had left NOL and was working with a radio manufacturer in Chicago. In his spare time he was doing more radio astronomy with the big parabola in his backyard. He excitedly told me that he had detected strong radio signals from the sun. We were then (1945) entering a period of increased sunspot activity and apparently solar radio emission increased during these periods because he hadn't previously detected any signals from the sun.

The story was not published until after the war, but solar radio emission had also been observed during the war in England. A number of anti-aircraft gun-control radars in the south of England suddenly became inoperative because of a very strong noise signal. It was feared that the Germans had developed a new kind of radar jamming system and that a massive air attack was imminent. But Dr. J.S. Hey, a British scientist (and later radio astronomer), investigated the reports and concluded that the interference was due to strong solar radio emission associated with large sunspots on the solar disc at the time.

Then in August 1945 came the announcement that the U.S. had dropped an atomic bomb on Hiroshima. When I had been working on the cyclotron in Ann Arbor and listening to lectures by Fermi, Lawrence and others, the practical demonstration of atomic energy had seemed a long ways off. Now only 10 years later, the atom's awesome energy had been unleashed in a devastating blast of incredible power. It was hard to believe.

We quipped that soon there might be no need for coal or oil and maybe an aspirin-sized tablet of atomic fuel would drive our automobile for a year! But three decades later cars still used gasoline, although there were atomic power plants. However, these plants and many other peaceful applications of atomic power were taking longer than expected for development. Sometimes things come quickly; sometimes they come more slowly if at all. It was man's misfortune that with all the atom's great potential for good, it was the bomb with all its malevolence that came first. And whereas it often takes many experimental attempts to get a new device to function, the very first experimental atomic bomb worked!

Three days later on August 9 a second bomb was dropped on Nagasaki. The end of the war was in sight and RRL began an orderly winding down. Many of the staff started to leave for other jobs. Dr. Terman encouraged me to stay on to work with a small group writing a book on the developments made at the lab during the war. Secrecy restrictions would be lifted to allow open publication.

So in a matter of days I went from researcher to author. I stayed on for several months writing and editing. Equipment and systems we had developed at the lab had such great potential for many peace-time applications that it was regarded as very important to document the work carefully in book form.

As the lab closed down, its staff scattered to all parts of the country. Dr. Terman returned to Stanford University as Dean of Engineering.* Andrew Alford set up in business for himself in Boston, manufacturing antennas and related equipment. John Dyer of the receiver group, who in earlier years had been radio operator on Admiral Byrd's first Antarctic expedition, formed with several others a radio research organization called Airborne Instruments Laboratory, and Sam Beraducci, of my group, joined it. Lab members were scattering to all corners of the U.S. but for the moment I didn't go anywhere. I had no job.

---

*Later he became Provost and Vice President of the university.

CHAPTER 13

CORKSCREWS

No job but many offers. I had received nearly a dozen from industry, some of them excellent. A particularly good one had come from North American Philips on the Hudson River above New York City. Dr. Ora Duffendack, the Research Director, invited me to visit him for an interview. The offer he made was very attractive but it involved only research. What really wanted was a university position where I could both teach and do research. The combination, I felt, was important, especially so at the graduate level. The research would make me a better teacher while teaching would give impetus to my research.

So far I hadn't received any university offers of this kind. I had gotten offers from the University of Texas, at Austin, where I went for an interview, and another from the still-on-paper not-yet-established U.S. Navy Postgraduate School at Monterey, California, but the Texas offer involved only research and no teaching while the Navy offer involved only teaching and no research. I declined both.

It seemed certain that universities would soon be over-run with post-war students but the administrators didn't yet appear to be concerned about staffing for the coming flood. Should I accept the North American Philips offer or should I wait for a university offer that might never come? The decision was not easy but I declined Duffendack's offer.

I had written to several universities without any results. Meanwhile I spent endless hours at our small home in Newton Center, Massachusetts, studying books on mathematics, physics, and electromagnetic theory. To some extent it was a review but I went beyond material I had previously studied. I wanted to be ready when a university offer did come.

Then one day in January, 1946, I received a letter from Professor Erwin E. Dreese, Chairman of the Department of Electrical Engineering at the Ohio State University in Columbus. Ohio State was one of the universities to which I had not written. Professor Dreese had sent his letter early in December but it carried a Washington address and although eventually forwarded to me in Massachusetts, it had taken a number of weeks. He explained that he was seeking someone to fill the position vacated by Professor William Everitt, who had gone to the University of Illinois. The job could involve both teaching and research. Would I be interested, he asked. Yes, I replied, very much so.

Dreese then invited me to Columbus for an interview and one morning in February I met with him in his office on the campus. He was stockily-built, jovial, energetic and radiated a contagious enthusiasm. I was impressed by his progressive, positive attitudes. He explained that although the university did not have money for research in its general fund, there were several special funds which might be used. Soon he made an offer of an associate professorship at $5000 a year starting in June. Although the salary was much less than I had been offered on several industrial jobs, I accepted. We then walked to the Administration Building where he introduced me to President Howard L. Bevis.

Crossing the campus with Professor Dreese on our way back to his office we reminisced. I knew that he had graduated from the University of Michigan and had taught electrical engineering there for several years; also that he had been the engineer-in-charge of the U of M's broadcasting station WCBC which I had listened to in the early 1920's with my galena and catwhisker receiver. I reminded him that I had met him once while he was in charge of WCBC. In 1925 he became Chief Engineer of Lincoln Electric in Cleveland, Ohio, a large manufacturer of welding machinery and equipment and in 1930 he came to Ohio State University (OSU). He told me that he had had a long-standing interest in astronomy and while still an undergraduate at Michigan had considered astronomy as a career. He was enthusiastic about my physics background because "the physics of today is the engineering of tomorrow." Historically, OSU's electrical engineering department had at one time been combined with physics in what was known as the Department of Physics and Electrical Engineering.

Before I left that afternoon, "Deke" Dreese, as he was often called, said that there would be a special $5000 research fund waiting for me to help on my research. I was delighted.

Professor Dreese asked me to teach a graduate course on waveguides and transmission lines when I came in June. This was the second in a series of three courses which I was to develop. The first course was on basic electromagnetic theory with the final course on antennas and I was to teach these during the following fall and winter.

Back home in Newton Center, I spent many hours each day studying electromagnetic theory, and preparing lecture notes for all three courses, making numerous trips to public libraries and coming home each time loaded down with more books on electromagnetic theory and its applications. Each time I thought I had found the perfect book for my needs but each time I eventually encountered questions which the book failed to answer. I inched through long calculations involving differential equations, complex variables, and boundary conditions. It was hard work but I persisted through the spring and into June.

My lecture notes for the summer quarter began to take shape. Professor Dreese had suggested that I have them mimeographed when I came. Gradually my thoughts swung toward expanding them into a book. But that seemed a long way off.

Finally by June after the movers had loaded our household goods and departed, Alice and I packed our personal effects into our Pontiac sedan and with our sons Jack and Nelson, aged 4 and 2, we drove west, with stops in New Hampshire, to see Alice's parents and in Ann Arbor to see mine.

At Ohio State there were many war veterans in my classes. They were mature, hard-working and eager to learn. To me they were a stimulus and a challenge and I did little else but study, prepare notes, give and correct problems and exams.

The summer quarter drew to a close. A few weeks later the fall quarter began. I was now teaching the first and third courses in the electromagnetic theory sequence. I gave the basic or first course to a class at eight o'clock in the morning and I presented the third course on antennas and radiating systems to a class which met two nights a week from seven to eight thirty. This class had been scheduled in the evening to permit engineers working at many of the industries in and around Columbus to attend. Both classes were large. I also taught a circuits lecture and lab course.

I was up nearly every night to midnight preparing lecture notes. I looked forward to the weekends and holidays because they afforded me large blocks of uninterrupted time for study and preparation. Teaching was hard work but was rewarding when I could see students progressing in their understanding. I was content. I also became accustomed to being called "John Kraus from Harvard." This amused me because I had always thought of myself as from Michigan.

Paul Raines of a large eastern laboratory visited OSU in November 1946 and gave a seminar. I attended his afternoon lecture on traveling wave tubes in which he described his work on these devices for amplifying signals of very short wavelength. In these tubes an electron beam is fired down the inside of a long helix. After the lecture I chatted a bit with Dr. Raines. Having previously speculated some about trying a helix as an antenna I asked,

"Do you think a helix might work as an antenna?"

"No," he replied, "I've tried it and it doesn't work."

The finality of his statement got me to thinking. Perhaps he had had no luck with the helix as an antenna because he had used too small a diameter for the helix as in a traveling wave tube. I had in mind a much larger diameter. Using Alford's intuitive type of reasoning, I theorized that if a helix were as large as one wavelength in circumference it would have to radiate in some fashion or other. Just how, I had no idea, but I wanted to try. If Raines had said "Yes, maybe it will work," I don't think I would have been half as eager to find out.

Leaving the lecture room I went to my office where I had a 12-centimeter wavelength oscillator the size of a quart can. It was a war-surplus unit which I had acquired as a gift from General Electric before coming to Columbus. I planned to take the oscillator home, make a helix, and see if it worked as an antenna.

I decided to do it at home for two reasons: first, I had no lab space of my own on the campus—the department was very crowded—and second, I felt a certain embarrassment about trying it. No one had ever made a helical antenna. Furthermore, Dr. Raines had said it wouldn't work so it was probably a foolish thing to do, and I didn't want anyone looking over my shoulder and asking questions.

When I left my office for home late that afternoon with my briefcase crammed with lecture notes and exam papers, I tucked the GE oscillator under my arm. At supper Alice and our boys must have thought I was in a trance but when I was thinking I was usually uncommunicative. That night my thoughts were about helices and right after supper I took the GE oscillator downstairs to our basement to rig it up on the workbench.

It was Monday and too cold to hang clothes outside so Alice had hung our family wash on ropes strung near the ceiling. The workbench was hidden behind sheets, tablecloths, shirts and underwear. I ducked and dodged through the white forest and put the oscillator on the workbench. From my radio amateur junk box under the bench I extracted a couple feet of copper wire and a section of a cardboard mailing tube about an inch in diameter. I wound 7 turns of wire on the tube forming a helix about 6 inches long. Sliding the wire helix off the tube I connected one end to a terminal on the GE oscillator can. The helix was held horizontally a few inches above the workbench looking for all the world like a large corkscrew projecting from a tin can.

But to test it I needed a receiving device. From scraps of wire and metal I cut and soldered together a dipole antenna 2 inches long which looked like a small bow tie. Adding a crystal diode to the center of the dipole I mounted it perpendicular to the end of a two-foot long wooden dowel rod and connected it to a pair of headphones. The oscillator operated directly from the 115 volt 60 hertz power line, so I should hear a 60 hertz hum in the headphones if I picked up its signal. The apparatus was very simple and crude but I hoped that it would be adequate.

It had taken only a minute or two to wind the helix and mount it but I had spent most of an hour getting the crystal receiver with headphones rigged.

16. "I wound 7 turns of wire forming a helix looking for all the world like a large corkscrew projecting from a tin can." It was the first helical beam antenna. When I rotated the rod in my hands so that the little bow-tie shaped antenna at the end spun around like a propellor "nothing changed which could mean only one thing, the radiation from the helix was circularly polarized."

About eight thirty I was ready for the test. Alice was upstairs in the kitchen and the boys were on the second floor in bed. I turned on the oscillator and using the dipole antenna with crystal as a probe I began to explore the fields along the side of the helix. There was some radiation because when I brought the little bow-tie close to the helix I could hear a distinct 60 hertz hum in the phones on my head.

After probing along one side of the helix for a while I decided to probe along the other side to see if both sides behaved the same. As I moved the probe to do this, the bow-tie passed near the open end of the helix.

"Z-o-o-m!" My headphones rattled, the signal was very strong; much,

much stronger than along the sides of the helix. I found it hard to believe that the corkscrew could radiate so strongly off the end. I wondered if the oscillator might be producing the beam. But when I removed the helix the beam disappeared. Then I tried an ordinary straight wire antenna. It radiated as it should so apparently the helix was responsible for the beam.

I put the helix back and asked myself a question. If the radiation was really coming off the end of the helix how would it be polarized? That is, would the bow-tie antenna receive it best when horizontal, vertical, or at some angle? To find out I stood facing the helix holding the dowel rod with its tiny antenna close to the end of the corkscrew. By rotating the rod the bow-tie antenna could spin around like a propellor through all possible directions. When I rotated it nothing changed. The hum or zoom in the phones was equally loud in all orientations. This could mean only one thing, the radiation from the helix was *circularly polarized,* that is, the field rotated through all angles! All of the antennas I had ever used before were linearly polarized, that is, the field had a fixed orientation, usually horizontal or vertical.

By now I was trembling with excitement. Not only did the helix radiate *off its end* but the radiation was circularly polarized! I called upstairs to Alice and asked her to come down and witness a demonstration. She pulled some of the sheets and tablecloths back a bit so she could see better. Putting the phones on her head I went through the whole routine: first a straight wire antenna, next the helix, probing first the weak field along the side and then the strong field off the end. Finally, I rotated the probe antenna to demonstrate the circular polarization. Alice heard what I had heard, so I wasn't imagining it, and she seemed impressed. Sensing I might require more room she began to take down and fold the wash. This gave me needed space and I began moving the probe across the beam of radiation to determine its "beamwidth." The beam was surprisingly narrow, which meant that the helix was a highly directional end-fire antenna.

It was almost too much to believe and I still had a nagging feeling that some strange circumstance was the cause rather than the helix. Maybe I should try some different sizes of helices. So I wound ones with smaller and others with larger diameters. They radiated in almost the same way. This was even harder to believe. No antenna I knew about was that insensitive to a change in dimensions. I tried much larger and much smaller diameter helices. At last the beam disappeared. Then I tried longer and shorter helices. This change also had an effect. The longer helices produced narrower beams. This was what one might expect so in one respect, at least, the helix performed in a predictable manner.

For many weeks I spent evenings and weekends at the workbench experimenting with helices of all kinds while at the same time trying to evolve a theory to explain how they worked. All this came on top of an overfull teaching load so I was even busier if that were possible. I improved my workbench measuring arrangement and began to fill notebooks with the results of field patterns, polarization, and beamwidths which I measured on helices of different diameters, turn spacing, number of turns, and wire size.

Gradually a picture began to emerge. A helix radiated off its end over a wide range of diameters and turn spacings. Within a certain range of these dimensions, the helices all behaved much the same. It was this non-criticalness which I had found so puzzling in my earliest measurements. And most remarkably, the dimensions I picked for my very first helix were optimum—right in the middle of this non-critical region!

Jack and Nels were sick a day or so with what was apparently the mumps but they had light cases. About a week later I became very sick. My neck swelled up so big that my head simply merged with my shoulders. There was no doubt about it, I had the mumps—a really severe case. I was in bed for several days and was unable to meet my classes or go to the campus.

One day Alice brought my mail home from the campus. I was still in bed but felt well enough to sit up and ask for it. Among the letters was a large envelope from the Institute of Radio Engineers (IRE) offices in New York. As a member of the Board of Editors of the IRE I frequently received manuscripts for review and one was enclosed but as I slid the manuscript out of the envelope my eye caught the title,

"A helical antenna for circular polarization."

I had an instant relapse. I dropped the manuscript and sank into the bed and groaned.

History was replete with instances where two individuals in different locations had independently invented or discovered the same thing almost simultaneously. My mind suggested that this must also be true of the the helical antenna. Some one else had already discovered what I had about the helix, I thought.

It was all of an hour before I regained enough strength to pick up the manuscript and read it. Harold A. Wheeler, a well-known and highly inventive radio engineer, was the author. As I read I became very puzzled. Wheeler described a helix, yes, but he mentioned nothing about the strong end-fire radiation which I had found. He described only radiation off the sides, that is, broadside to the helix. Slowly it became clear that Wheeler and I had independently found two entirely distinct and unrelated modes of radiation from the helix, one broadside and the other end-fire. Furthermore, Wheeler's mode occurred only on helices which were very small in diameter (compared to the wavelength) and the circular polarization occurred only if a critical diameter-spacing relationship was satisfied. Wheeler had deduced this mathematically without even constructing a helix to test his theory. By contrast, the end-fire mode which I had discovered occurred on much larger helices with circumferences equal to the wavelength, produced sharp beams of radiation, and was much less critical. Further, I had found the end-fire mode experimentally and was evolving a theory after the fact.

My temperature, if it had shot up, was soon back to normal and I felt much better. I gave Wheeler's article a good rating and recommended it for publication.

Before the mumps I had been preparing an article on the end-fire helical antenna based on my basement tests and after recovering I completed it and sent it to *Electronics,* which published it in April 1947.

During the spring and summer of 1947 I worked with two graduate students, Claude Williamson and Otto Glasser, to acquire more complete and exact data on the end-fire helical antenna. Money from my special research fund helped buy materials and equipment.

There was no available laboratory space so Claude and I rigged a helix for measurements in a barren, dusty nook of the attic of the old Communications Lab which had been an airplane hanger in World War I. The studios of the university's radio station WOSU were below. There was not even a floor, just exposed ceiling joists over which we placed a few large sheets of plywood. Access was by a tall ladder. We constructed many helices and made extensive measurements. After several months we began to understand something about the complex manner in which the helix radiated.

We worked well into the summer on the problem. Williamson wrote a master's thesis on the results and we jointly published an article in the *Journal of Applied Physics.*

The *Electronics* article and this one stimulated considerable interest in the helical antenna and I began to get a steady flow of phone calls, letters and visitors. Two of the early visitors came from Sweden but at different times. One was Eric Hallen, Professor of Electrical Engineering at the Royal Technical Institute in Stockholm. The other was Bengt Josephson of the Swedish Research Institute in Stockholm. Both were large, heavy men but they managed to clamber up the ladder to our improvised attic "lab" and see our helix measuring apparatus.

Josephson became so interested in examining the equipment that he didn't realize he had stepped off our temporary plywood floor onto the fiberboard ceiling below. Suddenly he exclaimed in Swedish, "Vad i Guds namn? (What in God's name?)," and I turned just in time to see him descending through the ceiling as it gave way under his weight. I grabbed him as he clutched for a plywood board. I tugged and he landed flat on the plywood. As I helped him to his feet I could see there was now a gaping hole where he had almost fallen through into the WOSU broadcasting rooms below. WOSU personnel were able to patch up the ceiling but admonished us against this unorthodox way of dropping into their studio.

Concurrently with Williamson's work, Otto Glasser and I set up another helix projecting from a second floor window of the lab. Otto used a special device to measure some helix characteristics at different wavelengths and found that the helix performed without much change over a 2 to 1 range in wavelength. This remarkable characteristic would make the helix useful for many applications. Glasser prepared a master's thesis on the results and we jointly published a paper.

From our studies, we had made tremendous progress in less than a year in understanding the helical antenna but much more remained to be done. We needed to accurately measure the width of the beam from the helix at many wavelengths. For this, another student, Milford Horton, helped me set up equipment in an empty field at the corner of Neil and 19th Avenues on the campus where Caldwell Laboratory with my office now stands. Here we measured many helices into the fall and winter of 1947.

About this time the university constructed an all-wood two-story building across the street. The building was supported entirely above ground on a number of concrete pedestals two feet high. The building had been salvaged from an army base, dismantled board by board and moved to the campus. It had seen rough use and although nailed back together reasonably well it swayed and vibrated as one walked about inside. But this was nothing compared to the way it bounced and shook when someone went up or down the stairs. By contrast an earthquake of maximum intensity 9 on the Richter scale would have passed unnoticed. However, the building provided much needed space for two classrooms on the first floor. There were also a few rooms on the second floor and I acquired one of these as my office. At long last I now had my own office, not just one desk amid dozens of others in a big room in the Communications Lab. Best of all, next to my office was a room which could be outfitted as a lab. Here Milford Horton and I could construct helical antennas and prepare them for tests across the street. We also moved the apparatus used by Williamson and Glasser from the Communications Lab to our new "lab."

From our many months of measurements I prepared an article emphasizing the practical applications of the helix and published it in the IRE *Proceedings.* Also I presented a talk with demonstration on the helix

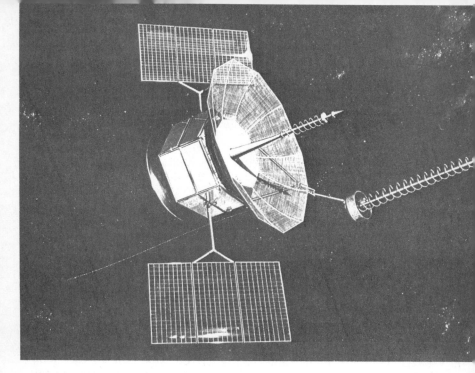

17. Communications satellite with helical antennas jutting out like huge corkscrews to gather in voice, television and data signals from many locations world-wide, including ships and aircraft, and relay them back to other places. Four such satellites in stationary orbit give global coverage.

before a big crowd at the IRE National Convention in the Grand Central Palace in New York City in March 1948. Alice accompanied me. It was our first visit to the city together since I had proposed to her atop the Empire State Building seven years before.

I started a pair of new graduate students, Carroll Bagby and Tom Tice, on further studies of the helical antenna. In a concluding paragraph of his thesis, Bagby pointed out that the helix was an important and fundamental form of nature and he suggested that the helix might be important on an atomic scale, a prediction borne out by the discovery a few years later that polymeric molecules are helices and in 1953 by the announcement of Watson and Crick that the DNA molecule is a double helix.

           *   *   *   *   *

To meet the needs of my classes I worked long hours to get my lecture notes into book form and made careful drawings of the hundreds of figures. I had arranged with Edwards Brothers in Ann Arbor to lithoprint the book as a low-cost paperback edition. Mr. Long, founder and owner of Long's College Book Company on High Street across from the OSU campus, agreed to underwrite the cost of the printing and handle the sale and distribution of the book which was called "Elements of Electromagnetics."

During the summer of 1949 I corrected proof which came in batches at almost weekly intervals. We needed the book for the start of the fall classes. Edwards Brothers were on a tight schedule but expected to run off the copies in time if I could transport them to Columbus. Just before the start of the fall quarter I drove to Ann Arbor, loaded enough copies for the fall classes into my car and delivered them to Mr. Long the next day.

We used the book in my course. Mr. Long also promoted it with a post-card mailing to other universities and the printing was soon sold out.

While I had been working on "Elements of Electromagnetics" I was also laboring long hours including many on weekends and holidays on a much bigger book entitled "Antennas." It had hundreds of figures, equations, and problems with chapters on all different kinds of antennas including one on the helical antenna. I sent the foot-high 20-pound manuscript to McGraw-Hill in the summer of 1949, and for months thereafter proof arrived in installments. Finally, by mid-year 1950 the book appeared. It was 553 pages long and I estimate that I had spent close to 5000 hours over a five year period preparing the book and getting it published. It was the ninth book in a new series on Electrical and Electronic Engineering

18.   Atlas rocket blasting off from John F. Kennedy Space Center, Cape Canaveral, Florida, with helical antenna at top of launching tower for transmitting commands to the rocket.

done under the consulting editorship of none other than Fred Terman, my former RRL boss. The book was well received. It became a standard reference on antennas and many universities adopted it as the text for their courses.

The helical beam antenna soon came into very wide use on land, sea and in the air. At OSU we put it to use in our first radio telescope and later Jim Douglas employed vast arrays of helices in the radio telescope he built at the University of Texas. After Sputnik the helix became the work horse of space communications. Satellites carried them, Cape Canaveral bristled with hundreds of them, and they were much in evidence at satellite communication stations around the world.

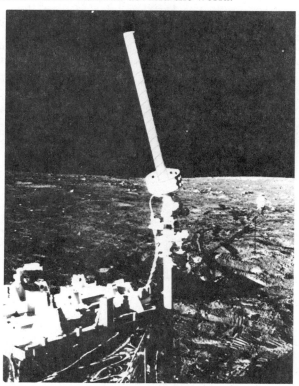

19. Helical antenna placed on the Fra Mauro highlands of the moon by the Apollo 14 astronauts Alan Shepard, Jr., and Edgar Mitchell for radioing information back to earth about conditions there. The helix wire is supported by a thin plastic tube.

Then when the Apollo astronauts travelled to the moon, they took along helical antennas which they installed there to transmit data back from lunar experiments by radio telemetry. These continued to send information on conditions on the moon years after the last Apollo astronauts departed.

The helical beam antenna is one of the most unique and widely used antennas ever invented. I discovered it only because I tried what some might have called a foolish experiment.

CHAPTER 14

CAROLINE LOVEJOY

Everyone in Columbus burned soft coal. The smoke often accumulated during the night, hanging over the city in a giant black cloud until nearly noon of the next day. Driving to my eight o'clock class one chilly, spring morning, the rising sun loomed through the cloud like a huge, glowing red ball suspended in the eastern sky. The density of the cloud was perfect for seeing the sun's disc clearly, better than looking through a smoked glass. A big black splotch stood out prominently on the disc halfway between its center and edge.

"Can that be a sunspot," I thought, "or is it a thick place in the 'Columbus cloud'?"

As I continued driving the splotch didn't budge from its position on the disc so I concluded it must be a sunspot. I had never seen such a big one and Hey's and Reber's war-time observations flashed through my mind.

"Such a big spot probably will be accompanied by strong radio emission," I said to myself. "I really ought to see if I can detect it!"

Between classes I connected a yard-square corner-reflector antenna to a war-surplus receiver which had a sensitive indicating meter. I carried the antenna out onto the second floor fire-escape platform of our wooden lab building and pointed it alternately at the sun and away while watching the indicating meter. I observed no movement on the meter. I presumed that there were radio waves associated with the spot and that I got no indication because my equipment was too primitive. This turned out to be the case but I came much closer to detecting the sun than Art Adel and I had in Ann Arbor over a dozen years before!

I wanted to try a bigger antenna and a more sensitive receiver but my teaching, experiments with the helix, and writing of books and articles gave me no opportunity. There was also committee work.

Several professors and I had to interview all the candidates for graduate work in electrical engineering. We had a large number of candidates, many from other institutions or with a potpurri of courses taken in a variety of military or defense engineering programs. The candidates were all men except for Joy Eaton, an attractive, young brunette, who had majored in music and mathematics in Texas before the war and in electronics in a war-time army curriculum.

We interviewed the candidates individually. When Joy's turn came, the professor acting as our chairman took one look at her as she entered the room and, muttering "All the bitch wants is a man," turned his chair completely around so his back was toward her. I was aghast at his rude display of male chauvinism. He had closed his mind to the fact that a woman might make a first-rate electrical engineer.

He refused to speak to her so I took over as chairman and proceeded with the interview. I was impressed with Joy's educational qualifications and the sincerity of her interest in electrical engineering. She appeared more competent and better prepared than many of the men we had interviewed. I gave her my vote and she was admitted. Some years later she became the first woman to obtain a doctor's degree in electrical engineering at OSU. As her advisor, I supervised her dissertation on a radio astronomy topic. After receiving her doctorate she joined a large California space lab and has had a very successful engineering career while being a homemaker too. She has told me that most male engineers treat her as an equal but that once in a while she still encounters the same highly-biased attitude exhibited by the professor that day at OSU.

One day I received a letter from Sam Lutz, chairman of the electrical engineering department at New York University (NYU). He was seeking more staff and offered me a full professorship at a substantial increase in salary. "Deke" Dreese couldn't match the NYU salary but did recommend me for a promotion. At 39 I was a full professor.

Visitors continued to drop in to learn about the latest on our helix experiments. One of these was Ron Burgess, an English radio-physicist, with a broad range of interests. I showed him our lab filled with dozens of helices of all sizes lying on the workbenches and hanging from the walls and ceiling. As a wry, fanciful speculation he wondered if they might not come to life at midnight, pirouetting and prancing around the lab.

His insights were both poetic and practical. He talked about many things including radio telescopes. His familiarity with the ones at Cambridge and Manchester, England, enabled him to indicate quantitatively what would be needed in the way of an antenna and receiver to detect the sun and other radio sources. I realized that with some effort we could have a working radio telescope at OSU and in the weeks that followed Burgess' visit I started to plan seriously to build one.

I had no funds and if I managed to get some money I wanted to stretch it as far as possible so the designs which began to fill my notebook were for *low-cost* antennas. "Deke" Dreese suggested that I try the Caroline Lovejoy Memorial Fund. Ellis Lovejoy, a mining engineer and OSU graduate of 1885, had willed one-third of his nearly half-million dollar estate to the College of Engineering in memory of his mother, Caroline Drew Lovejoy. Interest from the endowment amounting to $5000 per year was available for research projects in the college. I applied for funds to assist in the construction of our radio telescope and was granted $2000.

John Cowan, a young instructor, helped with the design of the antenna structure. We figured that the $2000 from the Caroline Lovejoy Fund would buy 10 tons of steel with which we could build a tiltable flat framework 160 feet (50 meters) long by 12 feet (4 meters) wide. I had not yet decided what kind of antennas we would mount on the frame but went ahead and ordered the beams and angles, converting the entire Caroline Lovejoy grant into steel and launching us into radio astronomy.

Since then I have wondered if Caroline Lovejoy, as a teen-aged girl

100 years before, had thought much about the stars and planets of the firmament soon to be pierced by our new kind of telescope. At that time (1851) Samuel Morse's telegraph was only 7 years old and it would be another 37 years before Heinrich Hertz produced and measured his radio waves.

The tiltable framework would consist of 8 sections each 20 by 12 feet. As soon as the steel was delivered we welded the first section together, covering it with a coarse mesh wire screen to form a flat surface on which the antennas could be mounted.

With Sol Matt, a graduate student, we constructed an array of 24 dipole antennas on the newly assembled frame but when we tested the arrangement we discovered that the antennas were very critical and we had great difficulty adjusting them. We replaced them with six helical antennas, each helix being equivalent to 4 dipole antennas. This worked very well.

Sol and I wound the helices of half-inch diameter aluminum tubing. Each helix had 11 turns and was about 7 feet long and one foot in diameter. The helices were supported on slender wooden slats and projected like six giant corkscrews from the 12 by 20 foot steel frame. We worked on the array at such odd moments as we could. The array was just a few feet from Neil Avenue and occasional passersby came over to inquire what we were doing. We didn't hesitate asking them to hold a helix or a wooden slat while we drilled and bolted it into place. Before they realized what was happening they became our impromptu extra "work force." Among those stopping by was Ken Baker, a newspaper reporter who both asked questions and took pictures.

20. Array of 6 helices outside Caldwell Laboratory which Ken Baker dubbed a "big ear".

The next morning the *Ohio State Journal**, a Columbus morning newspaper, carried a four-column splurge on the front page with a big picture of the antenna and its six helices with me, hand on a helix, standing alongside. The headline announced,

"OSU Will Listen in on Stars."

The caption under the photograph stated,

"Dr. John Kraus inspects a section of the antenna he designed for listening to stars billions of miles away. There will be seven more sections like this. He hopes the antenna will reveal secrets of space."

Baker went on to ask,

"What does Venus whisper to Mars during their lonely flight through space? They utter a frying sound which has often been called 'cosmic static.' That frying sound — actually it's caused by radio waves from distant stars — can be recorded and it can tell scientists about the stars and whole universes that are so far away they can't be seen by optical telescopes."

If one dismissed the Venus to Mars conversation as amusing fantasy and changed "stars" to "radio stars," the report was reasonably accurate. The photograph was carried on the Associated Press picture wire and it appeared the same day in hundreds of newspapers across the country along with snatches of Baker's story. I received many letters, a few from astronomers and radio engineers but most were from the curious general public. And angry backlash came from an unexpected direction.

An editorial, in what I had always thought was a reputable Christian journal of national circulation, criticized me severely for suggesting that radio stars could emit a "frying sound." The editor implied that we must be tuned to the wrong place; celestial objects should produce only beautiful music.

Actually "frying sound" *was* an apt description. "Hissing steam" was another, but I don't think the editor would have liked it any better. To most persons the word "radio" implied speech and music and since you didn't look through a radio telescope then what was it that you heard? This was a common question and when Ken Baker asked it of me I replied that any emissions we expected to detect from distant radio sources, then often called "radio stars," would have a faint hissing noise like the sound of a radio receiver tuned between stations. The sound itself contained no information. It was the *increase* in the volume as the radio star passed through the antenna beam that was significant, since this revealed its presence. Carrying the "listening" analogy further, Ken Baker had referred to our radio telescope as a "big ear."

"Not bad," I thought, "not bad at all."

The six helix array was easy to adjust and worked fine. But where could we put a 160-foot antenna consisting of eight arrays like this one?

The Ohio State University had a large and vigorous College of Agriculture. The quip, "Millions for agriculture but not one cent for engineering" was not entirely without substance. Agriculture was big and important in Ohio and the Agricultural College and its Dean had clout with the state legislature. The Engineering College and its Dean did not, in spite of the fact that Ohio was highly industrialized.

Adjacent to the campus, the Agricultural College farmed thousands of acres of open land. Leo Rummell, the Ag College dean, was a good

---

*In later years combined with the *Columbus Citizen* as the *Citizen Journal.*

friend and neighbor. I approached him about "giving" us a couple of acres northwest of the campus as a site for a radio telescope. He drove me around the farms while I suggested some possible locations. He was agreeable to the site I liked best. At the time, the transaction was all verbal like the legendary deals of Texas oilmen although sometime later Leo did dictate a memorandum for the record.

The university had in storage a used 8 by 20 foot van which had been the trailer part of a semi rig. I acquired it and had it pulled to the new observatory site on the university farms. Our antenna would be immediately adjacent to and south of the trailer van which would house the receiver. Next we installed the first 12 by 20 foot frame with its six helices.

For several months Sol and I had been working on a receiver in Caldwell Lab on the campus and by May (1952) we installed it in the trailer at the farm site and connected the antenna. With help from EE shop personnel we concurrently completed another 12 by 20 foot frame and installed six helices on it.

By August 1st we had all 12 helices connected to the receiver and everything seemed to be in readiness. The next morning was Saturday and I turned the steel frames so the helices were aimed at the point in the sky where the sun would transit at noon. I went home for an early lunch after which I took Alice and our boys to the circus which had come to town. Watching the animals, clowns, and trapeze acts I kept wondering if we would get a record of the sun. On our way home we stopped at the observatory. As I put my key into the padlock on the trailer door I held my breath. Going inside I walked over to the Esterline-Angus recorder and there it was! Between noon and one o'clock on the chart loomed a big peak right where the sun should be. At long, long last we had detected a radio source! We were now a radio observatory in fact, not just in fancy! With Art Adel in 1933 and from the helix lab in 1947 I had tried unsuccessfully to detect the sun. Now in 1952 with a bigger antenna and a better receiver we had done it.

Once having detected something we had a reference or benchmark against which to measure changes. Within days we were able to improve both the stability and sensitivity of our receiver greatly so that the sun appeared even more prominently.

From the sun we went on to search for the next strongest radio objects in the sky and soon had good records of Cygnus A and Cassiopeia A (Cas A for short). These two radio sources were a great mystery to astronomers since it was not possible to identify them with any visible or optical object. Radio astronomy was revealing a new class of celestial objects, and, metaphorically, opening "a new window" on the sky.

For many months Sol Matt and I met several hours a week in an empty classroom to study and discuss a set of mimeographed lecture notes on radio astronomy which had been prepared by H.C. "Hank" van de Hulst of the Leiden (Holland) Observatory. Sol and I took turns writing van de Hulst's material on the blackboard, while we discussed the significance of each equation as we wrote it part by part. Sol got no credit for taking our "course" nor I for teaching it. We did it as an extra because we had a lot to learn and wanted to cover it as quickly as possible.

During the summer Ed Ksiazek (Kay-zak), a graduate student from the University of Vermont and an avid skier, joined our group and by fall Hsein (Sen) Ching Ko came from Formosa (Taiwan) where he had studied antennas using my book. With more personnel, work progressed more rapidly on the helix array and by October 18 (1952) all eight sections of the antenna with 48 helices were completed and connected to the receiver. The increase in antenna size gave us greatly improved results and we began to search for weaker radio sources.

However far into space our telescope might transport us there were often earthy distractions closer at hand. Our observatory site was in the extreme north-west corner of the university farms across from the OSU campus. I had selected it because it was a good quarter mile from the nearest highway and remote from most of the farm activity. (Automobile and tractor ignition systems could cause interference.)

21. **Ed Ksiazek adjusting the helix array at the observatory on the university farms.**

When Dean Rummell agreed to the observatory site he bypassed his farm manager. I don't think the manager was pleased because during our first winter at the observatory the manure from all the big barns was dumped just west of the observatory. The pile soon grew into a veritable mountain of manure hundreds of feet long. I rationalized that its penetrating ammonia vapors helped clear our sinuses but Sol, Ed and the others in our group weren't quite so philosophical. Much later radio astronomers discovered ammonia trillions of miles out in space. We discovered it in 1952 right next door.

In 1952 radio telescopes were few and far between. They were new and strange. OSU was the third university in the U.S. to possess one, the others being Harvard and Cornell. However, the U.S. lagged in radio astronomy in spite of the fact that the pioneer radio astronomers, Jansky and Reber, were Americans.

Setting the pace were groups in England, Holland and Australia. At Malvern, England, a group under J.S. Hey pin-pointed the strong source Cygnus A, using a modified war-surplus radar unit, while at Cambridge University Martin Ryle and Graham Smith located the intense source Cas A using a newly-rigged interferometer radio telescope. At the University of Manchester a 218-foot (66 meter) diameter fixed parabolic radio telescope was constructed by a group under Bernard Lovell and with it Hanbury Brown and Cyril Hazard detected faint radio emission from the great Andromeda galaxy, twin and nearest neighbor of our own galaxy. In Australia there were several active groups. Two Australians, John Bolton and Gordon Stanley discovered radio emission from the Crab nebula, a billowing, gaseous remnant of an exploded star, using both a newly constructed interferometer radio telescope and a modified war-time radar unit. It was the third strongest radio source in the sky, other than the sun, ranking in strength behind Cas A and Cygnus A.

Graham Smith, with a special interferometer radio telescope which Martin Ryle and he had built at Cambridge, England, measured an accurate position of Cygnus A and airmailed it on August 22nd, 1951, to Walter Baade of the Mount Palomar Observatory. On his next observing session on Palomar Mountain with the big 200-inch telescope on September 4th and 5th, Baade took long exposure photographs in blue and yellow light and noted the tiny, faint smudge of a strange-appearing very distant galaxy at Smith's position.

This was a great milestone in radio astronomy, for if such a strong radio source corresponded to this faint, distant optical galaxy it suggested that other strong radio sources might correspond to very distant objects and that radio astronomy might play a very important role in probing our universe to its ultimate depths.

At the time, Baade speculated that the Cygnus A object represented two galaxies in collision but later thinking leaned toward the theory that Cygnus A was a single galaxy which had undergone one or more violent internal explosions.

Another important milestone was the detection of narrow-band radio radiation from atomic hydrogen in interstellar space by Harold Ewen and Edward Purcell at Harvard University on March 25, 1951, and soon thereafter by groups at Leiden, Holland, and in Australia. "Hank" van de Hulst of Leiden had earlier suggested that a search for the radiation might be productive. This narrow-band radiation, coming from diffuse hydrogen gas in seemingly empty space, contrasted with the broadband continuum radiation received at many wavelengths from the sun, Cas A, Cygnus A and other radio sources.

22. Our observatory "building was dwarfed by the big antenna . . . and its 96 helices up-turned toward Heaven."

In Canada in 1946, Arthur Covington began systematic observations of the sun establishing a close correlation between radio emission and sun spot size and number.

This was the status of radio astronomy around the world as we began our first serious quantitative measurements early in 1953, and within the year we published three articles about our telescope and the results obtained.

An additional grant of $3000 from the Caroline Lovejoy Fund and $9200 from other university funds enabled us to start widening the antenna frame from 12 feet to 22 feet to accommodate another 48 helices and also to begin the construction of a building the size of a two-car garage to house the receiving equipment. The trailer van was proving unsatisfactory. It was too small, but worse, it jiggled and shook and was so poorly insulated that we couldn't hold it at a constant temperature. The receiver was a delicate, sensitive instrument and required a vibration-free, stable-temperature environment for good results.

I laid all the concrete blocks for the building while Gabe Skitek (Skee-tek), a graduate student from Missouri, helped me by mixing the mortar in a wheelbarrow and together we did the wood framing, paneling and roofing. By the summer of 1954 we had completed the building and moved the receiver into it. By this time the additional helices had been installed bringing the total to 96. We were pleased with our big antenna and proud of our "observatory building."

The receiver units and associated equipment were neatly installed in steel racks arranged side-by-side, forming a solid wall seven feet high by 16 feet long, a veritable mosaic of glistening aluminum panels with meters, clocks, chart recorders, dials, knobs, switches, and lights. This dazzling tapestry of electronic equipment was displayed behind a large plate-glass window separating it from the other half of the building where visitors could stand and gape.

The receiver worked much better because the temperature was more constant and vibration was absent. The receiver was supported by sturdy steel racks on a solid concrete floor which Gabe and I had mixed and poured by hand. Professor Chadwick of the Horticulture Department planted a few junipers around the building and Gabe set out some jonquils. The building was dwarfed by the big antenna with its 96 helices up-turned toward Heaven, but the junipers and jonquils helped join and blend them to earth.

Not long after our building was completed, it was "discovered" by some of the university's administrative bureaucrats. They were annoyed and angry that a building had been erected on OSU property without their knowledge and approval.

"How in hell did Kraus do it?" they asked. To make sure it didn't happen again, a directive was circulated specifying that henceforth all orders for building materials required special approval and an agreement by the requisitioner that the materials were not to be used for the erection of any new building or the modification of an existing one.

The procedure we had used to acquire the materials without attracting attention was to specify that they were for a "receiver enclosure," which in fact it really was. No one questioned the tons of materials required for the antenna, either beforehand or after. We could have built one across the whole university farm if Dean Rummell had okayed it and no one would have stopped us. A building was another matter. If we had stated that the materials were for an "observatory building," we would have been in for interrogation by committees, delays and red tape and spent more time talking about it than it took us to build it.

Gabe and I were amused. We thought that we should have gotten a medal; we had constructed a sturdy, serviceable building quickly and at minimum expense. Gabe and I had contributed the labor; the only expense was for materials. There were no blueprints or architects' fees. We had been energetic enough to go ahead and do something that needed doing.

While we were constructing our observatory building, a brilliant, young zoology professor I knew had left OSU in disgust because of frustrating delays while trying to get the university to erect a small building, really nothing more than a shed, to house some of his experimental mice. The mistake he made was to mention the word "building."

Soon after "Elements of Electromagnetics" was published, I began a revision. This took thousands of hours culminating in "Electromagnetics," published in 1953.

Both "Antennas" and "Electromagnetics" grew out of lecture notes I had prepared for my courses. "Electromagnetics" had a good reception in both the U.S. and abroad and was adopted by hundreds of institutions. "Antennas" was translated into Japanese and "Electromagnetics" into Spanish.

It had taken a herculean effort to complete "Electromagnetics" along with research on the helix, building a radio observatory, and teaching a heavy schedule of classes. Some might question the effort involved but the professional reputation of an institution depends in large measure on the books and articles its faculty produces. Both "Electromagnetics" and "Antennas" were books which, I thought, reflected credit on the Ohio State University. Books are an author's personal messengers and in a sense those of the institution he represents. Students, often good ones, are attracted to a university because of them. Through my books I not only taught thousands of students at OSU but hundreds of thousands around the world. Sometimes one copy served many as in a mideastern country where an instructor shared one copy of "Electromagnetics" with his large class until the pages literally wore out.

I could have become even more involved in book writing because McGraw-Hill wanted me to become the editor of a new handbook on antennas. McGraw-Hill offered to provide a staff of editorial assistants and most anything else I needed. Reluctantly I declined. The decision was especially hard because before the war one of my ambitions had been to publish a handbook on antennas. (My book "Antennas" was not a handbook, that is, a compendium of data on antennas, but rather a textbook for teaching how antennas worked while including practical applications to illustrate the theory.) Here a chance to do a handbook was handed me on a silver platter and I declined! It seemed like a crazy thing to do but I didn't want to get so bogged down with editing that I had no time left for radio astronomy, to me a challenging and exciting new frontier.

Then an unexpected and startling thing happened. Harlow Shapley, the dean of American astronomers, picked a radio map Hsien Ko and I had made as one of the year's ten top astronomical highlights. In fact, he listed ours first, stating,

"Out of the abundance of amazing contributions in the field of radio astronomy — contributions from Holland, England, Australia, the U.S., and Canada — especially noteworthy was the work of John Kraus and H.C. Ko of the Ohio State University."

He went on to say, "They mapped much of the northern sky as it would be seen by an eye sensitive only to radiation of meter wavelengths. The Milky Way is clearly recorded, as well as the Virgo cluster of galaxies, the intensely bright galactic nucleus, and some special hot spots in Centaurus, Cygnus and especially Cassiopeia."

The citation was circulated nationally in a press release from Harvard University, Dr. Shapley's institution. Columbus newspapers called us to get our personal reactions and one sent a photographer to the observatory to take pictures.

Photographs of our 96 helix telescope appeared in newspapers and magazines and on the front covers of many journals. Press releases went out over state and national wires, and newspaper articles about our telescope appeared in Sunday supplements. Reporters vied with each other in describing our work in novel, wierd and unusual ways. According to the papers we "tuned in on space" while "stars hissed" at us, "spoke" to us, or "gave off radio waves in B flat minor." The reporters said, quite correctly, that our telescope could function night and day, in clear weather or cloudy, because it could "see" right through the clouds often detecting radio signals from points in the sky where no stars or other objects were visible. Headlines announced that we were "intercepting star talk," "star hunting by radio," "snagging star sounds," and "keeping an eye on the universe." Our telescope was a "star snooper" which received "music from the stars." But the headline caption I liked best was,

"Tinkle, tinkle little star,
Do I hear you way out thar?"

And as runner-up I picked,

"There's more in the sky than meets the eye."

I received many invitations resulting in talks on radio astronomy to a wide variety of audiences from sixth grade classes, Rotary and Kiwanis clubs, to groups of professional astronomers and engineers, as well as

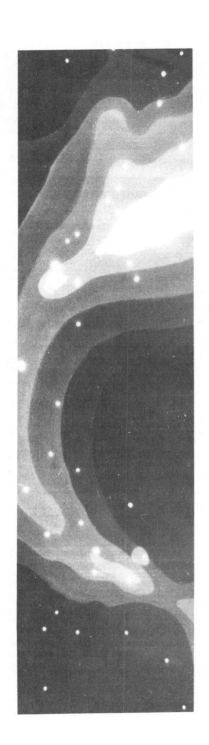

23. This is how the sky would look if our eyes were sensitive to radio waves. This panorama was made with the 96-helix array. The bright arch is the Milky Way or plane of our galaxy. None of the dots, representing radio sources, correspond to any visible star. "The radio sky is no carbon copy of the visible sky; it is a new and different firmament, one where the edge of the universe stands in full view and one which bears the tell-tale marks of a violent past."

The panorama is a Mercator projection. A more realistic impression would be obtained if the left and right edges were pulled around behind your head and the top stretched over it so that you view the panorama as though it were the real sky above and all around you.

appearances on television. I had used the statement that "radio astronomy is opening a new window on the universe" so many times that I thought perhaps the "window" should at last be kept up and open for good, and not mentioned again.

One summer Walter Baade, who took the first pictures of Cygnus A, gave a series of lectures in Ann Arbor which I attended. Baade was a "galaxy man" and had studied many galaxies including our own. He had found that the stars in a galaxy could be separated into two "populations," the young, blue giant and supergiant stars he called Population I, amid the gas and dust of the spiral arms, and the older, redder, fainter stars in the dust-free regions outside he called Population II. Galaxies were a source of radio waves but just how the waves were generated was a matter of conjecture. Chauffeuring Baade around Ann Arbor to the post office, laundry and haberdashery after his lectures, I had an opportunity to discuss many topics and to learn much from him.

In the fall of 1954 Professor Geoffrey Keller of the astronomy department and I presented a graduate course on "Radio Astronomy and Galactic Structure," OSU's first formal course involving radio astronomy. We alternated giving the lectures to a small but enthusiastic group of students.

We had been conducting observations continuously with the 96 helix radio telescope and publishing many articles. In one of them Hsien Ko, Sol Matt and I listed over one hundred radio sources we had observed. The only previous published lists were ones by Martin Ryle of England with 50 sources and by Bernard Mills of Australia with 77 sources.

In the few years that we had been at the observatory site on the university farm, we had experienced much interference from motor vehicles and from nearby radio and TV stations. We wanted to increase the size of our telescope antenna but because of the interference and threat of rapid urbanization of the area, it didn't seem wise to do it there. My thoughts turned to a bigger telescope at another location.

CHAPTER 15

TWENTY ACRES MORE OR LESS

A bigger telescope in a more secluded location was what we needed. I considered sites in the relatively undeveloped hill country of southeastern Ohio but a three hour drive from the campus made them impractical for students attending classes.

Geoffrey Keller, the Director of Perkins Observatory, suggested a nearer site. Perkins, surrounded by some 200 acres of farm and woodland, belonged to the Ohio Wesleyan University of Delaware, Ohio, a town two miles north of the observatory. Geoff thought that an open 20-acre field in the middle of this tract might suit our purpose. I liked it because it was large enough for a big radio telescope with a buffer zone around it of more Wesleyan land, and it was only a 30 minute drive from the OSU campus. Perkins with its 69-inch telescope and excellent astronomical library was owned by Wesleyan, while staffed and operated by Ohio State. The location looked good but would Wesleyan be agreeable to our building a radio telescope on it?

On a warm May afternoon in 1956, I called on Vice President Donald Hornberger in his small office in the basement of old University Hall on the Wesleyan campus. First we reminisced a bit. Hornberger's younger brother, Ted, had been a star quarter-miler on the University of Michigan track team in the early 1920's and I vividly recalled his winning a close race during a Big Ten meet at Ann Arbor.

Then I asked if Wesleyan could provide the site and guarantee not to use the surrounding land in any way that would be detrimental to the radio telescope. Ohio State would assume all other responsibilities. Hornberger's answer was short and to the point.

"Take what you need," he said.

After months of discussion and searching we had a site!

Later in the year a formal Joint Observatory Agreement was signed by President Arthur Flemming* of the Ohio Wesleyan University and President Howard Bevis of the Ohio State University in which OSU was given access to "20 acres more or less" for a radio observatory. Further, according to paragraph 4 of this document, Ohio Wesleyan agreed "to restrict the use of the property in the vicinity of the aforesaid

---

*Two years later, Flemming left Wesleyan to become Secretary of Health, Education and Welfare in President Eisenhower's cabinet. In 1972, President Nixon named Flemming to head a federal commission on geriatrics.

Radio Observatory site in such a manner as to prevent interference, radio or otherwise with the Radio Observatory."

So began "The Ohio State-Ohio Wesleyan Radio Observatory." Now two observatories, Perkins and the Radio Observatory, would be involved as a joint enterprise of a state and a private institution. This arrangement has frequently been cited as a good example of inter-university cooperation.

*   *   *   *   *

A big radio telescope is simply a big antenna with a receiver attached. The antenna's job is to collect radio waves from as large an area as possible and focus them so they can be conveyed to a receiver. I considered many designs. Why couldn't we move the 96-helix array and enlarge it by adding more helices? This was an attractive idea but had the disadvantage of restricting our range of wavelengths. The helix was a broad-band antenna but not broad enough. It could cover a 2 to 1 wavelength range but I wanted a 10 to 1 range. This narrowed the choice to a parabolic reflector.

A conventional radio telescope antenna consisted of a parabolic dish which could be elevated and rotated to point anywhere in the sky, but this was an expensive arrangement. If motion were restricted to elevation only and combined with the earth's rotation for pointing to any part of the heavens, the cost would be less. This would be a very acceptable scheme for systematically surveying the whole sky. But how could one obtain the largest collecting area or aperture per dollar? Cost increased roughly as the cube of the antenna height. Thus, doubling the height made the cost eight times as much but doubling the width made it only twice as much.

Following these lines of reasoning, I developed the design finally adopted. It involves a fixed standing parabola into which the radio waves are deflected by a tiltable flat reflector. The parabola is wider than high and is supported directly from the ground at many points (like half a bowl on edge). Being fixed, the steel required is less. Originally, I envisioned a height of 200 feet (61 meters) for the parabola with a (maximum) width of 2000 feet (610 meters). With this design we could build and use initially any part of it, adding the rest later if money became available. This provided flexibility for funding.

The flat reflector needs to be as wide as the parabola and longer in slant height so that its vertical height matches the height of the parabola. Originally I selected 280 feet (85 meters) for the slant height. Although the flat reflector needs to be moveable, it is simpler to tilt than a parabola. Instead of constructing the flat reflector as a single, massive, rigid unit, it can be built of a number of independently moveable sections at a great savings in cost.

A major advantage of the whole scheme is that the focal point is close to the ground instead of teetering high in the air on long struts as in a conventional dish antenna. The weight and size of the feed system is not critical and, furthermore, the sensitive receiving equipment can be placed in an underground laboratory immediately below the focal point where it can be easily adjusted and maintained. The scheme has many attractive features but best of all it provides a large aperture or collecting area per dollar. It is a really cost-effective design.

There were no dramatic meetings, no heated discussions, no shouting, "Eureka, I've found it!" The idea for the telescope evolved gradually over weeks and months of contemplation and pondering various designs and alternatives. The final design crystallized quietly and without fanfare from my notes and calculations. I described the basic idea in an article in the March 1955 *Scientific American*.

*   *   *   *   *

Geoff Keller and I had hosted the American Astronomical Society meetings on the OSU campus in 1956. It was exciting to have so many eminent astronomers who turned out for a visit to our Radio Observatory with its 96-helix antenna on the university farms late one afternoon before the society banquet.

As the banquet speaker I had invited Cyril M. Jansky, Jr., a prominent radio engineer, to tell about his younger brother Karl's early work which marked the beginning of radio astronomy. Karl Jansky had died six years before at the age of 44. Tracing his brother's career C.M. Jansky told how their father, born in Wisconsin of Czech immigrants, had attended the University of Michigan earning degrees in both Physics and Electrical Engineering. He had been such an ardent admirer of his Michigan physics professor, Karl Guthe, that he had named his third son Karl Guthe Jansky.

"C.M." went on to relate Karl's early experiments culminating in Karl's paper on "Electrical Disturbances Apparently of Extraterrestrial Origin" presented before a Washington meeting in April 1933 and which subsequently appeared in the October 1933 *Proceedings* of the IRE. "C.M." referred to this article as "a classic and in effect a wedding ceremony. It weds the science of astronomy and the science of radio and electronic engineering. It ties these sciences together by inseparable bonds."

In response to my invitation, Karl Jansky's sister and his daughter and son also attended the banquet. So it was a Jansky family reunion to do homage to Karl, the founder of radio astronomy.*

At a special session on radio astronomy Lloyd Berkner, President of Associated Universities, a consortium of eastern universities, gave a paper on a "Plan for a National Radio Astronomy Facility" in which he outlined how such a facility should be organized and operated. He emphasized that it should not be considered as an independent activity, but as a means of supplementing, rather than replacing, the large-scale facilities of radio astronomers at their own institutions. He also did not want it operated as a government laboratory but by a university-type organization on a non-profit basis under government sponsorship to provide a university atmosphere of inquiry and penetration.

*   *   *   *   *

To obtain experimental confirmation on the capabilities of the new radio telescope design, I assigned Bob Nash, a graduate student, the problem of building and testing a scale model. After months of work building the model, he installed it on the roof of Caldwell Laboratory and with a receiving system two miles away on the roof of another building made measurements of the antenna pattern which confirmed our expectations. Bob proved to be an unusually capable engineer, gifted by a keen, analytical insight. He summarized his results in a thesis written as partial fulfillment of his masters degree.

---

*With a few other radio astronomers I had proposed that the unit of flux density or strength of radio sources be named the *jansky* after Karl G. Jansky but it was not adopted generally until many years later.

A grant of $23 000 from the National Science Foundation (NSF) had helped us in our work of building and measuring the scale model. A later NSF grant of $48 000 enabled us to start actual construction of the full-sized telescope. However, the grant was so much less than our estimated cost of an antenna with 2000 foot parabola that we scaled down our goal to one with a parabola 360 feet long by 70 feet high. Even with this reduction we knew that $48 000 wasn't enough and we didn't know whether we would ever get any more funds.

Our receipt of the NSF grant was heralded in many newspapers with stories of our plans. An article by Ray Bruner, the *Toledo Blade* science

24.   With Bob Nash on the roof of Caldwell Laboratory inspecting the scale model he made of Big Ear.

editor, had the prophetic headline, "Reaching for the Edge of the Universe." He quoted me as saying "the new telescope is expected to locate thousands of new radio stars" a prediction fulfilled many times over. "As larger radio telescopes are built," the quote continued, "it will be possible to probe farther into the most distant parts of the universe. The new venture is a pioneering step in the direction of super radio telescopes and if tests with the device are satisfactory still larger units of the same design may be built." These statements have since been borne out although it was not in Ohio but in France that a larger telescope, often referred to as a "Kraus type," with fixed curved reflector 1000 feet (300 meters) long by 100 feet (30 meters) high was constructed.

Our telescope was not only of unique design; its manner of construction was distinctly out of the ordinary. Customarily an astronomer who wanted a telescope would engage a design firm to draw up plans to his specifications. Based on cost estimates funds to construct the entire telescope would then be solicited. If funds were obtained a contractor was engaged to build the telescope and the astronomer's only concern would be that his specifications were met.

Our procedure was entirely different because (1) the funds we obtained were not enough to complete the telescope, (2) we drew our own plans to meet our specifications, and (3) we did all the construction work ourselves, "in-house," using part-time university students as our work force.

I made sure that my general performance specifications would be met by drawing up or approving the plans for all components of the telescope. I was involved in the selection of girder shapes, bolt sizes, and welded-joint designs down to the smallest details. As the students acquired more experience and proficiency I shifted more responsibility to them. Bob Nash and John Hoover were two of the students involved.

One day another student, Lou Malik, walked into my office and introduced himself. He said that he had had extensive welding and high structural steel experience. I hired him on the spot. Lou was such an expert welder that we had him teach the other students the fine points of electric arc welding and for months he taught a welding class every Saturday morning for our student crew until we had ten well-qualified welders.

Then there was Dave Lipphardt whose special interest involved time and motion studies. With Bob and John he arranged faster, more efficient methods for fabricating the trusses and towers for the parabola. Our construction crew numbered about 15 undergraduate students who paid $1.40 per hour on the average and one graduate student, Bob Nash, who received $2.30 per hour.

We acquired some war-surplus welding generators and scrounged and resurrected several old university-owned units. OSU had purchased a factory building from the Rockwell Saw Company. Located west of the Olentangy River across from the main campus, it took only a few minutes to reach it and we arranged to do our basic assembly work there. Ninety-six trusses 30 feet long fabricated of steel angle and rod were needed for the parabola and as soon as a number were completed we hauled them to the observatory site on a low-boy trailer rig.

Meanwhile work was progressing on the 70-foot parabola tower legs made of large steel pipe and angles. These were so large they had to be constructed on the site one at a time on a special jig set in concrete. 26 of these tower assemblies were required. As each set of tower legs was completed it was lifted off the jig with a borrowed crane. By fall the foundation pillars were poured. The following spring we began assembling the parabola and on June 10 (1957) we raised the first bay. We had 11 more to go. These were assembled and raised one at a time during the summer and fall. The parabola was beginning to take shape.

I visited the site several times a week to check on progress. It always seemed slow to me but the students were attending classes and the number of hours they could put in per week was limited. As an "office" for our blueprints and for housing some of our supplies the old trailer van from the helix telescope site was hauled in. The university supplied us with an old 2-ton flat-bed truck for transporting equipment and materials.

We had a gate with lock in the fence where the road entered the site but sometimes the students forgot the key. This resulted only in a slight delay because acetylene and oxygen tanks and a welding generator were carried on the truck. It was only a moment's work with the acetylene torch to cut through the plate holding the padlock. Then later in the

25. **Lou Malik rigging** cables to section of parabola before crane lifted it into place.

26. **Parabolic reflector of Big Ear with several bays up and one** more ready for raising.

day when leaving, it took only a moment to start the generator and weld the plate back together again.

After a heavy rain the site became a sea of mud and made working difficult. But in rain or sun the work on the big parabola progressed. While this was going on, other things were happening. The telescope we were building might soon reach for the edge of the universe but for a while I was distracted by objects closer at hand in our own solar system, some circling the earth itself.

CHAPTER 16

MY AFFAIR WITH VENUS

Bernard Burke and Kenneth Franklin* electrified the audience of a Washington, D.C. gathering in 1955 by announcing that they had received radio waves from the planet Jupiter at a wavelength of 14 meters. The radiation was sporadic, fluctuating and sometimes intense.

Jupiter is a giant planet with 100 times the surface area of the earth. It has large, strange red and white spots on its surface and even though bigger than the earth, it spins faster. A planet of mystery, perhaps the radio observations would help us to understand it. As I listened to their talk I became intrigued.

Could we detect Jupiter? It had been in the beam of our 96-helix telescope many times but we had observed nothing. Our telescope operated at a wavelength of one meter while Burke and Franklin's operated on 14 meters, so apparently a longer wavelength was needed and I decided to try one working at 11 meters since if it worked it would add information about Jupiter at another wavelength. The simplest antenna I could erect was an interferometer of a few half-wavelength wires.

There wasn't room at our site on the university farm for the antenna but on my 12 acre farm northwest of Columbus there was plenty of room so I decided to set it up there. Several students from the observatory and my sons, Jack and Nels, helped me get it rigged. The antenna consisted of horizontal wires strung from poles eight feet high with one set of wires west of our house in the sheep pasture and the other set east of our home near our chicken house. The two sets were about 400 feet (120 meters) apart. To a casual observer the antenna looked like a high fence. It was so inconspicuous that one could hardly discern it from a distance. Within a week or two everything was connected and I began to get records of the Jupiter bursts on a receiver-recorder I installed in the workroom of our house. Now I had three radio observatories, one on the university farm, one near Perkins Observatory and one right at home.

My home telescope demonstrated that simple equipment was sufficient to detect Jupiter. The total cost of antenna, receiver and recorder was about $500.

---

*Carnegie Institution, Washington, D.C.

Could Jansky have detected Jupiter with his telescope two decades earlier? This question nagged Grote Reber who endeavored to locate Jansky's original records but found that after his death in 1950, his records had been destroyed. Jansky's equipment was of adequate sensitivity and his wavelength of 15 meters was optimum for picking up Jupiter so it is unfortunate that his records had not been preserved. Reber's observations with his telescope were at much shorter wavelengths, about 2 meters, and his records did not reveal Jupiter.

During the day, my home telescope produced splendid records of radio signals from the sun. Solar activity and sun spots were near a maximum. At night there were occasional records of Jupiter signals. I reported on my results at the American Astronomical Society meeting in Columbus in 1956 and also in several articles. In one of these I stated that I had noted two periods of very intense Jupiter emission only a few days after great flares on the sun. I said,

"Although these sequences may be entirely coincidental, they do suggest the possibility that the mechanism producing the Jupiter radiation may be initiated or triggered by particles emitted from the sun."

It was a daring idea, to some even far-fetched, to suggest that particles shot out from the sun could drift all the way to Jupiter and produce an effect on its radio emission. The notion of a "solar wind" had not yet been formulated. Some years later more detailed studies by James Warwick in Colorado and T.D. Carr, Alex Smith and others in Florida showed that there probably was a correlation between periods of Jupiter activity and prior solar activity. As the years passed the idea grew more acceptable as it was realized that the particles from the sun became trapped by Jupiter's magnetic field and spiralling into it produced the radio waves.

27. With Hsein Ko and Bob Nash in front of the array of 8 giant helices we built for analyzing signals from Jupiter.

In addition to the more usual swishing sounds, I also reported hearing some clicking or spitting noises from Jupiter but other observers failed to detect them. Then, many years later these observers did hear them. Strangely, Jupiter had given up spitting for a while but then resumed it.

If Jupiter could produce such intense radio emission, what about radio waves from Mars and Venus? They were smaller planets but they were much closer to us. Might they also emit radiation at wavelengths of 10 to 15 meters? (We hadn't detected any at 1 meter wavelength with our 96-helix array.) I wondered about it and began to examine the records of my home telescope more closely.

At night the background noise on the record dropped to a low level so that it was possible to detect very faint signals. But aside from Jupiter and obvious interference from automobiles and other man-made devices, there was nothing evident; no signals at all from Mars, not even a hint.

Venus was always so close to the sun that it was necessary to search the day-time records for her, but during the day the situation was much different than at night. With the sun up there was solar emission evident to a larger or smaller extent over much of the day with a peak around noon when the sun transited the center of the antenna beam. During the day the earth's ionosphere or charged particle layer could also reflect signals from radio stations in places like Florida or Texas and these occasionally caused interference.

One evening I came home to find that there was no record at all; the pen had drawn a straight line on the chart all day. The receiver seemed OK so I went out to inspect the antenna. There out in the sheep pasture lay the answer; the antenna was down. Billy, our Shropshire ram, had apparently become entangled in a guy wire and in struggling to get free had dragged down the whole affair. I couldn't be sure as to details but bits of wool on the wires and a mischievous gleam in Billy's eye suggested this scenario.

Jack and Nels helped me put the antenna back up and within a couple of days I was able to continue searching day time records for signs of Venus. I calculated the pattern which should occur corresponding to any emission from Venus and looked for this pattern on the record. I was trying to translate some ink squiggles on a strip of paper into some sign, maybe just a wink, from Venus. Then one day I found a pattern which fit. There were the signals from Venus I had been looking for! My objectivity and caution were overpowered by what appeared to be valid evidence and I dashed off a short note.

While monitoring for radiation from Venus, I also had heard signals that came in distinct separated pulses. I wondered if they weren't interference from a terrestrial radio transmitter so I checked with a Federal Communications Commission monitoring station and with a military intelligence agency but neither had any knowledge of them. They seemed to be strongest when Venus was in the beam and seemed to follow Venus across the sky. I wrote a brief note about them and suggested they might originate on Venus.

I was unprepared for the flurry of stories which appeared when my notes were published. There were accounts in many newspapers, often with fanciful and imaginative headings. A few were: "From Venus with love," "Is Venus trying to get in touch with us?", and "Venus is calling but who cares; we have a Marilyn."

Compared to the papers the reaction of the scientific community was reserved. It was not an easy thing to confirm or deny and the attitude of most was to wait and see. But Bernie Burke at the Carnegie Institution took a positive approach. He arranged his antenna to observe Venus during the weeks of maximum elongation when she rose several hours before the sun. In this way he minimized solar interference. He kept me informed of his results by letter and phone and reported finally that he couldn't detect any signals at all from Venus. His observations convinced me that I was wrong and in due time I published a note acknowledging it. But how had it happened?

28. With Gerry Greshel (top), Bob Nash (right) and Sanjib Mukherjee and John Hung (left to right below) inspecting our 40-foot steerable parabolic dish antenna.

Venus is never more than three hours ahead of or behind the sun in the sky so most of the time she was in the main beam of my antenna, the sun was in the minor lobes. Small fluctuations of solar emission of the right rhythm could have given a pattern which might have been mistaken for Venus. This is what had mislead me.

And the pulse signals just had to be terrestrial interference, although it was some time before I found who the real culprits were. Induction heating machines were then beginning to come into use for injection molding of plastic parts. These machines use radio frequency oscillators and due to inadequate shielding radiate their signals far and wide whenever the sun is high enough to make the ionosphere reflecting. Each pulse I heard probably came from a machine as far as California when it was turned on for a couple of seconds to melt the plastic powder in a mold. The process was then repeated in about a minute, after the plastic part had cooled and was ejected. I had confused a plastic imitation with the real Venus!

My affair with Venus was a brief, passionate interlude lasting only two months. But it was a blunder, which taught me a lesson:

Things are not always what they seem.

Although I had qualified my notes by including the words *"Appear to come from Venus,"* indicating that I harbored some doubt, it was not enough. With all the experiments and observations I had tried before with negative results I should have recognized that this was another such case. It was an important lesson. On many occasions since then, it has prodded me into examining with care and objectivity what appeared to be new "discoveries" with our telescopes which in case after case have turned out to be either quirks in the equipment, unusual interference or improbable fluctuations in the background noise.

My mistake was that I tried too hard to make an important discovery to the extent that subjectivity overcame my objectivity. Not to diminish the gravity of my error, it was something that has also happened to other astronomers, physicists and chemists, including Nobel laureates, and continues to happen. When it does, I think I understand the situation better having been involved once myself. The path is not always forward from success to success but may involve setbacks and detours.

It spotlighted the difficulties of an observational science and of the many pitfalls that exist. One needs completely unbiased objectivity. When you dare to publish a new scientific observation or calculation you are under an enormous responsibility to be certain that your work is accurate, correct and factual. You tred a narrow line. You don't want to be found in error but you can be so cautious that you never publish. To publish always involves some risk; the only safe way is not to publish at all.

At the very time when I wrote those little notes about Venus, I was teaching, operating the observatory on the university farm, starting to build one near the Perkins Observatory, and also preparing some of the best, most profound and significant articles I have ever composed. So I might derive some small comfort from the fact that my overall "batting average" was reasonably good.

Even many years later, no long wavelength radiation of the kind received from Jupiter has been observed from other planets, except from the earth itself and from Saturn, both by artificial satellites outside the earth's ionosphere. Venus has been found to have insufficient magnetic field and this could account for the lack of radiation from her. Only Jupiter, the earth and Saturn seem to have the magnetic fields and other conditions required.

29. President Novice G. Fawcett presenting me with the Sulli-vant medal (1970).

CHAPTER 17

MUSIC OF THE SPHERES

"The Russians have a satellite up!" Jack and Nels exclaimed in unison as they burst into my study.

Looking up from my paper strewn desk, I dropped my slide rule.

"It can't be!" I uttered incredulously. "What makes you think so?"

"It's on the radio; we just heard it," Jack replied.

"They call it a sputnik; and it goes beep beep," Nels added.

"What's its wavelength and where is it now?" I asked.

"I don't know, the announcer didn't say," Jack answered.

I wanted more information, hard data. It was Friday evening, October fourth 1957. I thought a moment.

"Let's go to the observatory," I suggested. With my teen-aged boys trailing me, I rushed from the room. As I flew out the back door I shouted to Alice washing the supper dishes,

"We're going to the observatory to see if we can hear the sputnik."

"The what?" she called back, but the door slammed behind me before I could answer.

We piled into our station wagon. It was only a few minutes' drive to the observatory. We kept the car radio on hoping to get more information but all we heard was Elvis Presley strumming and singing "Jail House Rock." At the observatory Nels and I went in while Jack stayed in the car to listen for any further announcements. We had several shortwave receivers at the observatory and I thought perhaps I could pick up the new satellite with one of them but I didn't know on what wavelength or frequency to listen. Just tuning around listening for a "beep beep" wasn't productive, but I searched for nearly an hour. Then Jack bounded in to say,

"Sputnik's on 20 megacycles. They just announced it."

"20 megacycles," I said in disbelief, "that's the frequency WWV the Washington time service station uses. They won't like that."

I switched one of the receivers to the WWV 20 megacycle channel.

"Dit, dit, dit, dit," a pause, then, "This is the National Bureau of Standards, WWV. When the tone returns the eastern standard time is eight twenty P.M."

"No beep beep from Sputnik," I muttered.

"Did the announcer say where it was now?" I asked.

"No, he didn't," Jack replied.

"Well, rather than wait here all night let's go home. We can get my ham receiver out of the attic and hook it up and monitor 20 megacycles there." (I had dismantled the Jupiter telescope at my home earlier in the year.)

So we drove back home. It was dark but we rigged a horizontal wire antenna just above the ridge of the roof of our house. The center of the antenna was near the chimney so I dropped the feeder wires from the antenna down the chimney while Jack reached up and grasped them in the fireplace below. Having located my ham receiver and placing it on a table in the living room beside the fireplace, we connected the feeder and plugged the receiver into a wall outlet.

I tuned to 20 megacycles. There was WWV "dit dit ditting" along but still no "beeps." So Jack read from his books and I worked on my lecture notes as we continued to listen to WWV as background "music," and after WWV faded out, to a faint hiss from the loud speaker. We finally gave up and went to bed.

Saturday morning I turned the receiver on again. Still no beeps. Then the phone rang. A Columbus newspaper wanted to know if I had picked up Sputnik. I said I was very sorry but I hadn't; however, I was still trying. I had hardly put the phone down before it rang again. It was a Columbus TV station asking the same question. I gave the same answer. Soon the phone rang once more. This time it was the operator asking,

"Is this Dr. John Kraus, Director of the Ohio State University Radio Observatory?"

"Yes," I replied.

"Paris, France, calling," the operator said, "one moment, please."

Presently a man came on who identified himself as Monsieur Le Beau of a French broadcasting system. Had I heard Sputnik? What did I think about it? What was its significance for all of us? I tried to answer Monsieur Le Beau's questions as best I could but I kept wondering why he had called me, so finally I asked him.

"Oh," he said, "in France you are a famous person."

I was unprepared for that and I didn't believe it. Eventually, after what seemed like a very long time, Monsieur Le Beau thanked me and hung up.

During the day there were more calls and more questions. "If the phone doesn't stop ringing," I thought, "I won't be able to listen for Sputnik at all. Everyone wants to know if I've picked it up but they don't give me a chance to try."

That was Saturday's story; still no luck. Sunday morning I was up early but heard nothing except WWV. We had just finished breakfast and gone into the living room when we heard some faint "beep beeps."

I rushed to the receiver and adjusted the tuning. Instantly the "beep beeps" filled the room making our ears ring. Sputnik's frequency was just a bit higher than WWV.

"Maybe that's why we didn't hear Sputnik before," I thought.

Loud as Sputnik had sounded, the beeps grew relentlessly louder and louder. Alice said,

"Turn down the volume; it's hurting my ears."

"OK, OK," I said, as I rotated the volume control a trifle.

But the beeps continued to build up again until the whole room, the entire house, pulsed and throbbed. I felt that Sputnik would scrape our chimney or plunge through the roof into our living room at any moment. I could hardly breathe. Then gradually, but ever so gradually, the beeps became fainter and after many minutes the loud speaker grew quiet.

A Russian satellite had just zoomed over our heads! Incredible! The U.S. had spent millions, probably billions of dollars, building a DEW (Distant Early Warning) line with huge radar antennas all across the Canadian arctic to warn of the approach of Russian aircraft coming in over the north pole. In one stroke the DEW line was obsolete.

Who needed airplanes? Here was an object made in Russia coming by right overhead and no one could stop it. The "beep beeps" heralding its passage were like trumpet blasts proudly announcing to all the world, "Beep, beep, beep; here we come; beep, beep, beep; here we come!"

Russia had catapulted us into the space age.

Everyone had assumed that the U.S. would put up the first satellite. The significance of the Russian achievement swept over our country like an electric shock. The thought that we lagged was a blow. And to the military, Sputnik posed a dire threat. What if Sputnik didn't have a beeper to announce its approach but carried an atomic bomb instead? The U.S. was unprepared and frantic scrambling ensued. I thought that anything we could do at our observatory to learn more about Sputnik, or other satellites which might follow, would be useful.

Monday, right after my classes some of my students, Jim Albus, Bob Nash and Dick McFarland, helped me string an antenna at the radio observatory on the university farm to pick up Sputnik's signals. The antenna worked as an interferometer with a multi-lobed pattern like the fingers of one's hand.

We had been plagued by phone calls from newspapers, TV and radio stations wanting to find out what we knew about Sputnik, which wasn't much. A camera crew from a TV station arrived to take movies of us putting up the new antenna.

We connected the antenna to a WWV receiver and it in turn to a chart recorder. The recorder would make a permanent record of the signals of Sputnik whenever it passed over.

By the next morning we had some excellent interferometer records, a series of regularly spaced lobes, for several of Sputnik's passes, one of which was directly over Columbus. From the records we calculated Sputnik's altitude. We had barely written down the results when the Columbus *Dispatch* called. I reported that Sputnik had passed over Columbus at 7:32 A.M. at a height of 310 miles. Our measurements were featured on the front page of the afternoon edition.

We observed good records on all of Sputnik's passes over eastern North America. The satellite was traveling around the world once every hour and a half, circling the earth 16 times a day. It rushed along at 18 000 miles per hour which must have been some kind of a speed record. Then Sputnik's transmissions stopped. Apparently its batteries went dead. "What now?" I thought. "Should we just sit here or is there something we can do?"

A year or so earlier, Professor Lloyd Wylie of Wittenberg University, Springfield, Ohio, and his student, H.T. Castillo, had stopped into my office to talk with me about an antenna they were using to observe meteors. They tuned a receiver to WWV on 20 megacycles. At night, WWV faded out because the earth's ionosphere became too thin to reflect its signal back down. They had noticed, however, that during the night WWV might suddenly pop in loud and clear for a second or two, and then disappear again. This happened only a few times during the night and they associated these events with the passage of a meteor high in the earth's atmosphere leaving a momentary trail of ionized particles sufficient to catch and reflect WWV's signals down to Ohio.

I wondered if Wylie and Castillo's method might yield results on Sputnik, even though the circumstances were not quite the same. Sputnik travelled above the atmosphere in a highly rarefied region called the "Kennelly-Heaviside layer"* or the "ionosphere," a region sparsely populated with charged particles, that is, electrons and protons.

When there were enough charged particles, detectable radio waves could be reflected from them. Radio waves bounced off this layer as though from a huge mirror so that radio stations could communicate across continents and over oceans. If it weren't there, the waves from a radio station would shoot right out into space and never return to earth.

During the day the sun's radiation increased the ionization and the layer was highly reflecting. At night, however, the ionization decreased and the layer became thin and less effective so that it might not reflect any 20 megacycle signals back at all, but might a satellite, like Sputnik, disturb or bunch the particles enough to permit reflection? I didn't know although I suspected there might be some effect because we had noticed some strange behavior of the Sputnik signal the week after it was put into orbit. The signal was rough and hashy but suddenly became smooth and steady each time the satellite passed Columbus.

It would be easy enough to find out if there was a detectable satellite-induced ionization effect; all we needed to do was to tune to WWV and leave our recorders running. This we did and we also plugged in a magnetic tape recorder to catch the sounds. If a burst were seen on the chart we could run the sound tape and find if it were indeed from WWV.

Before we could draw any conclusions, a second Sputnik went up. This one, called Sputnik 2 to distinguish it from the earlier Sputnik 1, was much bigger and carried a dog, Leika. Sputnik 1 was a 20 inch (50 centimeter) diameter aluminum or magnesium ball with four long whip antennas. Sputnik 2 was several times as large and must have weighed hundreds of pounds. Sputnik 2 was easily seen streaking overhead just after sunset or just before sunrise, when the sun's rays illuminated the satellite high in the sky but with the earth below in darkness. I spent many evenings and early mornings watching it. Sputnik 2 also carried a transmitter but after a few weeks it stopped, so now there were two Sputniks circling the earth in silence.

From optical tracking data we knew when the Sputniks should pass and we examined our WWV recorder charts to see if any "events" occurred that might be associated with a satellite pass. There did seem to be bursts of WWV signals during the night after it had faded out, which were near the expected times for passes of Sputniks 1 and 2. The bursts were stronger and much longer than those due to meteors. I published a couple of notes about the observations.

These stirred up a great flurry of interest. I received many letters of inquiry but worse, my phone began to ring, *continuously*. I would no sooner hang up from one call before I got another. Back from a class or a meeting on the campus, I would find a stack of messages

---

*After two scientists, A.E. Kennelly, an American, and Oliver Heaviside from England.

our department switchboard operator had left me from persons who had called. But when I got to the phone in my office it was ringing! The only way I could call out was to use someone else's phone. The calls persisted all day, tending to come from points further and further west across the country as the day wore on. And they continued evenings and weekends at home. A few of the calls were from newspapers or magazines, such as *Time,* which carried a story about our observations with my picture, but most were from scientists and engineers at laboratories across the country who wanted to know more about the observations and the methods we used. There was doubt expressed by some because with large powerful radars no reflections had been detected from either the satellite proper or from what could be regarded as satellite-induced ionization. But when looking for ionization they had looked for a trail like that produced by a meteor. Their failure to find trails didn't surprise us because our observations had suggested that the ionization was more likely ahead of the satellite than behind it. We speculated that the satellite might knock particles ahead of it like a golf club driving a ball.

Then, on May 15, 1958, came Sputnik 3, a huge instrumented laboratory weighing more than a ton, big enough to hold several men, although it was unoccupied. To us the Russians loomed 10 feet tall and the story was circulated that some cows were aboard Sputnik 3: "the herd that was shot 'round the world."

Sputnik 3 transmitted on 20 megacycles, sending "dit dah dit dit," Morse code for the letter "L," over and over. We did not know that Sputnik 3 had been launched until the day after but our equipment had been on and when we looked at the charts and listened to our sound tapes we found that we had recorded Sputnik 3's transmissions during the night on its first pass over Columbus.

In the spring of 1958, preceding Sputnik 3, the U.S. had launched Explorer 1 followed by Vanguard 1. These satellites were tiny compared to Sputnik 3 and also transmitted on a different frequency of 108 megacycles, adjacent to the FM broadcasting band. We had installed a receiver for this frequency in order to record these satellites.

Whereas Sputnik 1's "beep-beeps" at two per second and Sputnik 3's rapid, staccato, insistent "dit dah dit dits" conveyed the impression of satellites in a hurry, blatantly clearing the path ahead like Paris taxis, Explorer 1 had a languid, slowly throbbing, continuous musical tone that was plaintive, ethereal and timeless. Vanguard 1 sounded similar to Explorer 1 but with a somewhat flatter, less musical note. We had first received Vanguard's signals while it was being launched into orbit from Cape Canaveral March 17, 1958. Sometimes the satellites would pass Columbus a few minutes apart sounding like two flutists of a celestial orchestra floating leisurely by. "Frying noises" and "hissing steam," were now balanced by "music of the spheres."

We had obtained better correlations of WWV bursts with passes of Sputnik 2 than we had for Sputnik 1. The correlation with Sputnik 3 was even better and we got some burst sequences during passes which were the best we had seen. During a 7 hour stretch from one to eight in the morning there were strong burst groups close to every one of the four successive passes of Sputnik 3 near Columbus and no bursts of significance at other times.

A number of things began to emerge. The WWV bursts occurred mostly in the interval of 20 minutes before to 10 minutes after the nearest approach of the satellite and at times when the earth's ionosphere was disturbed, following intense solar activity associated with sun spots.

We also occasionally observed bursts when Sputnik 3 was over the southern hemisphere at or near our magnetic "conjugate point." Magnetic field lines arch thousands of miles above the earth joining a point in the northern hemisphere to its "conjugate point" in the southern hemisphere. Charged particles can travel along these magnetic field lines between hemispheres in a minute or so. Could it be that Sputnik 3 was sometimes creating disturbances in the southern hemisphere that propagated along field lines to the northern hemisphere, producing detectable ionization effects there? This possibility focussed our attention more on the satellite position with respect to the earth's magnetosphere (the magnetic field region around the earth) and in particular the auroral zone as well as the newly discovered outer Van Allen belt. Both dipped further south at the longitude of Columbus than anywhere else in the northern hemisphere with the Van Allen belt usually centered right over Columbus.

The electrons in the Van Allen belt not only oscillate back-and-forth between hemispheres but also drift eastward. A satellite traveling eastward might trigger effects which could build up enormously if its motion and that of the interhemispheric electrons were in synchronism. This amplification or resonance effect could excite shock waves* propagating rapidly out to large distances from the satellite, inducing detectible ionization effects.

Workers at other labs began to refer to the satellite ionization phenomenon as the "Kraus effect." A number of labs set up elaborate equipment to duplicate our observations but without success. We continued our observations with our inexpensive equipment and supported only by a small grant from the OSU Development Fund. Our satellite ionization work was carried on while the Delaware antenna was under construction and radio astronomy observations were also being made at the university farm site. And the phone kept ringing, although perhaps a bit less.

Many of the calls were not to ask questions but to extend invitations to speak. I couldn't accept them all but I did give many talks, addresses and colloquia before local, state, and national meetings of astronomers, physicists and engineers, at technical sessions, banquets, and dinners. (If my speeches were not astronomical they were at least gastronomical!) I spoke to Rotary clubs, women's organizations, scientific honorary societies, and high schools. I journeyed to Michigan and Florida and to the east and west of Columbus. I was on radio and TV panel shows. My subject ranged the entire cosmos. Many of my talks began,

"We live in a large and mysterious universe" from which I went on to convey, as best I could, something about the size of the universe and man's relation to it. I explained how astronomy takes us out of our smug, arrogant, self-centered view of ourselves. I pictured us as dwelling on a frail, little, spinning ball, we call the earth, that is but a tiny speck, lost and dwarfed by the immensity of our galaxy and the vast space which surrounds it. I expressed my feelings of awe with a quotation from the ancient psalmist,

"When I consider thy heavens, the work of thy fingers, the moon and the stars which thou has ordained;

What is man, that thou art mindful of him?"

As the commencement speaker at the OSU graduation exercises in

---

*Waves of the Magneto-Hydro-Dynamic or Alfven type (after H. Alfven, a Norwegian scientist).

March 1960, the first of the new decade, I spoke on "The Challenge of the Space Age" before 10 000 persons filling St. Johns Arena. I related man's past, present and future by saying, "Man's history is one of accelerating development. It was over a million years from man's first faltering, upright steps to the Wright Brothers' first flight at Kitty Hawk. But now 57 years later we stand on the threshold of man's first flights into space."

I stressed the challenge of the new and unknown by noting that "our knowledge is like the area inside a circle and the unknown like the area outside. The more we learn the greater the circle becomes, but so also does the edge of the circle or frontier of the unknown. The conquest of nature and of the unknown constitutes an endless frontier that will challenge man as long as he is capable of thinking and wondering. If man no longer searches for knowledge and truth for its own sake, he is no longer man. And where better can this creative effort be accomplished than in our universities? They are one of our greatest resources for the future and their support should receive the highest priority."

Speaking further, I said,

"Woman brain power is our greatest untapped natural resource." I thought it should be used a lot more; this a decade before women's lib!

Commencement speakers at OSU had included so many distinguished figures of national prominence in politics, business and education that I felt greatly honored to be invited, especially since OSU faculty members were rarely asked. In more recent years the roster of OSU commencement speakers has included screen and TV personalities and even President Gerald R. Ford, another Wolverine at that!

Although most of my talks were done gratis, I often received modest honoraria. I put these into the OSU Development Fund to assist our radio observatory research. Just talking about our work helped pay for some of it.

One day an editor of *Life* magazine called. At that time (1960) *Life* had the greatest circulation of any U.S. weekly.

"We're doing a special article on the International Geophysical Year and what it accomplished and want to include a photograph of your radio telescope with all the helices," he said. "Would it be OK if we sent a photographer out to Columbus next week to take some pictures?"

"Sure," I replied, "we will look for him."

He came for a day and took many pictures but that didn't end it. During the next two weeks three more *Life* photographers came, each shooting hundreds more. From these myriads of photographs *Life* published one, showing our helix array resplendent in a huge two-page spread with the caption

"Morning sun glints through gigantic wire corkscrews of bizarre radio telescope at Ohio State University."

It was a strange, surrealistic view that must have been a double exposure with a diffraction pattern of the sun's rays highlighting the helices. I certainly would have thrown it out but the editor liked it. Of the hundreds and hundreds of pictures the photographers had taken from every conceivable angle and under every kind of lighting condition, the one they used was a cockeyed double exposure!

Following a visit by General John B. Medaris to our radio observatory, we received a substantial contract to help us in our satellite work. Medaris was in charge of the group which had launched the first U.S.

satellite, Explorer 1, on the first of February 1958. We acquired additional equipment for our studies. One of the biggest items was a huge 20 kilowatt radio transmitter which we installed on the top floor of Caldwell Lab on the OSU campus. With it we were able to send out our own pulse signals instead of relying on WWV. We installed a vertical antenna on the roof of Caldwell Lab for the transmitter and a large rotating corner reflector at the university farm site for receiving. I hoped that we could obtain both distance and direction information on the satellite-induced ionization. Martti Tiuri from Finland spent a year at OSU working with me on the problem.

Our system worked well and we got some good records of satellite-induced ionization effects. We also received pulses from our transmitter which had travelled around the world and back to Columbus. Our pulses ranged over the whole world but a problem developed right at home.

The pulses were picked up by amplifiers in the WOSU studios next door and the staccato rat-a-tat of our radar was audible on all of WOSU's broadcasts. And in the adjacent Physics Building more than a dozen experiments throughout the building were immobilized because the pulses overloaded equipment. It took a week or two for the studio personnel and the physicists to discover where the interfering signals were coming from but they then rose as one to demand that I shut down our transmitter. They wanted me to move it off the campus and to promise not to run it again in Caldwell. I agreed only to turn it off and investigate the problem. The basic difficulty was that the studio and Physics Department equipment had inadequate shielding but this wouldn't be easy to fix even if I could convince everyone that better shielding was needed. So I took another tack.

We replaced the vertical antenna on Caldwell Lab, which had radiated horizontally over the campus, with a horizontal antenna, which radiated straight up. In the meantime we moved our receiving equipment from the west campus to the new radio observatory near Delaware where our big telescope was nearing completion.

Without telling WOSU or the Physics Department, we turned our powerful transmitter in Caldwell Lab on again and our system was once more in operation. We had no complaints. Months later when some of the physicists learned, via scuttlebutt, that the big transmitter was on again, they had difficulty believing that we could operate such a powerful transmitter so close and not bother them at all. We had done it with an appropriate antenna design.

Although some labs which had "duplicated" our experiment failed to duplicate our results, two scientists at the University of Chicago, R. Baron and L.S. Lerner, analyzed the situation and reported that these labs had in fact *not* duplicated our experiment but had modified it in ways which led to different results. For example, their radar wavelength was too short, they looked in the wrong directions, or their location was too far from the base of the outer Van Allen belt (we were right below it).

But a number of other labs were by this time obtaining results which did confirm ours. And one in Oklahoma obtained even better correlations of ionization effects with passes of Sputnik 3 than we had.

But the culminating evidence for satellite-induced ionization effects came from an unexpected quarter. One day, E.K. Bigg, an Australian statistician, walked into Jim Warwick's office at the University of Colorado in Boulder. Jim had a couple of big corner reflector antennas with which he had monitored Jupiter's radio emission for many years and had accumulated a large backlog of Jupiter records. Bigg asked Warwick if he could use his Jupiter records to find out if there was any connection between the occurrence of Jupiter emission and the position of one of Jupiter's inner satellites, Io. Unlikely as success may have seemed to Warwick he told Bigg he was welcome to use them.

In due time Bigg had a verdict to give. To almost everyone's surprise he had found a stunning correlation between the position of Io and the strength and duration of radio emission from Jupiter. The little moon, Io, revolving around the giant planet 87 000 miles (140 000 kilometers) in diameter was, if not actually producing the radio emission, certainly triggering or controlling it. Bigg's epic discovery was one of the great milestones in our understanding of Jupiter's ionosphere.

I think that Martti Tiuri and I may have been the only ones who were not surprised. Our work with Sputnik 2, Sputnik 3, and Echo 1 had shown it was very likely that these satellites of the earth interacted with ionospheric zones producing detectable effects. It appeared to us that the satellite-induced ionization effects and the "Io effect" were actually different aspects of the same phenomenon.

When Io penetrated a highly ionized shell in the magnetosphere of Jupiter, it swept up charged particles and produced Alfven waves which resulted in radiation from electrons in the shell. This radiation was easily observed at the earth some 375 million miles (600 million kilometers) away. When Sputnik 3, Echo 1, or other satellites of the earth penetrated a highly ionized shell in the earth's magnetosphere, the same phenomenon occurred in the Van Allen belt right over Columbus, sufficient to be observed by radar or radio reflection methods from the earth's surface just a few hundred miles below.

In a paper Martti Tiuri and I presented, we commented that "The similar circumstances involved in the satellite-ionization phenomenon and the decameter radiation from Jupiter suggest that both may be different manifestations of the same basic mechanism in which a satellite interacts with an electron shell in the magnetosphere."

In other words, was not the Io effect simply a Jovian version of the "Kraus effect?"

CHAPTER 18

BIG EAR
Ad Astra per Aspera

Work on our big parabola had begun in 1956. During that year and the next, Jupiter, Mars and Venus had been distractions. Then came the Sputniks and the U.S. satellites, diverting our attention well into the sixties. But all the while construction on the new telescope continued. In June 1957 the first bay of the parabola was raised into position. After a rain the mud was so thick that I had to fight to free my boots with each step I took. And at the other extreme, on hot, dry, windy days, dense brown clouds of clay dust were blowing everywhere.

By the following year all 12 bays were up and we turned our construction efforts to the tiltable flat reflector. Bob Nash and I had been working on details of its design for several years. To tilt a steel structure several hundred feet long by one hundred feet wide through a large angle was not a trivial problem, but, in addition, the surface had to be flat and accurate to within a few millimeters. Also we needed to be able to set the whole affair at any angle and have it hold without moving.

If the entire flat reflector had been built as a single rigid structure, the amount of steel required would have made the cost prohibitive, so we opted for a sectionalized reflector, made up of several units or bays which could be moved independently. The great economy of this design was that only single bays, not the entire reflector, had to be rigid. Alignment of all the bays could be achieved by a surveying or sighting instrument.

We considered many schemes for tilting the bays. Then one day at the county fair, where Jack and Nels had their sheep on display as part of their 4-H project, I studied the mechanism of the large ferris wheel on the midway. The huge chair-studded wheel was turned by a steel cable wrapped all the way around it. There were no gears at all!

"Maybe," I thought, "we can adapt such a scheme to raise and lower our flat-reflector, only we won't use a whole ferris wheel, just a part of one."

Further study showed that the arrangement was not only practical, it was economical as well. Instead of picking up a large circular dish antenna and building a massive, expensive supporting structure under it, so that it could be moved around as in a conventional telescope, the same area was made long and low with multiple short supports from the ground. Thus, an antenna of large collecting area could be constructed to a given surface accuracy at a great savings in cost, which is to say, our design would provide the largest possible telescope per dollar of cost.

30. First section of the tiltable-flat reflector. "After a rain the mud was so thick I had to fight to free my boots with each step I took but on hot, dry, windy days dense brown clouds of clay dust were blowing everywhere."

A French group at the Paris Observatory recognized the merit of our design and initiated plans to build a much larger telescope modelled after ours. The French telescope had a fixed curved reflector 1000 feet (300 meters) long by 100 feet (30 meters) high, giving an area four times that of our telescope. After we had started construction, Dr. Jean Louis Steinberg of the French group visited us on a number of occasions to discuss design details. The French group went forward rapidly with construction and by 1965 their big telescope was in operation.

Still later, about 1970, our design was incorporated in a Russian telescope built at Gorki by a group under Albert Kislyakov. Although smaller in physical size, with fixed parabolic reflector and tiltable flat reflector each 82 feet (25 meters) long this telescope is so precisely constructed that it works at the extremely short wavelength of one millimeter. The surface is smooth to one-twentieth of a millimeter (50 microns) approaching the surface quality of an optical mirror. (The shorter the wavelength the smoother the surface needs to be.) At one millimeter wavelength the antenna beam width is only 10 seconds of arc (or three thousandths of one degree), the sharpest single beam produced to date by any radio telescope in the world.

We thought our design had merit. The French and Russian groups did also. Low cost wasn't the only advantage. Still another was that the low profile made it much less susceptible to interference from earth-based radio, TV, and radar systems. The feed antennas are as low as one can get, right at ground level, making direct pick up of interfering signals less likely. We don't need 4000 foot mountains for shielding the telescope like conventional telescopes do; a woods with 80 foot trees suffices. Yet another advantage is that there is virtually no restriction on the size and weight of feed antennas and receivers at the focus. By contrast there are severe size and weight restrictions on what can be suspended at the focus of conventional dish telescopes.

Between 1957 and 1959 we had received additional NSF grants to complete the parabola and construct the flat reflector. During the summer months most of our student crew members worked full time and progress was more rapid. Foundations were excavated and concrete poured for all nine flat reflector bays.

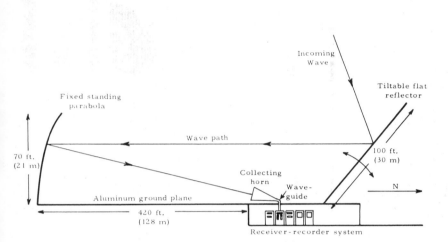

31. Big Ear in cross section. Incoming waves bounce off the tiltable flat reflector into the parabola which in turn focusses the waves into the collecting horns. Metal pipes or waveguides then convey them to sensitive receivers in the laboratory below where the waves are amplified and recorded. Movement of the flat reflector permits reception from different directions (declinations) in the sky.

By 1960 the flat reflector was essentially completed and construction efforts shifted to the three acre ground plane between the parabola and flat reflector, and to the underground laboratory situated below the focal point of the antenna. The ground plane acts as a guide for the waves traveling parallel to it between the flat reflector and the parabola. Although not a reflecting surface, like the flat reflector or parabola, it requires a metal surface.

Bob Nash and I weighed many alternatives for the ground plane design but finally decided on one of concrete several inches thick with thin aluminum sheet bonded to it.

While preparing the site for the flat reflector in 1959, it had been necessary to remove a great amount of earth which was dumped and spread over the area between the parabola and flat reflector until it was built up to the proper height for a concrete slab. For several weeks monster road building machines groaned and snorted like huge lumbering dinosaurs around the site, while 20 000 cubic yards of earth were moved at a cost of only 35 cents a yard.

Early in July 1961 we started to lay the concrete for the ground plane but frequent severe thunderstorms and torrential rains made the work difficult. After one rainstorm early in July the site looked like a three acre lake, a spectacle oft repeated during the month; it was the wettest July on record! In spite of this, the concrete was all down by August and the site took on the appearance of an enormous parking lot with a huge curved fence at the south and a big sloping structure at the north that resembled bleachers.

In September installation began on the aluminum surfacing, which came in large rolls five feet wide and which was glued to the concrete with a viscous asphalt-like adhesive. The work had to be done in dry, hot weather and the workmen were broiled not only by the direct rays of the sun from above but also by reflection from the shiny sheet aluminum below. They consumed what must have been record amounts of water *and* aspirin!

Although the ground plane was the largest component of the telescope, it was the simplest to construct and the least expensive. It and the underground focus laboratory cost only about 10 percent of the total for the antenna. The parabola's share was about 35 percent and the flat reflector's about 55 percent.

In addition to a parabola, flat reflector, ground plane and focus laboratory many other things were needed to make the telescope operational. We required receivers, feed antennas, a computer, controls for operating the flat reflector winches and an arrangement for accurately setting the reflector. Al Herriman, one of my graduate students, designed a precision optical device for setting the bays of the flat reflector, and Jess Wolfe, EE department machinist, constructed it. Collecting horns for the focus of the telescope were designed and built.

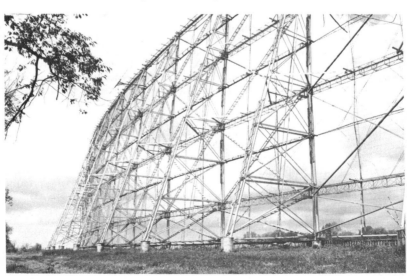

32. **The parabola from the southeast.**

Between 1958 and 1961 we received university grants of $23 000 for assistantships, $34 000 for site improvements, and $65 000 for receiving equipment. Altogether the NSF had provided about $400 000 for constructing the telescope antenna (parabola, flat reflector and ground plane) but of this the project allotment was about $250 000, the rest being the university's overhead charge. For one-quarter million dollars we had designed and built one of the world's largest radio telescopes! If Ken Baker could call the 96-helix array a "big ear," then this much larger telescope qualified as a *really* big ear.

To lock the flat reflector bays when they were not being moved with the hoisting winches, Bob Nash had designed massive brake arms which clamped against the sides of the ferris wheel assemblies. Aluminum does not slide easily when pressed hard against aluminum. Rather, it tends to grab and lock. Bob Nash took advantage of this property by equipping the brake arms with aluminum shoes and making them clamp against aluminum plates fastened to the ferris wheel.

In simplest terms a radio telescope is an antenna and a receiver. Without a good receiver the best antenna is of little value. We had an excellent, large antenna. What we desperately needed was a good receiver. In particular, the front end or preamplifier for the receiver was crucial. It should be of the lowest noise and highest sensitivity possible. Amplifiers which we might purchase as stock items from manufacturers were not sensitive enough so we explored other possibilities.

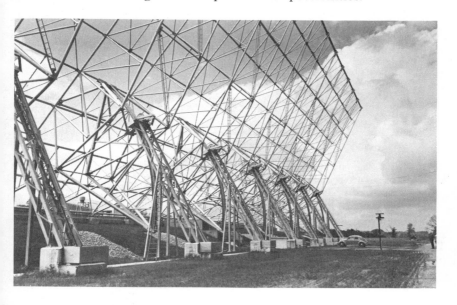

33. The flat reflector from the northeast.

At the Bell Telephone Laboratories in New Jersey, "Mickey" Uenohara (Wayne-o-hara) had developed a very sensitive parametric type amplifier for use in satellite communication relay stations. Mickey had received his doctors degree in electrical engineering at OSU a year or so before. Bell Labs was willing to have Mickey build us one of his best parametric amplifiers or "paramps" for a 21 centimeter wavelength if we provided the basic hardware required costing about $6000. We were delighted with this arrangement, and in 1963 Steve O'Donnell and Bob Townsend from our observatory drove to Murray Hill in a rented truck to pick up the amplifier. We connected it to our "big ear," and turned it on. It has kept going 24 hours a day, 365 days a year ever since with only a few days of down time for maintenance.*

34. Workmen on ground plane installing aluminum sheet while being "broiled by the sun from above and by reflection from the shiny aluminum below."

The combination of our big antenna and this very low noise amplifier made our radio telescope the most sensitive in the world for many years. To keep the amplifier cooled required the addition of a couple liters of liquid nitrogen per day at a cost of about 20 cents per liter.

Although the underground prime focus laboratory, measuring 16 by 32 feet, had ample space for our receivers, recorders and associated equipment, we needed a building at the site for offices and for construction and repair of electronic components. A young architect, Pierre Zoelly, was recommended to design the building. In due time Zoelly produced sketches for a Frank Lloyd Wright type of soaring, gravity-defying structure

---

*Some years later Mickey left Bell Labs to return to Japan where he became director of research for Nippon Electric, one of Japan's largest electrical and electronics companies.

35. Big Ear completed. Office building is at top center with automobiles alongside.

of steel and concrete. I'm sure it would have won many prizes but estimates of its cost ran over $100 000 to which the NSF gave a flat no. So we paid Zoelly's fee of $400 and settled on a one story Armco Steel prefab building 40 feet square costing $15 000.

Along with the telescope construction and all that this entailed I had many other irons in the fire. We were making radio astronomy observations and also artificial satellite observations with the instruments at the old site on the university farm near the campus. I was also teaching courses on electromagnetic theory, antennas, transmission systems, and radio astronomy plus advising graduate students who were using the instruments for a variety of experiments. Then too there was the perennial committee work on curricula, policy matters, and funding. My mail was full of letters with questions about antenna design or radio astronomy problems and I answered these as a free consulting service. Meanwhile, I continued to give many talks. Some were local but many were out of town at such places as Chicago, Boston, Princeton, and Cape Canaveral. I flew to Washington at the request of the White House to serve on one of President Eisenhower's science advisory panels where I met with Dr. George Kistiakowski, the President's science advisor. At other times I served on special radio astronomy panels meeting in New York, Washington, and Green Bank, West Virginia.

Ideas come at odd moments as when driving to or from the campus and I always carry a few blank cards on which to jot them down when I am stopped at traffic lights. Sometimes when I awake in the middle of the night, solutions appear to problems which have puzzled me so I keep a pencil and pad of paper handy by my bed and even though my notes are written in the dark they are legible provided I print them.

One morning when I awoke I found I had written myself a note suggesting that I check the parabola foundations. I did so and after long calculations concluded that the concrete foundations were not heavy enough to prevent the parabola from overturning in a 100 mile per hour wind from the south at a time when the ground was completely soaked and unable to restrain the foundations, the worst possible combination of circumstances. I calculated that we needed to add many tons to each foundation column. To do this it would be necessary to excavate a trench around each of the columns to a depth of five feet and pour a massive concrete collar around it. The quarters were too cramped to use excavating machinery; the job would have to be done manually.

To obtain some notion of how much work would be involved, I demonstrated my abilities with pick and shovel, excavating one of the circular trenches through the hard clay in five hours. No one offered to try and break this "record" so I multiplied by a factor of 2 to get 10 hours as an estimate. This turned out to be close to the time it took the students to dig each of the circular trenches. After some weeks the trenches were dug and filled with concrete and we felt more secure.

I wrote many articles during the early sixties. I also devoted huge blocks of time to the manuscript for a book on radio astronomy. My lecture notes for the first courses in radio astronomy I gave with Geoff Keller ten years before were the starting point. Martti Tiuri wrote a chapter on his specialty of radio telescope receivers. It became a family project in that my son Nels typed the final manuscript. The book, 481 pages long, was published in 1966. It was, and still is, the only radio astronomy text book with problems and is used at many universities. It is also in great demand as a reference. On a visit to the National

Radio Astronomy Observatory in Green Bank, West Virginia, I found that
although the library had 17 copies of "Radio Astronomy," *all* were checked
out! The book is much used abroad and a Russian translation has been
published. This translation appeared before the U.S.S.R. recognized any
copyright agreements so there probably aren't any rubles for me in a
Moscow bank with which to buy a bottle of vodka if I visit there again.

36. These are the funnel-like horns into which the parabola
focusses the faint signals from the depths of space after their
journey of millions or billions of years. The signals, thus gathered,
go by pipes or waveguides to the receivers in the laboratory
below. The large horns on the left collect the 21 centimeter waves
while the smaller ones at the right, with Gene Mikesell checking
them, are for 11 centimeters. The big horns are all of aluminum
and were constructed by Gene at the observatory.

Anyway, I didn't write the book for the royalties involved. Writing
the book, like building "Big Ear," took a great amount of time and
effort and both were done in spite of obstacles and the fact that I was
doing many other things. No one had asked me to write the book or
build the telescope; I did both because I wanted to. It was as simple
as that. Many people have accomplished many things in this world in just
this way. Their dedication bespeaks a love for what they do and among
persons in various walks of life many engineers, astronomers, teachers
and writers possess such a love.

Even though our huge radio telescope was taking solid form in steel
and concrete, it did not prevent my mind from constantly searching
for better and less expensive ways of constructing large antennas or

radio telescopes. I considered many schemes. One of the more practical types I evolved consisted of a wire mesh or grid shaped like the mortar pattern of a brick wall. In 1961, Nels helped me cut and solder hundreds of wires together to make an array of many meshes covering a couple of square yards on a large plywood sheet to test the idea. Working at a wavelength of a few centimeters this antenna would serve as a small scale model for one covering hundreds of square yards working at longer wavelengths.

When we set up the antenna in a field and measured the pattern I discovered that the radiation was in a double or split lobe instead of a single broadside beam as I had expected. I theorized that the radiation for the two beams was coming from the two halves of the array separated by the feed point at the center. So I moved the feed point to one end of the array and that did the trick! The radiation was now in a single narrow beam tilted at an angle from the broadside direction. By changing the wavelength the beam could be tilted through a range of angles without physically moving the antenna. This was fantastic!

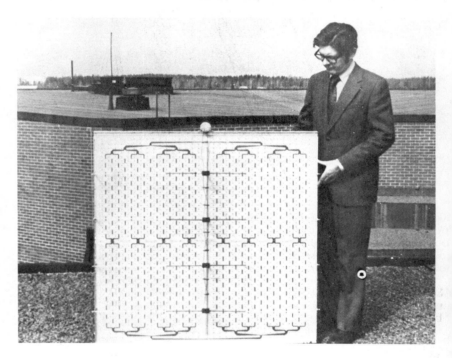

37. Martti Tiuri on the roof of the Helsinki Institute of Technology Radio Laboratory with grid antenna he constructed for installation on helicopters used to direct icebreakers in and out of ice-locked harbors. The grid antenna is "shaped like the mortar pattern of a brick wall."

It would be possible to build a big fixed array close to the ground and sweep or scan the beam across the sky by simply changing the wavelength. Or alternatively by having several receivers tuned to different wavelengths you could háve several beams in the sky at once like the fingers of your hand. I workéd out the mathematical relations between the antenna dimensions and the beam angle and compared these theoretical angles with ones I measured. The agreement was good so I felt that I understood enough about the way the antenna functioned to publish my results.

38. Helicopter over the Baltic Sea with grid antenna mounted under the fuselage. "The antenna does not move but its beam scans below and to both sides . . . searching for the thinnest ice."

The grid antenna has found many applications. In Finland, Martti Tiuri has installed it on helicopters for measuring the thickness of ice ahead of icebreakers to locate the best route in and out of ice-locked Baltic Sea harbors. The antenna does not move but its beam scans below and to both sides of the helicopter searching for the thinnest ice.*

---

*The system operates like a radio telescope except that the grid antenna "looks" down at the ice instead of up at the sky. Radar is not effective for measuring the ice thickness.

*   *   *   *   *

Central Ohio became the site of a spectacular oil strike while construction of the telescope was still in progress. We wondered if rivers of oil underfoot might distract us from things celestial. Big producing wells had been drilled in Morrow County, northeast and immediately adjacent to Delaware County where our telescope is situated. Oil fever swept the state. Many farmers began planning how they would spend their millions. Oil prospecting crews swarmed into Delaware County and a gusher was brought in just north of the city of Delaware, only four miles from our radio observatory. The dynamite charges of prospecting crews were heard often. Oil derricks began to appear as drilling rigs started to bore their way down through the shale and limestone, often working around the clock.

What if oil were found right under the radio telescope? Ohio Wesleyan would certainly be overjoyed but would activities of an oil field interfere with the radio telescope? Meetings of Ohio Wesleyan and Ohio State officials were called and discussions held. We concluded that if wells and drilling activities were no closer than 400 meters (¼ mile) from the telescope, we might get by provided we could apply noise silencing devices to any equipment found to produce interference. We also called attention to the long term problem of settling of the ground if large amounts of oil were removed since this could seriously misalign the reflectors. We were concerned about the telescope but on the other hand we did not wish to prevent Wesleyan from having an oil bonanza.

We were prepared for any contingency but all of the wells drilled within two miles of the radio observatory site were dry. A few somewhat more distant wells, which had at first seemed promising, fell way off on production and were capped. No new wells were drilled. Exploration crews moved elsewhere. Gradually the oil fever subsided.

The big oil strikes in Morrow County occurred about 1961. By 1963 the fever had spread to Delaware County but by 1965 it was all over, except in Morrow County, and we could once more turn our attention from the earth to the sky.

Oil wasn't the only thing which at first loomed big and then faded. For a long while I had endeavored to increase the university involvement in radio astronomy. I believed that it should be an integral part of the university program and budget the same as optical astronomy. Astronomy was the science of the universe and whether observations of a celestial object were made with light waves or radio waves, it was still astronomy. Both light and radio waves are electromagnetic in nature, differing only in wavelength. The fullest understanding of a celestial object might require observations at both optical and radio wavelengths.

With the construction of our big telescope underway I intensified my efforts. Most of the construction cost was being paid by an outside source, the NSF, and it was likely that the NSF would help support the costs of operation, but not forever. I met with many persons, Dreese, Carson, Heimberger. Deke Dreese was for it. Gordon Carson was the new Dean of Engineering. Carson wanted to introduce an item for radio astronomy as part of the regular college budget.* Fred Heimberger,

---

*Carson had organized a "Committee of 100," made up largely of OSU engineering graduates holding key positions in Ohio industry. He felt that such a group could be an effective lobby with the state legislature and provide some clout for engineering to balance that wielded for so many years by the Agricultural College and its Experiment Station.

Vice President for Research, was enthusiastic about the idea and hoped "to develop a very powerful total approach to astronomy" both optical and radio at OSU.

When astronomy became a separate department (it had been with physics) my title became Professor of Electrical Engineering and Astronomy.† Even though optical and radio astronomy were in different departments there was a lot of cooperation.

However, some of our most ambitious plans failed to materialize. The EE and Astronomy departments jointly endeavored on several occasions to add distinguished astronomers to OSU's faculty but without success. Also Carson's and my hopes for a line item in the budget for radio astronomy were unrealized. So was the ambitious 10-year plan for radio and optical astronomy which Robert Stephenson, Director of OSU's Research Foundation, had proposed and which he had hoped to accomplish through a long series of meetings and conferences. But we did achieve some lesser objectives. The engineering college assumed responsibility for our power and telephone bills, operating costs of the observatory truck, mowing of the fields around the telescope, paving and maintenance of the road into the observatory, and the construction of a substantial fence around the site to keep the cattle from neighboring farms from wandering onto the aluminum ground plane. Although not all that I had hoped for in commitments to match the lofty aims, it was something.

One day I was visited by a prominent Milwaukee industrialist and the engineering dean from Marquette University of Milwaukee. They wished to discuss the problems of establishing a large radio telescope in the Milwaukee area. Their reasons were intriguing. In our new technology, new industries were locating near centers of scientific achievement and research potential so they reasoned that a large radio telescope would be an important factor in attracting scientific talent and in fostering technological and industrial growth in the Milwaukee area. I had thought of radio astronomy as an important basic science. These men recognized its potential as an economic force. I showed them our telescope and offered to help all I could. I congratulated them on their foresightedness and wished them success in raising a parabola "to make Milwaukee famous." I also wished that more Ohioans had their vision.

Our telescope construction by part time student help committed us to slow progress. So while our work continued at a snail's pace I received many invitations to radio telescope dedications elsewhere. Other institutions had started planning long after we began construction and reached completion while we were still years from finishing ours.

I received invitations from Fred Haddock at Michigan and Harold Weaver at California for the dedications of their 85-foot dishes and from George Swenson of Illinois for the dedication of his huge antenna. I also received invitations to the dedication ceremonies for the 140-foot dish at Green Bank and the 1000-foot bowl at Arecibo, Puerto Rico. The 140-foot dish had cost over $10 000 000 and the Arecibo bowl nearly that much.

The Michigan dedication in October 1959 was an impressive affair with an address by Governor John B. Swainson. His remarks about the importance of research to industry and the general economy were reminiscent of the views expressed by my Milwaukee visitors. Governor Swainson said,

†Prior to that time my title had been Professor of Electrical Engineering, Physics and Astronomy.

"Here, at the University of Michigan, much is being done to bring Michigan to a position of preeminence in the field of scientific research. Our state was away to a slow start in the field of space research but there is absolutely no reason why we can't catch and pass the front runners. The observatory instrumentation being dedicated today is a giant step in that direction."

He then commented on the new Institute of Science and Technology authorized for the University of Michigan, predicting that it would become "one of the great centers of scientific research, capable of attracting new types of industry related to the space age, and, in fact, every type of research oriented industry. Properly developed and supported, this institute can become one of the world's foremost centers of scientific knowledge and will pay for itself many times over in developing Michigan's economy and industry. This observatory is another important development in the enlarging of our facilities for scientific research in Michigan."

I thought that we ought to have a dedication for our telescope too but I wondered if it was really appropriate to dedicate a partially completed telescope. Initially our plan was to build a 720-foot parabola but because of insufficient funds we started construction on half of this or a 360-foot parabola. And at 21 centimeters the effective telescope size was only 180 feet, since this was the parabola width over which we had reflector wires with small enough spacing. So from 720 feet we had shrunk to 180 feet or down by a factor of 4. Eventually we did receive funds for an increase to 340 feet but that was so many years later (1969) that all thoughts of a dedication had long since vanished.

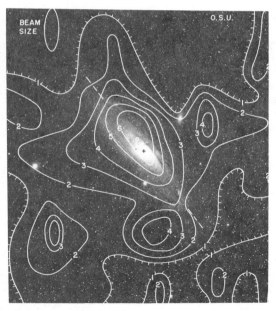

39. Radio contours measured with Big Ear extend like a 4-spiked halo beyond the Andromeda galaxy suggesting "a much more violent past . . . than hinted at by the photograph" taken at the Perkins Observatory.

In spite of the incomplete status of our telescope we began an astronomical observing program with it in 1963. For several months I observed the great Andromeda galaxy. The sensitivity and resolution of our telescope was sufficient to make a map of the galaxy with the greatest detail obtained up to that time, and I published the results in an article bearing the intriguing title "Does M31 Have a Halo?"

*   *   *   *   *

M31 is the Messier catalog designation for the Andromeda nebula. Charles Messier was a French astronomer of the late seventeen and early eighteen hundreds. In that era comets were among astronomy's most exciting objects and Messier was a comet hunter. Many faint, diffuse, nebulous objects in the sky are easily confused with a comet so Messier complied a list of 101 of these objects and published it in 1784 for the convenience of comet hunters.

If they discovered what they thought was a comet they checked Messier's list and if their object was at the position of one of Messier's objects they didn't waste any more time observing it but continued searching elsewhere.

Messier's nebula M31 in Andromeda is now known to be a great neighboring galaxy similar to our own as is also Messier's object M81.

In 1784 astronomers hunted for comets; now two centuries later astronomers still hunt for comets but also, as we shall see, for pulsars, quasars, black holes, big redshift objects and signals from distant civilizations. The universe has become bigger, more complex, mysterious and exciting than Messier or his contemporaries ever dreamed, yet we have really just begun to explore it.

*   *   *   *   *

I superimposed our radio contour map on a photograph of M31 taken at Perkins Observatory. Although the strongest radio emission occurred near the bright center of the galaxy, there were four prominent spurs in the radio map pointing approximately north, south, east and west, which had no optical counterpart, the spurs extending far beyond the optical limits of the galaxy somewhat in the manner of a halo. The implication was that an explosion in the galaxy at some prior time had ejected energetic electrons into the spurs which emitted radio waves but no visible light. Geoffrey Burbidge of the University of California at San Diego reproduced my radio-optical presentation in a *Scientific American* article probably because it suggested a much more violent past for the galaxy than hinted at by the optical photograph.

The Latin words "Ad Astra per Aspera" ("To the stars with difficulty") are engraved on the door to our radio telescope receiver room. We put them there because building and operating a radio telescope has its problems; it takes fortitude, patience and perseverance. When you have invented a telescope, designed all parts of it electrical and mechanical down to the last bolt, gotten funds for it, built it, used it, interpreted your data from it and published the results, you have a broad and unique perspective few can appreciate.

Some histories of radio astronomy have been written by persons who have never built a radio telescope. John Bolton, pioneer Australian radio astronomer and telescope builder, was a bit annoyed by one such historian who depreciated the exciting early days of radio astronomy as of little consequence. In a review of the historian's book John said,

"If the writer had had to build a radio telescope, his story of radio astronomy would be another story."

CHAPTER 19

BUSTED BOLTS

"The antenna has crashed!" Joe Cox blurted over the telephone from the radio observatory. I asked for details but Joe was incoherent. I had just returned home from the observatory and I immediately went back. It was a 10 minute drive but that Sunday morning it seemed more like two hours.

As I approached the observatory, I could see that the east end of the flat reflector was in disarray, the top tilted down and the lower part canted up at a crazy angle.

When I got there, Joe tried to explain what had happened. He and George James had been moving the flat reflector to a new setting. While George was operating the winch motor on bay 7, the bay suddenly fell backwards with a tremendous thundering, grinding crash.

George and Joe were puzzled and confused, and so was I. Had a cable broken, had it jumped off the huge pulley wheel? Why hadn't the brakes arrested the fall? We didn't know. George insisted that everything had seemed to be operating properly. He had released the brakes on bay 7 and had just started the winch motor when the crash occurred.

We needed Gene Mikesell, our chief telescope operator, but couldn't reach him by phone. I guessed that Gene probably was in church and suggested that Joe should drive over in his car for him. My surmise was correct, and it wasn't long before Joe returned with Gene.

Gene, Joe, George and I now began a more detailed investigation. First, we checked against the possibility of any further movement or damage. Even though bays 7 and 8 were tilting back at a precarious angle and some 15 feet out of alignment, they seemed to be holding steadily. The bays are joined by bridging sections and the backward tilt on bays 7 and 8 was placing a severe load on bay 6 as evidenced by a downward deflection of several feet at its top east end. Each bay is 40 feet wide by 100 feet in slant height and weighs 15 tons.

Then we noticed that the winch cable on bay 7 was hanging loose. We opened up the piano-sized box enclosing the winch. Superficially it looked OK. There were even several turns of cable on the winch drum, but we were startled to see that they were wound on *backwards!* Both ends of the cable were still securely attached, and there were no breaks. So the cable had not failed. The cable is 3½ inches in circumference and rated at more than 50 tons load so cable breakage had seemed unlikely, but how had it gotten wound on the winch drum in the reverse direction? We examined the winch drum more closely and found that it turned easily by hand. This was incredible!

The drum was rotated by a huge worm gear assembly which ordinarily held it immoveable except when the drive motor was operated, so something had broken in the winch! Looking more closely, we found iron fragments and bolt heads scattered about. These we traced to the end flange of the winch drum where it had been bolted to the drive block by six 2-centimeter (¾ inch) diameter bolts. Chunks of the flange had broken away around the bolts, and all the bolts had sheared off.

The bits of evidence now began to fit together, and we postulated a sequence of events. With brakes released on bay 7 the full load of the bay came on the winch. When power was applied to hoist the bay, the end flange of the winch drum disintegrated around some of the bolt holes. The load which had been carried by these bolts then transferred to the remaining bolts. These could not carry the load alone, and all of the bolts sheared off. The drum then spun free, paying out cable as bay 7 fell. We had incorporated a safety switch for applying the brakes when there was loss of tension in the cable. This caused the brakes to come back on automatically. This braking, plus the restraint of bay 7 through the bridging sections, kept bay 7 from falling farther than about 15 feet. But this was enough to spin the freely-turning winch drum so fast that although the bay stopped falling, the drum kept turning. All the cable paid out, and the still-spinning drum then wrapped the loose cable onto itself backwards or opposite to the direction it had been wound before. We later calculated that the whole thing must have happened in a few seconds.

Our observations with the telescope were stopped. The flat reflector was badly damaged, but fortunately no one was injured. I telephoned OSU officials in Columbus and advised them of the disaster. Word of the collapse was in the newspapers and on TV the next day (Monday). The Delaware, Ohio, *Gazette* had a front page story with pictures. The story began

"Failure of a power winch Sunday at the Ohio State-Ohio Wesleyan Radio Observatory south of Stratford resulted in damages that may run over $100 000. . . ."

Dr. Everett Hurlburt of the National Science Foundation (NSF) in Washington, had seen the news release and telephoned me to inquire about the extent of the damage and how long it might take to make repairs. Dr. Hurlburt was Program Director for Radio Astronomy, and his branch handled our research grants. I replied that we were assessing the damage, and right then I really had no idea how long we might be shut down. It was clear that the NSF could not help on the repairs. I was deeply concerned.

The telescope had been constructed and its research program financed by grants from the NSF. The telescope was the property of the university, but OSU, like all state institutions in Ohio, carried no insurance. State statutes did not allow it. And we all knew that the university operated under a very tight budget. If a university classroom building burned down, one could expect an eventual state appropriation to replace it. But the radio telescope was a research facility, and it had been built mainly by federal, not state funds. Although a research facility is like a classroom and laboratory for students both graduate and undergraduate, this is not widely recognized. So, how would the university react? Would it accept any responsibility, and if so, how much and in what way? I did not know, and my concern grew deeper as I discovered in the next few days that no one I talked to at the university had any definite answers. Certainly there was no automatic procedure available and no precedents.

But I did find concern and interest on the part of many OSU officials and a genuine desire to discover a solution. A meeting was set up for Wednesday, March 15 (1967) at the observatory.

In the meantime I ordered steel beams installed and welded in place under all bays of the flat reflector so that they could not move. If one winch had failed, we could not preclude the possibility that failure of others was imminent. Gene, Joe and George worked frantically to get this done. We wanted to prevent further failures.

I wanted an independent calculation by an engineer of the highest repute of the stresses in the winch that failed. Professor Mike Marco, Chairman of the Department of Mechanical Engineering at OSU, responded promptly and inspected the winch and hoisting system. He prepared a report with complete calculations. These showed clearly that the method of flange attachment was of inadequate strength and greatly reduced the winch capability.

Bill Brundage, our electronics engineer, and Gene Mikesell embarked on a meticulous inspection of all the winches and Mike Miller of the engineering college, assessed the damage to the flat reflector.

By meeting time on March 15th we had accumulated considerable quantitative information. Bob Green, Associate Dean of Engineering, presided. Many others including Joe Byrd, of the Engineering Experiment Station, were there. It was the first time I had met Joe.

After inspecting the telescope, we met in my office. It was soon clear that remedial action required: (1) repair of the flat-reflector structure, (2) winch repair or replacement and (3) other changes or improvements in the hoisting system. Under (3) we gave consideration to a faster-acting brake system which would prevent the bays from falling appreciably in case of any future winch or cable failure. Our original design provided for an automatic application of the brakes in case of loss of cable tension, but it was not fast enough to be completely effective.

Joe Byrd made a detailed inventory of the damage to the flat reflector structure and prepared a list of the corrective measures required. He transmitted the list to Dean Green on March 23 with the recommendation that an outside contractor do this work.

It was also determined that the winch drums were all *cast iron* and not steel as the manufacturer had indicated. Thus, the drums were more subject to fatigue and cracking. On some drums there were cracks in the cylindrical core around which the cable was wrapped. This meant that the cable was crushing the drum core like you crush an egg in your hand. Even if failure at an end flange had not occurred, the drum core would eventually have collapsed.

It was evident that all winch drums should be replaced. The primary failure had occurred in the flange of the winch drum. The winch was rated at 80 tons and had failed at about 15 percent of this load. It was actually a hidden defect in the winch, because it was assembled so as to make it almost impossible to determine the thickness of the flange wall where it was bolted. It was necessary to take the winch completely apart to measure the thickness. Bill Brundage and Gene Mikesell's measurements on all of the winches disclosed that the web thickness where the flange was bolted varied from 12 millimeters maximum to as little as 4 millimeters on the different winches. The smallest value was on the winch that failed!

Joe Byrd prepared drawings and specifications for new drums. The new ones were to be made of *steel* pipe and plate assembled by electric arc welding.

By mid-April the specifications for flat reflector repairs were put out for bids with the OSU Research Foundation underwriting the cost. The contract was awarded to the Otto Bess Company of Columbus and they moved their equipment to the observatory the middle of May. As the repair cranes lifted the bays back into place, nearly all of the bent steel members straightened out. Even the 100-foot long 8-inch diameter pipes forming the main bay structure all sprang back straight. Fortunately, they had not been stressed beyond their elastic limit! Only a few smaller members remained bent and had to be replaced. Progress was faster than anticipated, and within two weeks most of the repairs to the flat reflector had been completed.

We might have resumed observations with the telescope, but we did not want to risk moving the flat reflector until a fail-safe hoisting system had been installed. However, there was a way out. If we conducted our survey by raising the flat reflector small amounts on successive days, we could keep the upper brakes applied all the time. These would keep the bays from falling in case of any winch or cable failure, but we could not move the flat reflector back down if we needed to repeat previous measurements. We elected to resume the sky survey in spite of this restriction. If we made sure that we had sufficient observations of good quality at each flat-reflector setting before moving to the next one we could manage.

On June 6 observations resumed. We had been off the air nearly three months. We now began scanning the sky systematically for Installment III of the Ohio Sky Survey.

The question of liability on the part of the winch manufacturer had been raised at the first meeting on March 15. So another investigation had been progressing along this line. The purchase order for the winches had been placed through the OSU Research Foundation. When the original purchase order, dated July 1964 was pulled from the file, we were startled to read that it specified "Seven Broken Winches"! Our requisition had called for B r a d e n winches as a suitable type. By a typographical error these had become B r o k e n winches. We never got B r a d e n winches. Instead the supplier obtained a substitute which appeared to be of equivalent rating from another manufacturer which I shall refer to simply as "The Winch Company."

We later quipped,

"If we had gotten 'Broken' winches, they might not have broken like the Un-broken one got broken."

The supplier and The Winch Company's representatives were called, and they attended meetings at the Radio Observatory in March and April. Eventually the Winch Company acknowledged its liability and a settlement was made by their insurance company which covered the cost of repairing the actual damage. This was much less than the $100 000 we estimated originally, but we received no compensation for the three months loss of observing time and the attendant dislocation of our programs.

Soon after the winch failed on March 12, a number of us, including Gene Mikesell, Bill Brundage, Joe Byrd and myself, began to spend much time and thought on ways of making the hoisting system completely safe from failure. We had many meetings, formal and informal, in my office, in the shop, and 40 feet up at the brake assembly of a flat-reflector bay. We made scale models of various designs and even a full-size wooden mockup of one proposed system. A number of times we thought we had arrived at the ultimate solution only to discover some drawbacks as we pursued the idea further. Joe Byrd covered reams of paper with calculations.

After several months Joe Byrd evolved a system which had one of the two brakes always in contact with the ferris wheel plate. Motion of the ferris wheel was possible even with one brake shoe in contact, because the brake arm could be compressed a couple of millimeters. To move the flat reflector required that one brake open and close rapidly, in a small fraction of a second, while the other brake remained in contact. In this way, the flat reflector could be moved in small increments with one brake always in contact.

Joe Byrd's design was ingenious and effective. It required a dynamically well-designed system to open and close the massive brake assembly quickly. It also required a sophisticated electrical system with many controls, switches, and interlocks. In operation the electropneumatic brake action had the loud, staccato "bup-bup" of a rapid-fire machine gun. Bill Brundage designed the electrical system and was responsible for its installation.* Gene Mikesell made the mechanical modifications one bay at a time. It was a big job, and it was not until the following summer of 1968 that Gene and Bill completed the modifications, and the flat reflector could again be moved both ways. The "bup-bup" of the new brake system became a familiar and pleasant sound.

At the very first meeting on March 15, Joe Byrd had shown a lively interest in the hoisting system and methods of improvement. We were lucky to get his help on the brakes and equally fortunate to have his assistance on a variety of subsequent problems. He has proven that sometimes the person who can help you most is right next door. The problem is to find the person, and in an institution as large as OSU with 50 000 students and staff of 8000, this is not always easy.

Afterthoughts

For several years, after completing the flat reflector in 1961, we used winches with a 40-ton rating. Bob Nash and I wanted a larger safety factor. So in 1964 we purchased the new winches with 80-ton rating. The new winches were giants; they made the old ones look like pygmies. Each weighed one ton as compared to a few hundred pounds for an old one. When we finally installed the new winches, Bob Nash said,

"We won't have to worry now."

Two years later a winch failed. We had gone to great expense and trouble to double the safety factor but, due to a hidden flaw, had actually decreased it!

A year passed from the time of the winch failure to the time we resumed bi-directional motion of the flat reflector. A lot had happened, but there were some positive results.

For one thing, we now had a new, improved, second-generation hoisting and braking system. The original design by Bob Nash was basically

---

*Bill had continued on as electronics engineer following his master's degree. A year or so later he left to become chief electronics engineer on the 300-foot radio telescope at the National Radio Astronomy Observatory in Green Bank, West Virginia.

sound, but the brake action was too slow. Joe Byrd's new design required much more sophistication, but it was worth it.

As a result of the winch failure, we had been forced to resume the systematic sky survey (our Installment III) instead of making a variety of other observations as we had been doing previously. As it turned out, the survey was the most important thing we did, so in retrospect, it may have been fortunate that we were compelled to get on with it. And having resumed, we never stopped until it was completed.

The university had accepted responsibility for the repairs, and although later reimbursed by the insurance settlement, it had gone ahead without waiting. This was encouraging.

And, perhaps best of all, we had "discovered" Joe Byrd.

CHAPTER 20

A STATUE TO RUDOLPH DIESEL

Andromeda and Cassiopeia were twinkling overhead. Orion was just rising in the east while from the north came the roar of high-flying jets. Hal Johnson beside me said,

"I don't see them but it sounds like a whole squadron's up there. Maybe tonight's the night."

"All we can do is wait and see," I replied.

We continued to scan the cold, autumn sky and to listen. We were standing in the open field just west of our big radio telescope. Beside us was a Federal Communications Commission (FCC) van truck loaded with listening gear and bristling with antennas; through an open door came a steady hiss from the loudspeaker of one of the receivers inside. Hal was an FCC engineer who had been around with his truck for a couple of days. That night we had been at the observatory for several hours.

The sound of the jets grew faint and disappeared. Time dragged on and it became very late. Occasionally we paced back and forth to keep warm and sometimes we exchanged a few words but mostly we just stood near the truck watching, listening, waiting.

From the east I again heard jet aircraft.

"Maybe they're coming back," I suggested.

"Could be," Hal answered.

Suddenly, the sharp musical whine of a radar blared from the loudspeaker in the van.

"They're at it," Hal exclaimed as he bolted inside. An antenna atop the truck began to turn as Hal took a bearing. I moved a few steps away from the truck so I could hear the jets more clearly. They were off to the east and seemed to be traveling south.

"The bearing I get is east by southeast," Hal shouted from the truck.

"That's where the sound is coming from," I called back.

After some minutes, Hal called out,

"Where are the jets now?"

"Way off to the south," I replied. "I can hardly hear them anymore."

"My bearing hasn't changed much but the altitude has decreased," Hal responded. "It was a chaff drop all right. I think we're getting somewhere!"

"Good!" I called back. "I'm going to the focus room to see how badly they messed up our charts."

In the underground laboratory below the focus point of the big telescope, Bob Townsend had been attending the receivers which lined both sides of a central corridor. As I entered the room, it was alive with lights glowing from the mosaic of panels and the whirring noise of blowers cooling the equipment,

"See anything unusual?" I yelled.

40. Big Ear's prime focus laboratory with Bob Townsend, "alive with lights glowing from the mosaic of panels and the whirring noise of blowers cooling the equipment."

Bob was standing midway along the corridor of equipment peering down at the wide sheet of chart paper spewing from the wall of panels. Turning, he smiled and shouted back,

"All hell broke loose about 20 minutes ago. Everything went off scale and has stayed there. Was there a drop?"

"Yes," I answered, "we think so, off to the southeast."

I went over and examined the charts with Bob.

"Wow," I said, "some signal. I hope nothing's damaged."

"Me too," said Bob.

"Hopefully, things will quiet down after a while and then we can compare notes with Hal," I replied. "I'm going back outside."

Later things did quiet down, the pens of our recorders came back on scale, and Hal, Bob and I held a conference about what had happened.

For a year or two, ever since our first test observations with the new telescope, we had experienced severe interference like this once or twice a week; strong signals would disrupt our observations.

Radio amateurs have a special designation for it. They call it "QRM," meaning "interference, man-made." The hams have another "Q" signal, "QRN," which means "interference, natural," the so-called static produced by thunderstorms or by lightning discharges. There were no storms or lightning when the interference occurred so what we were dealing with was QRM; it was man-made. I felt caught in a race to gather the message of the universe before it was drowned out in the din of man's devices. But what could we do?

We kept accurate records of the QRM, dates, times, intensities, but we had no good clues as to the cause. Then we found bits of evidence which had literally fluttered down from the sky. Alice and I had purchased a heavily wooded tract of 60 some acres in Liberty Township, Delaware County, not far from the new radio observatory. We enjoyed walking through the deep woods, learning the flowers, trees and birds. While alert to nature's signs we also picked up some unmistakable artifacts of man in the form of slender strips of aluminum foil. Some were only 5 or 10 centimeters long but many were 20 to 25 centimeters long and 6 millimeters wide. From my years at the Radio Research Laboratory I recognized these as "chaff," the code name used for aluminum foil dropped from aircraft to blind or confuse radars.

I reported my findings to the observatory staff and a chaff hunt was on. Soon I began to receive pieces of chaff picked up in backyards and along roads in and around Columbus and in Delaware county. I pasted the foil carefully on paper sheets, classified them as to type, and filed them. The word was out,

"If you find some aluminum strips, get them to John Kraus. He collects them."

Now chaff arrived by the bushel. We also learned that farmers some miles west of the observatory had found large amounts of aluminum foil in their fields and were concerned that it might be eaten by their cattle.

Only the Air Force could be dropping so much aluminum, I thought. There was a Radar Counter Measures (RCM) squadron at Lockbourne* Air Force Base in central Ohio and we suspected that it might be responsible. What an ironic twist that this RCM technique, born at the Radio Research Labs (RRL) where I worked during World War II, was now coming back to clobber our radio telescope. Apparently the Air Force had selected central Ohio for its RCM training missions.

I called the Air Force headquarters. A few days later a colonel, who had been a student of mine, called on me at the radio observatory. I showed him our records of interference with dates and times and the piles of chaff I had accumulated.

The interference seemed to be of two types, I explained. Some of it might have come from airborne radar jamming transmitters which covered wide bands of the radio spectrum including our radio astronomy channel. But more often it seemed related to chaff drops which produced a high altitude cloud of aluminum strips which slowly fluttered to the ground. I theorized that the cloud caught the strong signals from radars all over Ohio and reflected them down into our telescope. Ordinarily the radars did not bother us because of the low profile of our antenna

---

*Now Rickenbacker Air Force Base.

with feed horn right at ground level. But with the chaff cloud high in the sky, it was exactly as though there were a dozen high power radars up there beaming down into our antenna.

We were receiving in a channel reserved for radio astronomy listening but some of the radars operated very close to our channel and tended to splatter spurious radiation into it. Our receivers were so sensitive that even the smallest amount of radar signal drove our recorders right off scale. With every chaff drop we were wiped out. That is, we thought it was from chaff drops. Our evidence was really circumstantial.

The colonel expressed interest, but explained that he had no control over the training missions. However, he said that he would inform the proper persons about the problem.

We had also informed the FCC. Because the interference occurred in a channel reserved for radio astronomical listening, the FCC had a responsibility to investigate it.

Hal showed up with his van some weeks after the Air Force visit. What we needed, he felt, were observations to establish that when the interference occurred there were jets flying nearby and that a chaff cloud could be located and followed down during the period that the interference persisted. He had brought equipment in the truck for taking the bearing and altitude of any such cloud.

As Hal, Bob, and I compared notes following our vigil that cold fall night, Hal said,

"I think I have enough data to make a good case. I'm going back to Washington tomorrow."

Many weeks passed but we heard nothing from either the FCC or the Air Force. Then, one morning there was our answer on the front page of the Columbus *Citizen-Journal*. From Washington (D.C.) came this story,

"Scientists at Ohio State University were peeved. Something was jinxing their powerful big dish radio telescope that picks up sounds from space.

"The Federal Communications Commission (FCC) was called. It sent a specially-equipped vehicle to Columbus to track down the gremlins.

"For two days last fall the FCC engineer cruised the area. He discovered the interference was coming from the sky, according to a report released by the FCC yesterday.

"More detective work disclosed that the jamming, which drove ink-line recordings of space sounds right off the charts at OSU, was caused by chaff dropped from Air Force bombers during training missions.

"Chaff consists of light aluminum foil pieces which are discharged by planes and drift slowly to earth distorting enemy radar. In this case radar signals were bouncing off the chaff, jamming OSU's radio telescope.

"Where were the bombers from and how near Columbus did they drop the chaff?"

"The Air Force, slightly embarrassed, says certain effects of radar and countermeasures are military secrets, so it can't answer these questions. But it is dropping its chaff somewhere else!"

And it was true; no more chaff and no more interference caused by it! Somewhat later we heard that the RCM squadron based at Lockbourne had been moved out west. We never knew whether the move was related to the QRM or not.

The FCC news release came in January 1964. We have had many other cases of interference. Each one is a story of its own and I relate a few in this chapter to give a perspective on this aspect of observational radio astronomy.

Whereas we interfered with no one, others might easily interfere with us. Radars and radio stations on nearby channels could spill over into our channel, chaff drops accentuating this interference, also the ignition sparks of gasoline engines could completely jam our equipment. The great sensitivity of our receivers made our telescope extremely vulnerable to the weakest emission which could drown out and obliterate the ultra-weak signals we were trying to receive from the depths of outer space. Interference to our radio telescope might come from a distant radar station, an airplane overhead, or a farm tractor in the next field.

One radar in particular had caused us considerable interference, not continually, but for a few hours a day several days a week. It was an extremely powerful radar operated by the Air Force at Bellefontaine, Ohio, about 40 miles west of the radio observatory. If it hadn't been for the low profile of our telescope, it might have bothered us continually but most of the time its radiation passed right over our telescope without being picked up. Occasionally an atmospheric temperature inversion produced bending of the radio waves back to earth so that the radiation slanting upward from the radar was bent back down into our antenna. The effect was similar to that produced by a chaff cloud, only weaker. This "tropospheric bending," as it was called, occurred often enough to make the interference a serious problem.

The Bellefontaine radar transmitted on a wavelength slightly longer than the 21 centimeter wavelength radio astronomy channel on which our receivers operated. If all the radar transmitter power had been confined to the radar wavelength there would have been no problem, but, like most radars, it also emitted appreciable amounts of spurious radiation on nearby wavelengths including our radio astronomy channel.

We had acquired a complete war surplus direction finding unit developed at RRL and installed it at the observatory. It had one of the rotating antenna spinners which I had designed. With it we determined that the interference was coming from the direction of Bellefontaine. I called the Air Force area headquarters and in a few days received a letter from the base commander at Bellefontaine. He apologized for the interference and extended an invitation to visit the base and discuss the problem in more detail.

With Steve O'Donnell, our electronics engineer, and Fred Dietrich, an EE graduate student, I drove over to Bellefontaine. The commanding officer, Jim Snyder, was most cordial. Following a round of introductions, he said,

"After we tour the site and have lunch I suggest that we have a press conference with a reporter from the Bellefontaine newspaper in attendance. Is this agreeable?"

"A press conference?" I gulped, "What for?"

"Well it's this way," Snyder explained. "This radar base with its big towers and radomes is just outside Bellefontaine on the highest point in Ohio. It's a landmark that's visible for miles and makes the Bellefontaine residents jittery. They think that it will be Russia's number one target in the event of a nuclear attack and that the first missile the Russians fire will over-shoot the radar station and land smack dab in the middle of downtown Bellefontaine."

"So," I said, "what does this have to do with us?"

"Well," Snyder replied, clearing his throat, "if some radio astronomers and, ah, respectable university people like yourselves have visited the base and the word gets out then maybe the Bellefontaine folks will believe that we're not all bad and maybe not such a target after all."

I laughed. "You're very flattering," I said, "but we came to discuss an interference problem and I don't think it would be an appropriate time for a press conference."

"That's perfectly OK," Snyder answered, smiling. "Please excuse me a moment while I ask my assistant to call off the conference."

This aspect of our visit was unexpected but it made me recall attitudes that I had noted many times during World War II. For example, at the Naval Ordnance Lab in Washington, the opinion was often expressed that in case of a German attack on continental U.S., the Naval Ordnance Lab would be their number one target. Precisely the same feeling was voiced by many at the Radio Research Lab at Harvard; they thought the Radio Research Lab would be the prime target. Maybe one could generalize and say that things close at hand tend to take on more than their actual importance, leading to such conclusions.

The tour of the base was impressive. On the big radar display screen, blips from aircraft flying over Ohio and surrounding states could be seen and their motions followed. The radar was so powerful that extreme precautions had to be taken that no one got in the path of the antenna beam and sizzled into an instant French fry. Because electrical power from public utilities might fail in a crisis, the base generated its own with huge diesel-driven generators which raised a deafening din in the big building housing them. Never had I seen an engine room so clean, tidy and spotless.

After the tour we got down to business and took up the interference problem. Snyder had called in his engineers and together they explained that they could shift to a longer wavelength more remote from the radio astronomy channel which might reduce or eliminate the interference. However, they couldn't use the longer wavelength all of the time. Occasionally they would have to use the one nearer our channel but they would endeavor to use it as little as possible. We expressed appreciation for their interest and cooperation. As we were leaving I said,

"Maybe the next time we come over we can have that press conference." Snyder laughed.

After our visit the Bellefontaine radar interference was greatly reduced. We occasionally were bothered but many days or even weeks would go by without any problem. Months passed and a year or two. Then we read the announcement that Robert McNamara, Secretary of Defense, had ordered the Bellefontaine base closed down as an economy measure. Soon after that the Bellefontaine QRM dropped to exactly zero and stayed there.

But other radars gave us problems, such as the one at London, Ohio, operated by the Federal Aviation Authority (FAA). This one was 35 miles southwest of the radio observatory. I wrote letters about the interference to the FCC and the FAA.

About the same time the Harvard Radio Observatory in Massachusetts had complained about interference from an identical FAA radar station located near there.

To correct the situation the FAA proposed to install a special filter in the waveguide between their transmitter and antenna to reduce the spurious emissions they were radiating into the radio astronomy channel. This would take time, they indicated, and be expensive; they estimated a filter would cost $100 000. Many months passed and we continued to lose large amounts of data due to the interference. Finally London called to report that the filter was in. However, they told us it appeared to be defective and radiation was leaking from the waveguide and triggering the alarm system installed to warn of dangerous levels of radiation. The operators were very unhappy about the filter and were using it reluctantly. We concluded that they actually weren't using it at all because the interference persisted; it appeared as a series of spikes or pulses on our records and made them useless. We weren't getting anywhere.

More letters and more phone calls. Weeks later London called again to say that the filter was in and the leakage eliminated. We confirmed that the filter worked, wiping out the interference. Since then the London radar station has not been a problem except very occasionally when it operated without the filter. We understood that the FAA installed an identical filter at their Massachusetts radar station eliminating the interference to the Harvard radio telescope.

The score was now two radars down but there were still more to go. There were two at Port Columbus, the city of Columbus airport, 20 miles south of the radio observatory which got onto our records. We conducted tests with the radar personnel at Port Columbus and eventually evolved a solution.

We experienced other types of interference. Highway US 23 just west of the observatory site is a heavily travelled 4-lane road. A straight downhill stretch past the observatory entrance encouraged excessive speeds. The Ohio Highway Patrol had painted stripes across the highway at ¼ mile intervals so that an airborne observer could time the vehicles and radio word about speeders to a patrol car parked at a pull-out near the observatory entrance. During speed checks the Highway Patrol airplane often circled close to the radio telescope causing interference.

I wrote a letter to Robert Chiaramonte, Superintendant of the State Highway Patrol, and suggested that the patrol plane circle on the other side of US 23 which would be sufficiently remote from the radio telescope that interference should be reduced or eliminated. I received a reply by return mail thanking me for my letter and stating,

"I am instructing our pilots to honor your request."

Result: no more interference from the Highway Patrol planes. Few of our interference problems were solved so quickly and simply. A single letter did it all in a matter of days.

For years we had experienced interference from tractors operated by farmers in fields adjacent to the observatory site. The problem was most severe during spring plowing when the tractors might be operating all day and far into the night. Our usual cure for this was to go to the farmer, explain the problem and get his permission to install noise suppressors on the ignition wires of his tractor. This usually reduced the interference considerably but did not always eliminate it. The farm nearest us was owned by Earl Mussard. He was extremely cooperative. But he had several tractors and each time he acquired a new one we had to go through the routine all over again. Then one day I received word that he had purchased diesel tractors.

"Beautiful!" I exclaimed. "May all the world go diesel!"

Diesel engines have no electrical ignition system and produce no radio interference. The main reason Mussard bought the diesels was that they were cheaper to operate. Economics had come to the rescue of our radio telescope and I contemplated erecting a statue to Rudolph Diesel.

We now had reasonably interference-free reception. From radars, airplanes and tractors we had experienced interference and had taken steps to eliminate it. However, some new menaces loomed involving potential sources of interference which we anticipated before they occurred.

One case involved the Peoples Broadcasting Corporation (PBC) of Columbus which had applied for a license to operate a TV station on channel 47. It turned out that the 4th harmonic of this channel fell right in our 11 centimeter radio astronomy channel. Plans were to use high power and to locate the station only six miles from the radio observatory. I phoned the PBC offices in Columbus and offered to discuss the problem but no one there was interested.

Next I wrote to Ben Waple, Secretary of the FCC, who replied that if the PBC complied with FCC rules he didn't think they would bother us. Waple indicated further that the FCC was disposed to grant PBC the license. However, we had calculated that a great deal more attenuation would be required than in the FCC rules, so much in fact that it was beyond the present state of the art to achieve it.

There were no new developments in the case for about a year. Then, PBC changed its name to Nationwide Communications Incorporated (NCI) and requested the FCC for permission to make major improvements in its planned channel 47 TV station. These included increasing the transmitter power to 2 186 000 watts, making the station among the most powerful in the country, increasing the antenna tower height to nearly ¼ mile and sharing the tower with other stations. If the original plan was bad, this one was much, much worse.

One of the stations considered for sharing the tower was WOSU-TV belonging to the Ohio State University. Richard Hull, Director of WOSU-TV, had told me they had wanted to move the OSU station to a new location. Their antenna at that time was in the landing path of a new runway at Port Columbus and the FAA wanted it moved. We had already advised him of our concern about interference from channel 47. Now that OSU was involved, NCI had the impression that the radio observatory would have to go along with their plans.

I called Fred Albertson, a Washington lawyer specializing in radio legal matters. He felt that there was not much we could do short of an injunction.

So on January 16, 1968, I sent a memorandum to Gordon Carson, now Vice President for Business and Finance of OSU, requesting an injunction against the NCI station and also that OSU not enter into any agreement about WOSU-TV sharing the NCI tower unless we could be sure there would be no interference.

At this point Dean Bob Green of the Engineering College became actively involved. It was Green who had so effectively handled the winch affair. In a letter January 26 to Carson, he reviewed the situation and recommended that OSU have the Attorney General of Ohio file a petition with the FCC against NCI's channel 47 TV application. We had until February 19 to file.

We prepared a "Petition to Deny" with engineering affadavit which was filed with the FCC February 16 by William B. Saxbe, Attorney General of the State of Ohio.*

Nationwide responded in a few weeks with an "Opposition to Petition to Deny" in which its lawyer assailed our "Petition to Deny" with vigor.

---

*Saxbe later became U.S. Senator from Ohio, served as U.S. Attorney General under both Presidents Nixon and Ford, and went to India as U.S. Ambassador.

Citing many cases such as U.S. Cane Sugar Refiners Association vs. McNutt and the United Church of Christ vs. FCC, he endeavored to show that our petition was legally defective and out of order. He attacked the validity of our engineering affadavit and challenged the value of our radio observatory as compared to the benefits that would come from another TV station and the possibility that WOSU-TV could share the tower. He expressed surprise that OSU could oppose their plan and charged that Nationwide was the innocent victim of competing interests within the university. He pulled out all stops in a crescendo of accusations.

To this we prepared a rebuttal. Most of the rebuttal concerned technical and engineering aspects of the problem, but in my letter of transmittal I wrote,

"Radio astronomy is a service of the greatest importance to the technological advancement and security of our nation. Much vital information concerning the earth and its surrounding space environment has been gained and even more important discoveries are in process. The most far reaching effects of radio astronomy may as yet be completely unforseen. However, some of the practical benefits which have come from radio astronomy are the development of high-gain low-noise antennas and ultra-sensitive receivers which are essential for space probe communications and satellite TV relays.

"Radio astronomy studies of the sun, the planets, and more distant sources are a necessary prelude to successful manned space exploration. Radio astronomy has completely revolutionized the knowledge of our galaxy and deep space beyond. The energy unleashed by many celestial radio sources far exceeds what theory would predict and a better understanding of gravitational energy and its effects may well ensue.

"It is ironical that the technology of television, which was developed by many of the scientists and engineers now engaged in radio astronomy, might now be used to saturate the radio spectrum with man-made signals so that further advances are impossible."

I suggested to other radio astronomers that they write the FCC in support of our cause with copies to the National Academy of Sciences and the NSF.

Gordon Stanley, Director of the Cal Tech Radio Observatory at Owens Valley, California, wrote the FCC that among other things the OSU Radio Observatory "is one of the oldest radio observatories in the United States, and has pursued a vigorous and highly successful program since its establishment in 1951. Its director has made many contributions to the theory and practice of radio antennas, many stemming from his interests in radio astronomy, which have benefited the whole of the radio industry in the United States."

David D. Henry, President of the University of Illinois* wrote to the FCC,

"The Ohio State University Radio Observatory is one of the pioneer American research institutions in the field of radio astronomy. We believe that the important research which has been carried out by the Ohio State group at their present location for many years should not be interrupted. The presently-applied standards of spurious-emission suppression for television transmitters are inadequate to protect the observatory from a transmitter at the proposed site."

---

*George McVittie, of the University of Illinois and a reknowned authority on cosmological theories, had asked President Henry to write the letter.

Strong letters of support were also sent to the FCC by many others. All keenly realized that commercial and other interests wanting to exploit the radio spectrum could obliterate all chances of man's hearing the faint, distant messages of the universe around us, making the earth a noisy, babbling, self-centered sphere spinning through space while oblivious of its environment.

The "Petition to Deny" and the rebuttals put things into a stalemate. Then came a suggestion from Dick Hull to investigate the possibility of some channel changes. The radio engineering consultants Jansky* and Bailey of Washington, D.C., were engaged to study the problem. They eventually recommended a channel switch involving a TV station on channel 28 in Newark, Ohio, operated by the Newark Board of Education, and channel 31 assigned but not yet in use at Mansfield, Ohio. The proposal was that NCI exchange its channel 47 for channel 28 from Newark, that the Mansfield assignment be changed from channel 31 to channel 47, and that Newark get channel 31 from Mansfield, a 3-way switch. A detailed study of distances and harmonic combinations indicated that this would be a feasible solution to the problem if all parties would agree. After careful study, I OK'd it.

Bob Green called a series of meetings to pursue and implement the plan. NCI was agreeable. Channel 28 was at a longer wavelength and was actually more desirable than channel 47. Green and Hull met with the Newark and Mansfield people to discuss the plan.

In due time a "Petition to Modify" was filed with the FCC jointly by NCI, OSU and the Newark Board of Education. The antagonists were now partners in a 3-way switch! They had resolved their own conflict.

The FCC approved the joint petition by January 1970, and everything was all set for NCI to proceed but two years later NCI relinquished its claim to the TV channel. It also sold part of the acreage it had purchased for the new station and tower near Westerville, Ohio, to WOSU-TV.

If NCI had proceeded, Dick Hull had hoped to use its tower for WOSU-TV (channel 34) but with NCI abandoning its plans he went ahead with ones to build a university owned station and tower on the same site. This plan also involved some problems for the radio observatory. Before relating them I should tell about channel 37.

For many years radio astronomers had sought a reserved channel among the frequencies allocated for television which are divided up into many channels each 6 megahertz wide. George McVittie and George Swenson of the University of Illinois were principal proponents for reserving the 608 to 614 megahertz band designated as channel 37 because the large University of Illinois radio telescope was designed to operate on this channel. However, when the FCC assigned channel 37 to a TV station in Patterson, New Jersey, *Newsweek* quoted George McVittie as saying, "We were sure we had lost out to the watchers of the late show."

But the radio astronomers, myself included, made themselves heard and letters poured in to the FCC and to members of Congress. As a result the FCC withdrew the assignment and ruled that channel 37 would be kept exclusively for radio astronomy for at least 10 years. In its statement the FCC noted the "vast potential offered by radio

---

*C.M. Jansky, brother of Karl Jansky, as mentioned in Chapter 15.

astronomy for adding significantly to our knowledge of the universe" and that it "does not believe it to be in the public interest to close the door on, or even jeopardize, whatever benefits may be derived from such operations."

One of our receivers also used channel 37. The university station WOSU-TV operated near the campus in Columbus on channel 34. At that distance it did not bother us. But Dick Hull's plans to move the station to Westerville, which was closer to the radio observatory, and to increase power and antenna height, gave us concern. It was quite conceivable that the closer, taller and more powerful WOSU-TV might spill over a significant amount of power into the observatory's channel 37.

We made calculations and conducted field tests to check them. Dean Green called a series of meetings to deal with the problem. With Hull and his engineers we concluded that a special filter would be required ahead of the preamplifier at the observatory.

Later, just before the university's station went into operation at the new site, "Burk" Farquhar, the WOSU-TV chief engineer, presented me with the filter while Bob Green looked on and a photographer caught the scene.

The NCI TV threat had been met and thwarted. The WOSU-TV threat had been met and solved. But there were more problems impending. Some came from proposed FM stations and others from projected extra-high-voltage transmission lines.

Another menace of major proportions loomed in June of 1972. A real estate development organization headed by David Slyh and William Fox announced plans for a high density apartment and residential complex called Delworth Village that would put a community of 3000 people next door to the radio observatory. At the nearest point the development would be only one-quarter mile from the radio telescope. This was the width of the buffer zone around the telescope owned by Ohio Wesleyan. This urban type development, including a commercial center, at such close range gave us great concern. Not only was the development a threat to the radio telescope, but the street and other outside lighting would impair optical work at the Perkins Observatory. Our concern made headlines and I spoke against the development on the Columbus TV news.

The 171 acres, which the developers had purchased for the project, were zoned residential and agricultural. This meant that no more than one dwelling unit could be erected per acre. To accommodate the higher density up to 20 units per acre, the developers needed to obtain a rezoning permit. To this end the Slyh-Fox combination presented their plans before the Liberty Township Zoning Commission on June 14, 1972, in the Powell, Ohio, fire station. Fire engines were parked outside to make room for the crowd. Bob Dixon, Jerry Ehman and myself from the radio observatory, Dean Bob Green, and Jean Hansford, OSU campus planner, were in attendance. Hansford voiced our concern and objections and Bob and Jerry distributed handouts containing information about the possible adverse effects of the plan on the radio and optical observatories.

The developers agreed to work with OSU to "safeguard all interests within economic limits." For example, they said they planned to put all external wiring underground.That was good, but many more precautions would be required. We knew that the problem was vastly more complex than they realized.

A series of public hearings at township and county level followed through the summer and into the fall. All the while the radio telescope continued to grind away scanning the sky systematically, while time still remained, recording the faint, tired signals which had been speeding our way for billions of years.

Alice and I attended most of the meetings as did Bob and Jerry, who by now had also moved into Liberty Township. The 5-member Township Zoning Commission unanimously turned down the Slyh-Fox request for rezoning. However, the three township trustees unanimously approved it. A unanimous vote of the trustees was required to reverse a Zoning Commission ruling.

A number of township residents realized that the sudden impact of such a high density development would be catastrophic. It would more than double the population of the township, put a severe strain on the schools, the roads, and the services for fire and police protection. With these residents we formed a Civic Association, a democratic non-profit organization open to any township resident by the simple expedient of paying the dues of one dollar per year. The association motto was: "Be Informed." Monthly meetings were held and newsletters were mailed to the township residents. Alice became active in the association as did Bob Dixon and Jerry Ehman.

The only remaining course for stopping the Delworth Village development was to have the rezoning issue put on the ballot as a referendum. A petition signed by 60 township residents was required within two weeks to do this. The Civic Association went to work and, in spite of a raging December blizzard and over a foot of snow, the members got out and obtained signatures from 600 persons or half of the voting population of the township. I chauffered Alice from house to house. Buffeted by the wind in her bright red head-to-toe snow suit, she trudged through the drifts to knock on doors and personally obtained over 50 of the signatures.

On election day the following November the rezoning request was soundly defeated with over 85 percent of the voters opposed. The threat had been thwarted.

The next peril, like the chaff drops, came from the sky. But whereas the chaff was temporary and intermittant, the new problem was potentially more permanent. A stationary or synchronous satellite was to be put in orbit which would remain in a fixed position in the sky for transmitting TV programs to the rural areas of Appalachia. The satellite was to receive programs beamed up to it from the ground, which it would then amplify and broadcast back down to special TV receivers in Appalachia. The system was designed so that the channel beaming the program up and the one broadcasting it down were close to a reserved radio astronomy listening channel. However, the design engineer placed the up channel more remote from the radio astronomy one and the down channel immediately adjacent, the exact reverse of what he should have done. The radio astronomers learned of this before the satellite was launched but by then it was too late to change anything.

The radio astronomers pointed out that signals tend to spill over into adjacent channels and that the down channel from the satellite, which could beam directly into a dozen U.S. radio telescopes, should have been placed more remote and not immediately adjacent to the radio astronomy channel. A nearby up channel would not be objectionable because the radiation would be directed out into space away from the telescopes.

John Findlay, of the National Radio Astronomy Observatory (NRAO) and Chairman of the Committee on Potential Contamination and Interference from Space Experiments, was understandably perturbed. NRAO is at Green Bank, West Virginia, in the very heart of Appalachia!

"It was a blunder," he explained to me, "just plain stupidity." But instead of admitting the mistake and apologizing, the design engineer worked overtime to concoct reasons for the unfortunate choice, all of which Findlay termed ridiculous. He pointed out that anyone using a channel for transmitting should be alert and responsive to the requirements of the users of adjacent channels.

We have had interference from the satellite on several occasions and so have other radio observatories.

For the future, stationary satellites pose a serious threat. With them up there a secluded observatory site in an Appalachian mountain valley might have more interference than one on the flat plains of central Ohio!

These interference crises are by no means all that we have experienced. However, they are illustrative of the complexity and variety involving many technical and engineering considerations with legal and even political overtones. The possibility of interference remains always with us and new crises may come from any quarter. Our situation is not unique; all radio observatories, man's only cosmic listening posts, have similar interference problems.

If interference of any form is observed it is desirable to find out all we can about it and take corrective measures which may not be easy. But who knows, the first signals we receive from a distant other-world civilization may appear on our records in a form that we may initially believe to be "interference." After all, the first radio signals from Jupiter and the first ones from the pulsars were thought to be interference.

CHAPTER 21

MAPPING THE SKY

Radio astronomers had opened a new window on the sky, but their first maps showed only the strongest radio sources, comparable to a geographic map with only cities of over one million population. More sensitive telescopes which followed probed deeper and located larger numbers of weaker sources analogous to cities over 100 000 population. With bigger and even more sensitive telescopes the march to greater numbers of still weaker sources continued, like going successively to cities of 10 000, towns of 1000 or even villages of 100.

The astounding thing about the first sky surveys was that, with few exceptions, the radio sources had no obvious optical counterparts. To be sure, radio waves had been detected from the sun and the plane of the Milky Way, but for two of the strongest radio sources in the whole sky, Cas A and Cygnus A, optical astronomers could see nothing significant or unusual at their positions.

For many years radio astronomers labored to make more accurate position measurements while optical astronomers peered at the spots until it was eventually discovered that Cas A was the billowing, gaseous remnant of a star which had blown up several hundred years ago while Cygnus A was the result of a more ancient, vastly greater explosion of a million stars in a distant galaxy. Only a few faint wisps of Cas A could be seen because the sky in that direction was obscured by the gas and dust of our galaxy, while Cygnus A, the exploded galaxy, registered only faintly on the most sensitive photographic plates in the midst of vast numbers of brighter stars and other objects unrelated to the powerful radio source. Cas A was 12 000 light years distant and Cygnus A at the staggering distance of one billion light years, which is to say, the waves, radio and light, had been traveling from Cygnus A at 186 000 miles per second for one billion years to reach us.

The strong radio emission from Cygnus A actually did not come from the visible galaxy, but from material blown far outside. The visible galaxy emitted little or no radio waves while the regions outside emitted powerful radio waves but no light.

Cygnus A at one billion light years is one of the strongest radio sources. If it were ten times as far away it would be near the limits of the universe, yet it would be easily detectable by even a modest sized radio telescope. This suggested that many weaker radio sources might be more distant Cygnus As and observations of them would lead to a penetrating, in-depth view of the universe, a prediction amply fulfilled.

The contrast between early radio and optical astronomy was great, being further enhanced by the revelation that there was no detectable radio emission from any stars, even the brightest ones. If an object were identified with a radio source, it invariably turned out to be a galaxy, or a nebula, or the remnant of an exploded star, but never an ordinary star. *The radio sky is no carbon copy of the visible sky; it is a new and different firmament, one where the edge of the universe stands in full view and one which bears the tell-tale marks of a violent past.*

Radio sources emit such enormous amounts of energy as to boggle the mind; they blare vehemently forth that the whole cosmos is bursting with energy, though man on the earth is gripped in an energy crisis. The energy emitted by one radio source in one millionth of a second could fulfill all of man's energy needs for a million years at one million times the present level. Man's energy requirements are as nothing, absolutely nothing, compared to the stupendous flow from any one of the cosmic sources!

Our knowledge of the optical sky gave few clues about where to search for radio emission; a primary radio survey was required. A primary survey involves a systematic searching of the sky *which assumes no prior knowledge of what may be found.* This is a "true survey," a "finding survey" or a "primary survey." If you examine or study only objects you already know are there, it is not a true survey but a follow-up or secondary survey. The OSU and Cambridge, England, sky surveys I describe in this chapter are all true, primary, finding surveys.

The making of a primary survey is not a trivial matter. The experience of the Cambridge, England, radio observatory is a case in point. This observatory, founded by Martin Ryle, pioneered in making radio surveys. After a preliminary survey called the 1C (or 1st Cambridge) survey, with 50 sources, the Cambridge group used a new, large interferometer radio telescope operating at 3.7 meters wavelength in 1955 to produce a list of almost 2000 sources. This list, called the 2C survey, contained almost ten times the number of sources known previously and appeared to be a quantum jump in our knowledge. But when other radio astronomers pointed their telescopes at the positions given for the sources, they couldn't find any trace of most of them. The conclusion was a jolt to the Cambridge group; most of the sources in their list were spurious and not there at all. They had misinterpreted the bumps and squiggles on their records, and at an international astronomers' meeting in Paris the words on everyone's lips were, "The downfall of Ryle." Some who said it were distressed while others were gloating.

But Ryle picked himself up and with a new group of students set about making an improved survey at a shorter wavelength of 1.9 meters called the 3C survey which was published in 1959. It contained 471 sources, or only one-fourth of those in the 2C survey, but when other radio astronomers began checking these sources they found that the positions of many of them were in error and in some cases the 3C source couldn't be found at all. So with new antennas operating at a still shorter wavelength of 1.7 meters the Cambridge group made a reassessment of the 3C survey and three years later, in 1962, A.S. Bennett of the Cambridge group published the 3CR or 3rd Cambridge Revised list of radio sources. The number was now down to 328, and this list proved to be quite reliable. At last, after great effort and four attempts, the Cambridge group had produced a valuable list for radio astronomers and much of the progress and new developments in radio astronomy of the 1960s and 1970s stem from studies of these 3CR sources. Later the Cambridge group brought out a more extensive list of nearly 5000 radio sources known as the 4C catalog, a very good and valuable list.

While the Cambridge surveys were in progress, Ryle and his students were refining their methods of surveying the sky and developing a method called "aperture synthesis" whereby, given sufficient observing time, several small moveable antennas could produce results equivalent to those of a much larger antenna. For his outstanding contributions Ryle subsequently attained knighthood and in 1974 became a Nobel laureate.

It had taken many attempts over almost a decade to produce a good reliable list of radio sources. So I repeat "a primary survey is no trivial matter."

Our first OSU survey covered most of the sky and was made at 1.2 meters wavelength with the 96-helix radio telescope in the mid 50s. A map we produced at that time had gained the plaudits and acclaim of Harlow Shapley, prophetic of our later surveys in which maps, like radio "photographs" of the sky, became our trade mark.

Our next survey, at 21 centimeters wavelength, with our new big telescope a decade later yielded maps of the Andromeda galaxy and surroundings and included over a hundred sources even though the region was only a small part of the sky. My graduate students Bob Dixon and Shein-Yi Meng worked on these maps.

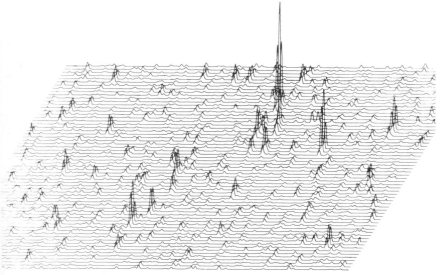

41. One scan with Big Ear yields a single trace with peaks corresponding to radio sources in the sky. Here many traces have been combined to form a map of a section of sky about 20 degrees square. The peaks indicate a number of relatively strong radio sources and many weaker ones. A contour map is a later step in the data processing.

Early in the 1960s another graduate student, Jim McLaughlin, began work digitizing the data output from the telescope, that is, converting the pen deflections into a series of numbers printed at 10 second intervals. With the data in digital or numerical form it could be processed by the newly perfected large memory, high-speed electronic computers. Another graduate student, Don Scheer, began with Bob Dixon to develop a program whereby the computer could assimilate all of the data, analyze it systematically and produce computer-drawn maps of the sky.

We were now at the culmination point of three important developments: (1) the big antenna was operational, (2) a high-sensitivity receiver with liquid-nitrogen-refrigerated parametric preamplifier was installed and working, and (3) computer processing of the data could be accomplished. Three technological developments joined to make a primary survey possible. All three were necessary. Ten years, even 5 years earlier, we could not have done it. Even with our big antenna completed, electronic and computer technology had not developed far enough to provide us with the receiver sensitivity or the computer processing we required.

By 1965 with much diligent systematic hard work Don Scheer had developed the program to the point where he was able to apply it to four months of observations he had made of a 1000 square degree area of sky (the total sky is 41 253 square degrees). With the assistance of a big computer he worked on the data reduction for a year and a half, and we published lists and maps summarizing the results as Installment I of the Ohio Sky Survey. It was also the 103rd publication of the OSU Radio Observatory. Don Scheer found 300 radio sources or more than one for every four degrees of sky. If we continued to survey the sky at this yield we would find thousands of sources.

In this survey we instituted a coordinate numbering system for the sources. For example, the source number OQ250 has the following significance. The "O" stands for Ohio, while the "Q250" is a concise notation for the position or coordinates in the sky.

The Cambridge survey had been conducted at 3.7 and 1.7 meters wavelength, while our survey was at 21 centimeters, a much shorter wavelength, in fact the shortest used up to that time for a primary survey. One of the remarkable results of Installment I was that we discovered a surprising number of sources we called "Specials" which were not in the 3C or 4C lists. They were strong at 21 centimeters but so weak at the longer Cambridge wavelengths that they weren't detected or catalogued. This abnormally strong centimeter wavelength radiation is now often called "centimeter-enhanced" radiation. It is the hallmark of the Ohio Specials.

We recognized the importance of learning as much as we could about the radio spectrum of the Ohio Specials, that is, what the strength was at many wavelengths. We had data at three wavelengths, 49, 21 and 11 centimeters with our telescope.

I wrote to radio astronomers at other observatories in the hope that they could measure the Specials at still other wavelengths. At the Algonquin Radio Observatory of the National Research Council (NRC), Canada, two radio astronomers, Jack Locke and Bryan Andrew, were very interested in helping. They had recently completed a 150-foot diameter steerable parabolic dish antenna with excellent characteristics. I went to Ottawa, the NRC headquarters, and to Algonquin to discuss the measurements with Jack and Bryan. Soon Bryan began to make measurements of the Ohio Specials at the very short wavelength of 2.8 centimeters and later at 4.6 and 9.4 centimeters. The most unusual source in our first group of Specials was OQ208 which peaked in strength at about 6 centimeters. We published a short article on the spectrum of OQ208 and several other Ohio Specials.

When we had begun observations in 1963, Big Ear's efficiency was low because the spacing of the parallel wires, which formed the reflecting surface of the parabola and flat reflector, was too large to be completely effective at 21 centimeters wavelength. Late in the summer of 1965 the wires were removed and replaced with five-foot widths of specially manufactured screen, with much more closely spaced wires. We expected that the smaller spacing would increase the efficiency of the telescope significantly. By October the screen was installed but the hoped-for increase in efficiency did not materialize. The new screen was too loose. It was slack and wavy, whereas for a good reflecting surface, it needed to be tight and flat. Increasing tension on the screen did not help matters.

This was not a problem which could be solved by sitting at a desk. With pliers and other tools I climbed a ladder half way up the sloping flat reflector and with Gene Mikesell tried using different techniques for flattening the screen. There were two aspects to the problem. We had to evolve a technique for fastening adjacent sections of the screen together and we had to stretch and pull the screen tight and flat like the skin on a drum head.

The first we solved by using steel hog-nose rings, employed by farmers to discourage rooting. Applying them with a special pliers, two sections of screen could be clamped or stitched together quickly and securely.

The second we solved by a tweaking technique whereby the individual screen wires were given a slight twist or tweak. Gene constructed a special tool for this purpose. The combination of hog-nose rings and tweaking produced the tight, smooth surface we desired and Gene with two helpers began to apply the technique systematically to the entire flat reflector and then to the parabola.

Meanwhile a student, Al Herriman, surveyed the parabola to determine what adjustments would be necessary to make the parabolic shape more accurate and after the tweaking was done Gene and his crew proceeded to make them.

The whole procedure took months, but while the work was in progress we could tell from test observations that the efficiency was coming up. When the job was completed our measurements indicated that the telescope efficiency had been increased by 50 percent which was all we hoped to achieve.

Bob Dixon went on with the 21 centimeter sky survey as soon as the screen installation and adjustments were finished, making observations through the winter and into April 1966. Then, for nearly two years he extended and refined the computer techniques for analyzing and reducing the data. The work was the basis for Bob's dissertation, and the published version was Installment II of the Ohio Sky Survey. Bob has a keen, methodical mind with a talent for the systematic management and organization of large amounts of data.

This installment covered more sky and included four times as many sources as the first installment. As in Installment I, maps were an important feature, covering all of the area surveyed.

The winch failure in the spring of 1967 shut down the telescope for three months. Immediately after operation resumed, Lew Fitch, another graduate student, continued the sky survey as his dissertation problem, making observations for seven months. These observations resulted in Installment III which covered twice the area of II and included twice as many sources. Areas and sources were increasing sharply from one installment to the next as we perfected our observing procedures and data reduction programs.

Lew Fitch was ebullient, witty, handsome and an excellent electronics engineer as well as radio astronomer. He was also a Latin scholar, being responsible for the "Ad Astra per Aspera" motto at the entrance to the prime focus laboratory.*

While the sky survey was in progress we also continued to upgrade the antenna and receiving equipment. Keith Carver, who had received his masters and doctors degrees with me on antenna topics, began a more accurate survey of the parabola surface.† The survey was completed later by Clarence Schultz, a professor on leave from Connecticut, assisted by Jan-Larry Holmberg, a student from Sweden. Gene Mikesell and two assistants then spent over a month loosening bolts, moving panels a few millimeters, and retightening the bolts until the entire 25 000 square feet of the parabola had been readjusted.

Dirk Baker, a graduate student from South Africa, investigated several problems involving the performance of our telescope. One of these, the determination of the electric fields in the focal region, proved to be a challenging one. Dirk solved it by lengthy numerical calculations using the big OSU computer — the problem would have been impossible to solve in the pre-computer era — and after two years work summarized his results in a dissertation. Dirk was talented, handsome and athletic and soon after coming to Columbus joined the OSU rugby club becoming its star roving wing.

Martti Tiuri and his students at Helsinki had designed and built parametric preamplifiers for our 49 and 11 centimeter receivers and two of the student engineers, Weikko Porra and Sepu Urpu, came to install and test the units. All of our receivers were now equipped with liquid nitrogen-refrigerated parametric preamplifiers of the most sensitive type.

Every few years the parabola and flat reflector required painting, a job for which the university hired an outside contractor. The task usually took months for a crew of several men. Although a rather straight-forward routine chore, it had its hazards. One noon Tim Cashen was painting from a scaffold hanging half way up the parabola when a sudden, violent gust of wind shook and bounced the scaffold like a leaf, hurling Tim 40 feet to the hard concrete ground-plane below. Although one leg was shattered, an arm fractured, his jaw broken and half his teeth knocked out, Tim was still conscious when we got to him. He sustained no internal injuries and six months later had recovered sufficiently to return to work.

---

*Lew once mentioned that he was a lineal descendent of John Fitch, who invented the steamboat in 1785, 22 years before Fulton's *Clermont*.

†Keith later became professor of electrical engineering at New Mexico State University in Las Cruces and together we prepared a thorough revision of my book "Electromagnetics," published in 1953, which appeared as a second edition by Kraus and Carver in 1973. To prepare and publish the new edition required huge blocks of my time for over two years.

He remarked that his prior experience as a sky diver probably saved his life because, although badly hurt, he landed in just about the best possible way to absorb the tremendous force of the fall.

Jerry Ehman, took major responsibility for the next portion of the sky survey, making 16 months of observations until April 1969. The results for this IVth installment appeared in the May 1970, *Astronomical Journal*. There were tables listing 4550 radio sources and 72 pages of maps. The article accounted for two-thirds of the May issue and helped to make it the biggest issue of the *Astronomical Journal* ever published. The Ohio Sky Survey now had over 8000 sources, more than the number of all other surveys combined!

Our sky survey had yielded many Specials, and with Bryan Andrew's help we had obtained considerable information about their radio spectra. Bryan had also measured the positions accurately leading to the next big step, the identification, if possible, of the Specials with optical objects. A graduate student, Jim Thompson, worked on this problem.

Jim's first task was to determine accurately the position of the Special on a photograph of a small bit of sky which included the Special's location. This required highly precise measurements. This drudgery completed, his next step was charged with excitement as he scrutinized the photograph for indications of some object close to the position which might be associated with the Special. Sometimes he found a galaxy, as for OQ208, and at other times a stellar object, that is, a single point of light. We didn't think that the stellar objects were really ordinary stars; we presumed that they probably were quasi-stellar objects (quasars or QSOs): objects which, though stellar in appearance, weren't single stars but perhaps very distant galaxies with a dense bright nucleus. Jim identified OJ287 as a quasar.

Occasionally he found no objects whatsoever at or near the radio source position; we called these empty or "blank fields." What was their significance? Perhaps the radio sources represented galaxies so distant or faint that they were not on the photographs. They were just one more expression of the duality of radio and optical astronomy.

We published identifications for 17 Ohio Specials in 1968. Of these 3 were galaxies, 2 were blank fields and the remaining dozen were red or blue quasars. We found the Specials and identified them; was there anything more that we could do? Yes, using optical telescopes we could obtain optical spectra from which the redshift might be determined and from this the distance deduced. We could take photographs or recordings in different colors and analyze the object by what is called "color photometry." We could repetitively photograph the object to see if it changed at all in brightness. We might attempt all these things ourselves, encourage others to do them or hope that still others, stimulated by our publications, might undertake them on their own. Actually all of these possibilities materialized to various degrees.

Maarten Schmidt recorded the spectrum of OQ208 with the 200-inch telescope on Mount Palomar and put its distance at about a billion light years. Alex Smith and his students at the University of Florida began a systematic program of photography to look for variability, and two OSU graduate students, Eric Craine and John Warner, took photographs and also examined old astronomical plate collections at Harvard and Oklahoma to determine if there was any long term variability.

Of the 17 Specials in our 1968 list Alex Smith, with his students including Karen and Richard Hackney, found, after two and one-half years of photographic monitoring with their 30-inch telescope, that eight showed definite variations while three more were possibly variable. Chief among their discoveries was that OJ287 was an erratic, rapid, violently variable quasar of the most remarkable type. The optical spectrum showed no lines so no redshift or distance could be determined but OJ287 was presumed to be a very powerful and distant, perhaps very compact, explosively energetic galaxy.

Eric Craine and John Warner found that OJ287 had a history of optical variability going back to 1940. They also found that OQ208 and ON231 showed evidence of fluctuations in brightness but of a more gradual kind.

Major responsibility for the Vth and next installment of the sky survey fell to another graduate student, Dick Brundage, a brother of Bill's. Starting observations right after those for Installment IV had been completed in April 1969, he continued until October 1970. With this installment the total number of sources in the sky survey rose to 12 000 in an area amounting to almost half of the entire sky.

Each installment of the survey involved mountains of data. For Installment V there were nearly 5 miles of foot-wide charts and over 100 million data digits recorded to an accuracy of one one-hundredth second in time. The job of analysis would have been impossible without the university's big computer. Even so, for each year of observations, it took another year to completely process the data, the work requiring the efforts of many persons working together in close cooperation.

The maps showed the position of each source while tables listed the exact sky coordinates and the strength. Our survey was an atlas of the sky analogous to a geographic atlas giving the location of each city and its population.

Part of the table of Installment V included the following 3 entries:

OH471	06^h	42^m	54^s	$44°$	$52'$	2.09 jan
OH472	06	43	19	46	07	0.26
OH473	06	44	06	47	48	0.19

The first column gives the Ohio name for the source, the next five columns the position and the last column the strength of the source in janskys. The published table also included an additional column for other names assigned to the source if it had been previously detected in other surveys such as the Cambridge. This column is blank for the above three indicating that they had been discovered in the Ohio survey. This was not surprising for OH472 and OH473 since they are weak, 0.26 and 0.19 janskys, respectively. However, it was surprising for OH471* because it has a strength of over 2 janskys and this fact immediately focussed our attention on it, making it a prime candidate as an Ohio Special. Much more work remained to be done at Algonquin to determine its spectrum and to obtain an accurate position, then to identify it with an optical object, and finally to obtain its optical spectrum and measure its redshift. When this was accomplished a few years later, OH471 became the first object known to have a redshift greater than 3, "the blaze marking the edge of the universe!"

After years of building and improving our telescope and more years of

---

*At first glance one might naively suppose that OH471 stands for OHio source 471 but we have seen that only the "O" stands for Ohio. The "H471 gives a concise, accurate position for the source in the sky

developing effective data reduction procedures, our sky survey was finally moving in high gear and with the completion of observations for Installment V in October 1970, we shifted immediately into an observing program for the sixth installment. We expected that this would be a big installment covering a large area of sky and would take longer. Previous installments had left many gaps in sky coverage and we planned to fill these. Jerry assumed principal responsibility for the survey.

By January 1972 we had done over a year's observations for Installment VI and we hoped that with almost another year's observations we would have completed our sky survey. The telescope was operating at its highest efficiency and producing the best results we had ever obtained. Our NSF funding had been at a steady level for seven years and although we didn't expect this to continue indefinitely, we were near the 90 percent mark in our survey and believed that we would receive enough support to finish the survey.

It was, therefore, a tremendous jolt when the NSF phoned me late in the afternoon of August 8, 1972, to deliver an ultimatum: the NSF was cutting off their support, and although we still had a few months funding still in hand, I was told that we couldn't use it for anything after August 31 except analyzing observations made prior to that date.

There was no previous warning or advice by the NSF and nothing in writing except a letter a few weeks before indicating that our funding would continue for another year at a slightly lower level than previously. After 15 years of constructing the telescope, instrumenting it, and getting our data reduction procedures perfected, we were told to stop. It was an incredible situation. Our observations required an immense amount of planning with schedules drawn up long in advance. Negotiations with students and other personnel to work at the Radio Observatory had to be made six months to a year ahead. We had already made many commitments to get the job done. To stop so abruptly was catastrophic and wasteful, like ordering a vessel returning from a long voyage with valuable cargo to be scuttled and sunk as it steamed into its home port.

Throughout the construction period and well into the survey observations, Everett Hurlburt, NSF Program Director for Radio Astronomy, had shown a keen interest in our radio observatory and its results and had visited it on numerous occasions. His was an era of planned, responsible growth and accomplishment. But with his successors we had entered a period of catastrophic curtailment. There was a shift away from support for universities and toward increased support for nationalized facilities, a policy completely contrary to that enunciated by Lloyd Berkner, founder of the National Radio Astronomy Observatory, and by every scientific advisory group since. They all had called for strong support of *both* university and national facilities and in that order. Their argument was that with only huge, grandiose, expensive national astronomy facilities and no suitable smaller ones, there would be a top-heavy imbalance that would be inefficient, ineffective, and wasteful like a Navy with all big battleships and no smaller vessels. But OSU and several other universities were caught by the changing NSF priorities.

The abrupt cutting off of support suggested a lack of interest and understanding about our scientific objectives. We wanted to complete our sky survey; we didn't want to publish a map of the sky with big gaping holes like a map of the U.S. with several large states missing.

Word of the ultimatum spread like a shock wave through our organization. Everyone wanted to know if they would still have a job. When a couple of welders making modifications high up on the flat reflector learned that their pay would terminate in three weeks they stopped in the middle of their welds, climbed down, removed their helmets and gloves and vanished. If they had stayed out the three weeks the modifications might have been completed. As it turned out, it wasn't until three years later that we were able to pick up where they left off and finish the job.

Bob Dixon, Jerry Ehman and I met frequently to discuss ways of salvaging as much of our data as possible. We were well along on a block of sky that we wanted to finish but to do it by the end of August we had to speed up our survey by scanning a zone only once instead of at least twice as in all previous installments. The change was unfortunate because it decreased the sensitivity of the survey, making the data of poorer quality, but there were no alternatives.

In the 16 years of NSF funding of radio astronomy at OSU, dating back to the 96-helix array, the NSF had contributed two and one-half million dollars. Of this three-quarters of a million dollars went into the university's general fund as an overhead charge, leaving a net amount of one and three-quarter million dollars which supported research with the helix array, the construction of the big new telescope with 360-foot parabola, and an observing program with it for a decade. Some of the university's overhead money had filtered back but now more of it returned to help keep the telescope in operation with a staff which had shrunk from 15 to 5, not including students. Marlin Thurston, who became chairman of the EE Department when "Deke" Dreese retired, shared "Deke's" faith in the value of the telescope, and helped where he could.

Observations for Installment VI had been terminated by the NSF fiat as of August 1972. It took nearly a year to complete the data reduction and send off the manuscript to "Lou" Woltjer, editor of the *Astronomical Journal*. The installment ran to 173 pages in the February 1974 issue and helped to make it the biggest *Astronomical Journal* ever printed. There were a hundred pages of tables with 6000 radio sources, more than in any previous installment, swelling the total number of sources in the Ohio survey to more than 17 000. We had now covered most of the sky observable from Ohio but more remained to be done and in September 1972 observations were begun without NSF support for the 7th and final installment of the survey.

*   *   *   *   *

Beverley June Harris was wearing a miniskirt and carrying a violin case as she stepped from the airplane on a late September afternoon in 1969 after her flight from Australia where she had just earned her doctorate in radio astronomy at the National University. I was at the airport to meet her and found her to be a demure, pretty brunette. Bev had arrived to spend a post doctoral year at the OSU Radio Observatory. She immediately began to study the Ohio Specials.

The next day Mirjana Mira Radivich arrived from Youngstown, Ohio, where her father worked in the steel mills. Mirjana had just graduated from Youngstown University and entered the graduate school at OSU majoring in radio astronomy. Mirjana was a shapely, attractive brunette, fluent in German and Russian and a second degree black belt. Fall quarter was just starting and Mirjana also began to work on the Ohio Specials.

Later in the year Patricia Chikotas began investigating the relation between Ohio radio sources and clusters of galaxies. Pat, a vivacious, good-looking blond, was a new graduate student from a small coal mining town in eastern Pennsylvania.

These students and our staff members Eleanor Hartquist, Mary Hilbert, Donna King, Rosemary Mardis, Peggy Shaner, and others gave rise to a widespread rumor that to work at the Radio Observatory a woman had to be not only intelligent but beautiful as well. I never denied that this might be true.

In the dead of winter with temperatures below zero (Fahrenheit) and snow in deep drifts, Bev Harris spent weeks helping Bryan Andrew observe Ohio Specials with the Algonquin radio telescope in the northern Ontario wilderness. Back at OSU she drew spectra for the specials and, working with Mirjana Radivich and another student, Phil D'Angelo, used the Algonquin positions to identify many of the specials with optical objects.

After receiving her masters degree, Mirjana continued to work on the specials, making many trips to the Algonquin Observatory to work with Bryan. Then back in Columbus she utilized the data to make additional identifications with optical objects.

In the fall of 1970 Bev Harris transferred to the University of Texas and a month or so later became Mrs. Wills. Her husband, Derek, was an astronomer at Texas who hailed from England. A bit later Mirjana Radivich became Mirjana Gearhart, marrying her Youngstown University classmate Norm Gearhart, now working for his doctors degree in physics. And in the meanwhile, Pat Chikotas became Pat Boeshaar. Her husband, Greg, was also a graduate student at OSU and had for a time worked at the Radio Observatory. Bev, Mirjana, and Pat all continued their careers in astronomy with Mirjana staying on at the Radio Observatory as staff astronomer.

Astronomy is often called the "Queen of the Sciences" and I like to think that the many women in astronomy are the jewels adorning her crown.

*   *   *   *   *

The 10 months of observing for Installment VII were completed in July of 1973. Curt Rinsland assumed major responsibility for the installment which we published in November 1974. The article was the 152nd publication of the OSU Radio Observatory, containing a list of 2500 radio sources and 50 maps. The total number of Ohio sources now exceeded 19 000.

At this point the Ohio survey was unique in that it covered a larger portion of the entire sky (70 percent) in more detail (19 000 sources) than any previous large-area survey and at a shorter wavelength (21 centimeters).

The seven installments of the survey had been published at an average rate of one per year over a seven year period and totaled 660 pages in the *Astronomical Journal*.

Within a year we brought out a supplement to the survey including a small additional area of sky and 239 more sources. With this supplement the big sky survey was complete but the work of sifting it for Ohio Specials and of utilizing it in other ways had just begun.

The Ohio Sky Survey is a unique collection of a large number of objects, giving the most detailed view of the radio sky ever afforded to man. Like the famous early catalogs of Messier, Herschel, and Dreyer, the Ohio Sky Survey marked a milestone in astronomy but as Dr. Heinrich K. Eichhorn von Wurmb of Florida remarked at the 1973 American

Astronomical Society meeting in Columbus, "it may not be for many years that the full value of the survey will be appreciated."

Starting with the first installments of the survey, astronomers at other observatories had found the lists and maps useful in many ways. For example, Dr. Ronald J. Allen, at the big Westerbork radio telescope in the Netherlands, wrote in 1969,

"We have found the Ohio catalog and maps very helpful in estimating the effects of nearby sources on the radio synsthesis picture of a galaxy."

Others like Alan Bridle and Ed Fomalont stated in the *Astronomical Journal*,

"The Ohio survey is uniquely valuable as a finding survey."

The Ohio Specials found in the survey were regarded by many as of great importance. Dr. Margaret Burbidge, Director of the Royal Greenwich Observatory in England, wrote in 1972,

"It is interesting that the Ohio 'peaked spectra' radio sources have proved to be such intriguing optical objects and that identifications from this source list have such a high probability of being correct."

The "peaked spectra" sources she referred to were, of course, the Ohio Specials. For many years Margaret Burbidge has been the world's pre-eminent quasar hunter. Stalking big redshift objects with the Lick Observatory, California, 120 inch (3 meter) telescope, she has found many powerful quasars, the mysterious distant objects which look like single stars but each of which probably is the condensed nucleus of a galaxy of millions of stars.*

Dr. Mark Stull of Stanford said in an article that "the Ohio survey is the only survey (at short wavelengths) which extends to a low flux density level and covers most of the sky visible from the northern hemisphere. Since it is reliable, it forms a good finding list for objects with peculiar properties." He estimated that about one-third of the previously uncatalogued sources in the survey may be Ohio Specials.

Later Alex Smith and his group at Florida were photographing the blank field at the position of an Ohio Special OE110 and found to their surprise a star-like object which wasn't there on the earlier Palomar photographs. During the weeks and months which followed, the OE110 object underwent rapid fluctuations in brightness and Alex concluded that OE110 was a violently variable quasar like OJ287.

Another Ohio Special OX-192, was found by Eric Craine and others at Arizona and elsewhere to be another such object which showed marked fluctuations in both its optical and radio strength, with brightness changes as great as a thousand fold!

The Ohio Sky Survey is like an inventory or census of the radio universe. An important function of such a survey is to provide a list of objects for study with bigger telescopes. In 1974 construction of a Very Large Array (VLA) telescope began on the Plains of San Augustin, New Mexico. This instrument is to have such a sharp beam that to scan the entire sky with it, searching for radio sources would take thousands of years. Clearly the VLA is not a survey instrument; for it to be used efficiently one needs to know where the sources are, as given by the Ohio Survey or the Ohio Specials list. Without these lists the $80 000 000

---

* Dr. Burbidge returned to the University of California, San Diego, in 1973 as professor of physics and astronomy. In 1975 she became president of the American Astronomical Society.

spent on the VLA would be wasted.

All evidence suggests that there will be many Specials in the Ohio survey with highly unusual properties, such as very large redshift or rapid variability, with the ones found so far representing only the first of many more to come. The Ohio survey may well prove to be one of the most valuable surveys ever made.

CHAPTER 22

TO THE EDGE OF THE UNIVERSE

When Hercules was nursing his mother, Alcmeme, Zeus' mistress, the strong muscular infant grasped her big, full breasts and squeezed them so hard that her milk spurted to the heavens and across the sky forming the "Milky Way." This earliest of Greek beliefs also gave us the equivalent name "galaxy" from the Greek word "galaktos" for milk. We like to think that we have come a long ways from such quaint ideas about the cosmos but what we know is still very little, a mere beginning.

From the ancient Greek astronomer Thales in the sixth century B.C. to Hipparchus to Ptolemy to Copernicus to Tycho Brahe, Kepler, and Galileo in the 17th century A.D., astronomy advanced in great strides, yet in 1633 Galileo was tried by the Roman Inquisition and forced to recant, at least publicly, his belief in the Copernican system in which the sun is the central body of the solar system. The accepted doctrine was that God had ordained the earth to be the central immovable object of the entire universe with the sun, planets and other celestial bodies revolving about it; to believe otherwise was heresy.

Gradually the idea that the earth and other planets revolved around the sun gained general acceptance. With the larger telescopes of the 18th and 19th centuries, astronomers like William Herschel, his sister Caroline, and his son John, focussed on stars and mysterious nebulas far beyond the solar system. They found that the stars seemed to be concentrated in a flat disc coinciding with the plane of the Milky Way or galaxy. Still later, astronomers determined that the sun and its planets were located far out from the center in the galactic hinterland. This struck another blow at man's ego: He had found that the earth was not the center of the solar system and now he found that the solar system was not at the center of the galaxy.

The nebulas the Herschels studied were of two types, wispy, amorphous clouds, generally believed to be in our galaxy, and highly structured spiral ones similar to Messier 81 in Ursa Major which looks like a celestial Fourth of July pinwheel. But the size of our galaxy and whether the spiral nebulas were inside or outside of it were uncertain.

Harlow Shapley of Harvard and Heber Curtis of the Lick Observatory (and later Michigan) met before the National Academy of Sciences in 1920 to argue the evidence. Shapley held that our galaxy was bigger than Curtis thought, but he also believed that the spirals were inside our galaxy whereas Curtis maintained that they were outside.

More work was needed and a decade later, Edwin Hubble, a lawyer turned astronomer, concluded from observations with the 100-inch (2.5 meter) Mount Wilson telescope that Shapley was right on the first point but wrong on the second. The spirals were outside our galaxy. They were island universes or galaxies like our own but at vast distances of millions of light years beyond it. Even more astounding, he found that the spiral galaxies were receding from us with velocities which increased in proportion to their distance. The universe was expanding, exploding outward from a point where some billions of years earlier all matter had been packed together before a "big bang" occurred! But it was not possible to say whether our galaxy was at the center of the universe or not, so man again faced more loss of prestige by the prospect that he lived in the boondocks of the universe.

How had Hubble arrived at his amazing conclusions? Chief among his tools was a celestial "yard stick" devised two decades earlier by Henrietta Leavitt of the Harvard College Observatory.

The clouds of Magellan are two bright patches in the southern sky containing myriads of stars and now known to be nearby galaxies. About the turn of the century Harvard installed a southern hemisphere telescope in Peru with which photographs of the clouds were taken at regular intervals. Studying the photographs of the smaller Magellanic cloud, Henrietta Leavitt found a type of star, known as a Cepheid variable, in great profusion. These stars varied or pulsed in brightness. About 1908 she reported that the brighter Cepheids turned on and off more slowly than the fainter ones. Since all were at approximately the same distance from us, this meant that the brighter ones with long periods, such as 10 days or more, were intrinsically more powerful than the fainter ones with shorter periods of only a few days. The distance of a few Cepheids in our own galaxy had already been established. It followed that the distance to any Cepheid could be determined by observing its period and apparent brightness. This was Henrietta Leavitt's "yard stick," known more esoterically as her "period-luminosity law." Using her Cepheids as "yard sticks," Shapley and others put the diameter of our galaxy at 100 000 light years and located the sun and its planets over half-way to the edge.

With the 100-inch Mount Wilson telescope, the largest then in existence, Hubble had been able to resolve some of the external galaxies into stars and among them he found some Cepheids. From a series of photographs and Henrietta Leavitt's "yard stick" he established their distance at a million or more light years. He also noted, with the help of Milton Humason, that the light from the galaxies was doppler shifted or redshifted, that is, longer or redder in wavelength than if the galaxies were stationary, like the decrease in pitch (increase in wavelength) of the horn of a truck or locomotive which is moving away. This meant that the galaxies were receding from us. Comparing redshifts with distances, Hubble concluded that the galaxies were moving away from us at velocities which increased in proportion to their distance, leading to the conclusion that we live in an expanding universe. This redshift distance relation is now known as Hubble's law.

The magnitude of the *redshift* is a measure of the ratio of the change in wavelength to the original wavelength. Thus, if the wavelength were doubled the redshift would be unity, or 100 percent, while if the wavelength were tripled the redshift would be 2, or 200 percent, and so forth.

The biggest redshifts Hubble measured were only a few percent, corresponding to galaxies a few hundred million light years distant — distances that stretched man's imagination. Earlier estimates of the entire size of the universe were much less than that. But Hubble's observations

42. With Grote Reber at my farm at the time he received his honorary doctor's degree from the Ohio State University (1962).

were only a starter, a mere curtain raiser.

Edwin Hubble was just reaching his dramatic conclusions in Pasadena, California, when Karl Jansky at Holmdel, New Jersey, was puzzling over charts recorded with his merry-go-round antenna and soon thereafter Grote Reber began measuring what he called "cosmic static" with his backyard parabolic dish antenna in the Chicago suburb of Wheaton. Still later, other radio astronomers began to probe the skies and strong sources like Cygnus A were discovered leading to flying leaps in man's exploration of the vast depths of space.

We have mentioned Edwin Hubble and Grote Reber. Could there be more than a cosmic connection between them, both being astronomers, one optical and the other radio? Yes, it turns out, there is. Around 1900 the Hubble family lived in Wheaton, Illinois, and as his 7th and 8th grade teacher young Edwin had a Miss Harriet Grote who later married a Schuyler Reber and bore Grote Reber as her first son. She often commented to Grote that young Edwin Hubble had stood out from the other students in his class and that she felt he would go far. In later years when Hubble's fame was spreading she took special pride in his accomplishments and that she had been his teacher.

Lesson: It's a small world but a great universe.

Two decades had passed since Hubble reported his results, when in 1951, using Graham Smith's accurate Cambridge position for Cygnus A, Walter Baade took photographs with the 200-inch Mount Palomar telescope and identified the source with a faint, peculiar galaxy. Later Rudolph Minkowski obtained its spectrum and a redshift value of 6 percent. Based on Hubble's law this placed it a billion light years away. Man was probing deeper.

Another decade passed, the Cambridge 3C list appeared, and attempts were made to identify the sources with optical objects. At some 3C positions there were objects which looked like stars but their optical spectra were different from stars. No one knew what they might be. Then, in 1963, Maarten Schmidt, a young Palomar Observatory astronomer, solved the riddle by showing that the spectrum of 3C273 could be explained on the basis of an unprecidentedly high redshift of 0.16 (16 percent) which according to Hubble's law implied a distance of about two billion light years, another big jump, far, far outside our galaxy.

3C273 was certainly not a star, like our sun; perhaps, it was thought, it was the very dense nucleus of a distant galaxy consisting of millions of stars so compressed and so far away as to appear to us like a star. The name Quasi-Stellar Object, quasar, or even more concisely, QSO, was applied to describe it; an object which looked like a star but wasn't one.

It was a great astronomical milestone and even got a big spread in *Time* magazine with Maarten Schmidt's picture on the cover.

Jesse Greenstein, another Palomar astronomer, and Schmidt published an article on the new quasar in July 1964. In the same article they listed a redshift of 0.37 for another quasar, 3C48, putting it at a distance of 4 billion light years. In the meantime, the first redshift greater than one-half was found for the quasar 3C147 by Schmidt and Tom Matthews, a radio astronomer at Cal Tech. It had a value of 0.55 placing it at a distance of 5 billion light years. Within another year redshifts of as much as 2 or a bit more were found for some quasars putting them at distances of 10 billion light years. Man, through his observations, was on the march to the edge of the universe but in the meantime theories were advanced predicting that no redshifts over 3 could be observed because there would be too much absorption of the light at these large distances.

In telling about the Ohio Sky Survey I have described how in 1970 we discovered a very strong source we named OH471 which was not listed in any prior survey. The inference was that its spectrum was unusual so it was added to the list of Ohio Specials. Using the big Algonquin radio telescope Bev Harris and Bryan Andrew observed its strength at a number of shorter wavelengths, the shortest being about 2 centimeters, and measured its position accurately. OH471 was one of the 3500 radio sources included in Installment V of the Ohio Sky Survey published in 1971. The same year we published its radio spectrum along with two dozen other Ohio Specials.

For some months before these articles appeared, Mirjana Gearhart had been working on the identification of a group of Ohio Specials, including OH471. Mirjana identified OH471 with a faint star-like object and published the identification along with 46 others in June 1972. Finding charts were included, that is, photographs of small sky areas with the objects identified clearly indicated.

The identification for OH471 was confirmed by means of extremely accurate position measurements with an interferometer radio telescope at the Royal Radar Establishment, Malvern, England, which reported its findings to Bob Carswell and Peter Strittmatter, two astronomers at the Steward Observatory, Tucson, Arizona. With the image-tube spectrograph of the Steward 90-inch telescope they subsequently photographed the spectrum of OH471 and found that it was a quasar with greenish-yellow emission from lines that were ordinarily in the ultraviolet and, hence, invisible. The lines had been enormously increased in wavelength, shifted

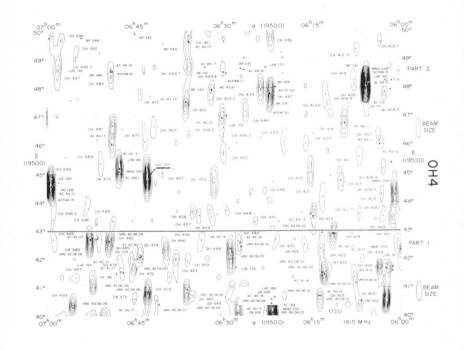

43. Contour map of 10 degree square block of sky from the Ohio Sky Survey showing OH471 (left of center) "the blaze marking the edge of the universe." (*Time* magazine).

to the red and lowered in pitch. It was as though the quasar were a cosmic soprano whose shrill, piercingly-high notes sounded to us like those of a deep basso profundo. The red shift value was 3.4 (or 340 percent) which implied that OH471 was rushing away at 600 million miles per hour at a distance of 12 billion light years!

The announcement of Carswell and Strittmatter's epic achievement appeared on the front page of the *New York Times* for April 8, 1973,

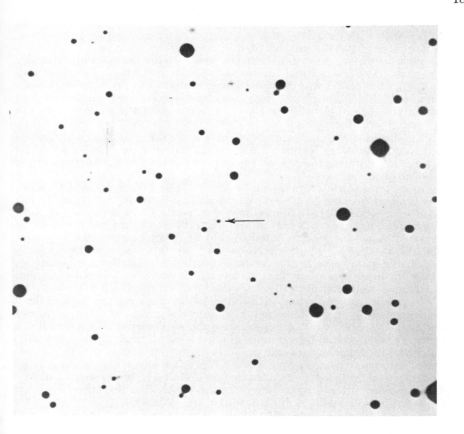

44. Photograph from the Palomar Sky Survey showing the faint star-like object (indicated by arrow) which Mirjana Gearhart identified with OH471. The area covered by this photograph is only 7 thousandths of one percent of that in the radio map with OH471, the area being that subtended by the tiny cross at the center of the contours for OH471.

Although OH471 is one of the strongest sources on the radio map, it is one of the faintest objects in the photograph requiring a big telescope to observe it. The photograph is a reversed (or negative) view with the stars appearing black against a white background instead of vice versa. Carswell and Strittmatter used this view to locate OH471 and measure its red shift with the Steward 90-inch telescope on Kitt Peak.

and their scientific article about it was published in *Nature* the same week. In this article they stated,

"If quasar redshifts are due mainly to Hubble expansion,* OH471 is the most distant object so far known as well as being the most intrinsically luminous." The last phrase "most intrinsically luminous" was their way of saying that OH471 was the most powerful object known in the universe.

The redshift "barrier" of 3 had been broken like Roger Bannister had broken the 4-minute mile in 1954! In both cases the barrier was not physical; it was psychological.

Some days later, the accomplishment was featured as *Time* magazine's lead article, and the editor climaxed his philosophic discussion of its significance with the metaphor "the quasar OH471, (is) the blaze marking the edge of the universe."

What is meant by the word "edge?" I have used it in the sense of a kind of horizon or observational limit related to the redshift. The speed with which OH471 is receding is 90 percent of the velocity of light which places it 90 percent of the way to the edge. A 100 percent recession velocity (velocity equal to that of light) would place an object right at the "edge" of the universe and for this its redshift would be infinite. This, however, is an oversimplification. The true nature of the edge and what may lie beyond may be argued by cosmologists with volumes of abstruse mathematics but riddles they remain nonetheless.

What gives a quasar like OH471 the tremendous energy needed for it to be detectable at these enormous distances? Current thinking suggests that quasars are young galaxies with dense nucleii in which millions of stars are converted into radiant energy — light, heat, x-rays, and radio waves — in a super-powerful, mind-boggling explosion. Matter is converted into energy on a grand scale.† When a nuclear device big enough to destroy a large city explodes, a few pounds or kilograms of matter are converted into energy. When just one star, like the sun, blows up, the effect is over a billion, billion, billion times greater.

If the sun blew up, the earth, Venus, Mars — the whole solar system— would vaporize and vanish in a flash. In a quasar like OH471, we are talking about the explosion of not just one, but millions of stars like the sun, drenching and saturating the universe around with blinding light, scorching heat and searing, over-powering radio waves.

What does it mean to say that our galaxy has a diameter of 100 000 light years and that we (earth, sun and other planets) are some 30 000

---

*The "If quasar redshifts are due mainly to Hubble expansion" in Carswell and Strittmatter's statement is a cautious hedge adopted by many astronomers to allow for the possibility that large redshifts may result from something other than expansion of the universe, such as from gravitational effects or individual quasar motion which isn't related to universal expansion. The prevailing attitude is that the effect *is* related to the expansion of the universe and does imply that the objects are both distant and powerful and that the larger the redshift the greater their distance and I interpret it this way here although I am very much aware of the fact that someday evidence may be forthcoming which will require a reinterpretation of the redshifts.

†Einstein formulated the conversion as $E = mc^2$, where E is the energy, m the mass and c the velocity of light. The velocity of light is a large quantity, squaring it makes the factor even bigger so when a significant amount of matter of mass, m, is multiplied by c^2 we obtain an enormous amount of energy.

light years from its center? Or what does it mean when we say that a quasar is 12 billion light years distant? It boggles one's mind. We can write down the numbers but do we really appreciate the immensity of the distances? When I say that it's 100 miles to Cleveland I can understand from personal experience how far that is, but when I say that a quasar is 12 billion light years away I recognize only that it's a staggeringly large distance, beyond my ken or that of any man. The distances are so great, so far beyond our ordinary experience as to be almost meaningless. But let's try to obtain even a slight comprehension.

The distance to the moon is 10 times the distance around the earth, yet light (and radio) waves travel it in about one second. In one day light travels 86 400 times farther and in a year another 365 times as far. That is *one* light year. The nearest stars are four times as far away, the center of the galaxy 30 000 times further and the distant quasar 12 billion times as far.

Now let's try another tack. Imagine that the earth and our entire galaxy have shrunk in size so the earth is the size of a pea. Then on this scale the nearest stars would be 20 000 kilometers (12 000 miles) away and the center of the galaxy would be 120 million kilometers (70 million miles) away while the quasar would be a half million times farther than that!

As still another approach to acquiring a concept of the size of the universe, I suggest that you look at the pictures in Kees Boeke's book "Cosmic View: The Universe in 40 Jumps."

45. Mirjana Gearhart at the time she identified OH471 with a faint quasar.

Mirjana Gearhart was 23 when she identified OH471 with a faint inconspicuous quasar on a sky photograph amid myriads of brighter stars and set the stage for Carswell and Strittmatter's spectrum which showed that it was the most distant and powerful object known in the universe! Man's efforts to probe the universe had resulted in another giant leap toward the edge.

The unique contribution of radio astronomy in exploring the cosmos is strikingly illustrated by the case of OH471. It is a strong radio source, yet optically it is a faint star-like object outshone by billions of much brighter stars. Without radio astronomers to guide the optical astronomers, hundreds of years might have passed before it was found through a systematic examination of the stars one by one.

If the stars are like the grains of sand on a vast stretch of sea shore, radio astronomy is like an arrow which leads us to the particular grain of sand which is unusual.

By a similar sequence astronomers were soon guided to another find. Three months after the announcement on OH471, a Lick Observatory, California, team of Joe Wampler, Lloyd Robinson, Jack Baldwin and Margaret Burbidge announced in *Nature* that they had measured an even higher redshift of 3.53 for another Ohio Special, OQ172. This put its recession velocity at nearly 91 percent of the velocity of light and its distance at more than 12 billion light years, pushing almost one percent closer to the "edge."

While the Ohio sky survey was in progress in 1967 we had discovered a strong radio source we named OQ172 which, like OH471, was not listed in any prior survey. Adding it to our list of Ohio Specials, Bryan Andrew measured it at centimeter wavelengths with the Algonquin radio telescope. OQ172 was one of the 2100 sources in Installment III, published in 1969 and we published its radio spectrum the following January. Later M. P. Veron, a French astronomer, made an identification. A very accurate radio position was measured at the Royal Radar Establishment confirming Veron's identification and this information was sent to Joe Wampler. Eventually, by 1973, the Lick Observatory team, using a new image-dissector scanner Wampler had built, obtained a spectrum of OQ172 establishing its redshift as 3.53. With OH471 and its redshift of 3.40, these Ohio Specials were the two most distant and powerful objects known in the universe.

To determine and document the radio spectra of OH471 and OQ172 as completely as possible, Mirjana Gearhart and I organized a cooperative international effort involving six U.S. observatories, three in Canada, and one each in Brazil, England, Germany and the U.S.S.R. For a year an international team of 23 astronomers from these institutions made special flux density measurements of these two sources at many different wavelengths from as long as 20 meters to as short as 3 millimeters.* The comprehensive results with charts and tables were published in *Nature* in midsummer of 1974 with Mirjana Gearhart's name at the head of the team of 23 authors. The editor of *Nature* wrote an editorial about the article, commenting on its significance both as an important scientific contribution and as an excellent example of international cooperation.

---

*The radio astronomers included Bryan Andrew, Ottawa, Canada, Martin Ryle, Cambridge, England, S. Ya. Braude, Kharkov, U.S.S.R., Otto Hachenberg, Bonn, Germany, and Pierre Kaufmann, Sao Paulo, Brazil.

In 1976 three years after their redshifts had been determined, OH471 and OQ172 were still the two objects with the highest known redshifts but more large redshifts had been measured for a number of other Ohio Specials. Of the 16 objects with highest redshift found in all radio surveys, 12 had been discovered in the Ohio survey. Three of the other four were also observed and catalogued in the course of the Ohio survey but had been found earlier in the 4C (Cambridge) survey.

During 1975 Margaret Burbidge and Harding "Gene" Smith of Lick Observatory had obtained spectra and measured the high redshifts on some of the additional Ohio Sources, like OF097 and OZ-187, of the top 16 and they wrote me,

"It is abundantly clear that the place to look for high-redshift quasars is among the Ohio centimeter excess (special) sources."

We had previously sent them positions and identifications for a group of Ohio specials and looked forward to hearing from them about their results. Whenever the phone rang I hoped it might be Margaret or Gene calling to say that they had measured another big redshift for an Ohio special.

Mirjana Gearhart and I made a study indicating that quasars with strong centimeter wavelength emission, that is, the centimeter-excess types, tended to have high redshifts. Nearly all Ohio Specials are of this type so the above statistics on the 16 highest redshift objects gave additional support to our suggestion. Erich Pacht, a graduate student, has continued studies of the trend.

Among the thousands of other Ohio radio sources may there not be many more with large redshifts and some as great or greater than for OH471 and OQ172?

When we observe quasars, OH471 and OQ172 for example, at distances of some 12 billion light years we are observing them as they were 12 billion years ago. This "look back" time enables us to see these objects as they were in the early formation stages of the universe.*

A modern story of Genesis might read:

"In the beginning the universe was a fireball. Everything was concentrated at one place in a sphere of super-dense matter which exploded into a collosal, gargantuan fireball of incredible heat and energy racing outward in all directions at the speed of light. As the fireball expanded stars and galaxies condensed out of the material left behind, our sun and the Milky Way galaxy being among those so formed."

This is the "big bang" theory of the formation of the universe devised to account for the expansion Hubble observed. Our own galaxy is billions of years old but when we observe such distant quasars as OH471 and OQ172 we may be viewing the universe as it was in the beginning and seeing these objects being born, each with a dense powerful nucleus which itself is exploding. All we are really sure of is the redshift value, the rest is theory and conjecture.

But whatever the true explanation, man's horizons have been widened spectacularly. From dimensions of some thousands of light years in 1920, man's probing has pushed his knowledge of the universe outward by 1973

---

*The radio waves from the quasar are very old when we receive them but the quasar was young or new when it radiated them. It's like the archaeological discovery of an ancient drawing of an infant monarch; the drawing is old but what it portrays is young.

46. This is the earth "hanging like a fragile, frosted blue Christmas-tree ornament above the lunar landscape, the first view of the earth from another celestial body." This is where we live as seen from the distance light travels in one second, a very close view.

to distances of billions of light years approaching what seems to be an ultimate "edge."

Astronomy has stretched man's perspective, yet the money he spends on astronomy is minuscule compared to the vast sums he pours into weapons of destruction.

"Will man be able to answer some of the riddles of the universe before he self-destructs?" may well be his most important question.

Astronomy has lifted man above his self-centered view of himself and given him a cosmic perspective. It has turned his viewpoint around. A dramatic example of this change is afforded by the photograph of the earth taken from the surface of the moon by the Apollo astronauts showing the earth hanging like a fragile, frosted blue Christmas tree ornament above the lunar landscape, the first view of the earth from another celestial body.

The questions astronomy stimulates man to ask about the universe, its nature, its origin, its destiny, and whether we are its sole intelligent inhabitants, are some of the most basic and profound he can imagine. *Astronomy presents man with the universe as his total environment and his endless frontier.*

Henri Poincare, the French scientist, once said,

"Astronomy is useful because it shows us how small is man's body, how great is his mind."

I believe that what Poincare means is that it is utterly fantastic that man's brain, a mere handful of matter, is able to grasp and appreciate, even partially, something of the enormity, complexity and vastness of the universe. But lest we become too smug we should project ourselves a few centuries or millenia into the future. Then, assuming man continues to progress, our current cosmologies may appear to be as naive, primitive and simplistic as the ancient Greek legend of Hercules now seems to us.

47. This is where we live. The arrow points to the place where we are situated inside a spiral arm of our galaxy but our sun is much too faint to be visible in this view from the distance light travels in 10 million years. The entire solar system including the orbit of Pluto is so insignificant that it is smaller than the tiniest dot in the picture and invisible among the 100 billion other stars of our galaxy which rotates like an enormous, gargantuan Fourth of July pinwheel 100 000 light years in diameter. Our galaxy in turn is but one galaxy among 100 billion galaxies and other objects which constitute the "astounding, baffling, stranger-than-fiction cosmos in which we dwell."

(This picture is actually a photograph of a beautiful spiral galaxy (M81) which is believed to closely resemble our own.)

CHAPTER 23

IS MAN ALONE?

With Big Ear we have explored the inanimate cosmos to enormous distances far beyond our solar system and our own galaxy, detecting quasars close to the edge of the universe. If Big Ear can do this could it not also hear signals from intelligent animate beings somewhere in all the vast space between us and the edge, or is man alone? If Big Ear can find *what's* out there, could it not find *who's* out there? Let's ponder the prospects.

The first question we need to consider is whether there are any places in the universe, other than the earth, which may be suitable abodes for life as we know it and, if so, what are the chances that life may have evolved there and developed to the stage of an advanced technological civilization capable of sending out radio signals?

The earth is like a space ship with four billion passengers circling a star called the sun. The sun is but one of 100 billion stars comprising our galaxy and our galaxy, in turn, is but one of 100 billion galaxies in the universe. If the chances of a star having a planet like the earth are only one in a million there would be 100 000 stars with planets in our own galaxy. According to some astronomers there might be more than this so the prospects here are encouraging.

What about the likelihood of life developing on these planets? The recent discovery through radio astronomy of clouds of water, ammonia, acetylene, formaldehyde, sulphur dioxide, formic acid, ethyl alcohol and other complex molecules in interstellar space has increased our estimates of the likelihood.

The amounts found for many of the molecules are enormous. In one cloud alone astronomers have found enough ethyl alcohol to make a billion, billion, billion fifths at 200 proof. This is a staggering amount.

It is now thought that many of the molecules basic to life originate in space and that these molecular clouds could seed planets. An alternative theory is that if complex molecules can form in cold, inhospitable interstellar space they are even more likely to develop on a planet where conditions may be more favorable. Either way, these molecules might eventually lead to simple, primitive living forms from which more complex and advanced types might evolve, ultimately culminating in intelligent beings and an advanced technological civilization. Many astronomers and exobiologists believe that this may be a normal, oft-repeated phenomenon throughout the cosmos. As long as there is the smallest possibility of the existence of other-men or other civilizations circling other stars we have

a chance.

Big Ear is a large radio telescope designed as a search instrument. With it we discovered thousands of radio sources during the Ohio Sky Survey. It is equally well-suited for a search of signals from other civilizations and has, in fact, been used for just that.

But before describing our search, let us discuss some of the problems and some of the strategies. It makes a fascinating story.

Radio engineers have designed and built systems for communicating between any part of the earth and any other part, between the earth and the moon, and between the earth and probes exploring the solar system. A system for detecting radio signals from an advanced civilization on a planet revolving around a distant star and possibly communicating with it involves much more.

I will consider an "advanced civilization" as one capable of interstellar communication but not necessarily of interstellar travel. This matches our present capability. We have just recently become capable of interstellar communication but our capability for interstellar travel is still far in the future.

If we were able to detect a distant civilization what might we expect to find? Would they be like us, or more advanced or less advanced? The answer to this question is more definite than some we have asked.

We have possessed the capability of interstellar communication for only a few years. We have "just arrived"; we are "cosmic rookies". Any civilization we detect is likely to be much more advanced, as will be explained.

The earth is about five billion years old, and man, as a distinct species, is a few million years old. Man's evolution has been a long process which is still going on.

There is no reason why intelligent creatures developing elsewhere should evolve at exactly the same rate as on the earth. With evolution from the most primitive forms to intelligent beings taking billions of years, a rate differing by as little as one percent could make the distant intelligent beings either millions of years behind us or millions of years more advanced. If they are millions of years behind us, their civilization, if it could be called such, would be primitive and we would be unaware of them. If they are millions of years more advanced, they should be very advanced, and they may provide clues of their presence, for example, by a radio beacon signal, as from a lighthouse. A beacon would require enormous power and this could imply that they had solved their energy problems which we as an emerging culture are just now beginning to face.

It boggles the mind to think what we might be like a million years hence if we are around that long. *If* we are around that long; that is the question. When a civilization reaches our stage of development, what are its chances of longevity? Will we annihilate ourselves in a nuclear holocaust, or will we destroy our fragile environment and suffocate in our own pollution? If so, how soon? Is this typical of all civilizations? If it is, the chances of our ever detecting a distant civilization become almost negligible. There would be no such thing as a civilization one million years more advanced than ours. Ours then might represent a terminal type.

Even if civilizations like ours can survive for a few hundred years or as much as a thousand years, it is not enough. It is necessary for advanced civilizations to be around for millions of years in order to have even a small chance of one detecting another. If we find a civilization that has been around that long, "they" may have an interesting story to tell and one from which we might benefit.

Assuming that advanced civilizations do exist, are there some places where they are more likely to be found than others? The sun has planets, one of which, the earth, has spawned what we smugly call an "advanced civilization." So we might argue that other stars of the same or similar type might be the most likely to have what we are seeking. The sun is neither too hot, nor too cold, and it and its planets are old enough for life to have had time to evolve on one of them (the earth).

The sun is a yellow-dwarf star of spectral class G. By spectral class is meant its classification determined by the emission and absorption lines in its spectrum as obtained with an optical telescope. These lines tell something of the star's chemical composition, temperature, and age. The classification systems employ a sequence of letters O-B-A-F-G-K-M-R-N-S. Young, giant, hot, blue stars are of the O and B type, other older, smaller, cooler, redder stars are further along or later in the sequence. Typically a B star has a temperature around 20 000 kelvins (centigrade degrees above absolute zero), while an M star's temperature is about 3000 kelvins, and a G star, like the sun, around 6000 kelvins.*

Finer subdivisions of spectral types are indicated by numbers ranging from 0 through 9. Thus, the sun is designated as a spectral type G2. So if a nearby star can be found of type G2 (or between G0 and G5), it should be quite similar to the sun with possibly better chances for having a planetary companion with intelligent life. Even late F types (such as F5 to F9) or early K types (like K1 or K2) can not be ruled out as possibilities. A B star would be much too hot and too young. At the other extreme an M star would probably be too cool and too old, but we really don't know.

Before considering civilizations on planets circling other stars let us think about the prospects closer at hand right in our own solar system.

The Apollo exploration of the moon reveals that it is a dead world. Data from space probes to Venus suggest that it is much too hot for life as we know it. Mars remains as the most likely abode for life. Mars is close enough that if there were Martians with radio transmitters, a radio telescope on the earth could readily detect them. But we could easily miss them unless we monitored the proper frequencies at the right times with the appropriate type of receiving system. To be certain that transmitters do not exist would require a very tedious, systematic search. To my knowledge, no such search for intelligent radio signals from Mars has ever been made.

The first pictures, July 20th, 1976, from the Viking 1 lander revealed a bleak landscape with no Martians on hand to welcome the new arrival. Viking's search for life will take time and who knows what may be found.

And what about the flying saucers or UFOs (Unidentified Flying Objects) and the reports that we have been visited, that we are being visited, or that we are going to be visited? Although some reports have raised questions, none have ever produced any tangible, real evidence which can stand up to the same unbiased, rigorous examination scientists apply to their own work. Carl Sagan gives an excellent insight into the difference in attitudes of the scientist and the saucerian in his book with I. S. Shklovskii on "Intelligent Life in the Universe."

If a space ship, or even parts of one, were acquired so they could be studied and analyzed in a laboratory and found to be of a composition or

---

*To remember the sequence, astronomers recite the sentence, "Oh-Be-A-Fine-Girl-Kiss-Me-Right-Now-Smack."

design alien to anything known on the earth, or if a "Little Green Man" with knowledge or abilities transcending ours was available for an interview, the saucerians would have a convincing case. But much of the so-called evidence is not hard data but stems from rumors, hoaxes, or erroneous observations. I know from first-hand experience that this is the case. For example, in some books and articles my report of pulse signals from Venus was eagerly cited as evidence of extraterrestrial intelligent beings, even though I had acknowledged that my interpretation of the signals was wrong! (Chapter 16). Actually, my evidence was as good or better than that which saucerians often give. As I stated in connection with my Venus observations, it is very easy to be misled.*

If probes we send to Mars show no signs of intelligent life there and if there is none elsewhere in the solar system, the next step in our search takes us to the nearest stars. These are 5 to 10 light years distant, a big step. One light year is the distance which light, or radio waves, travelling 300 000 kilometers per second, cover in one year. To get the distance in a light year we multiply 300 000 kilometers by the number of days in a year (365) by the number of hours in a day (24), by the number of minutes in an hour (60) and finally by the number of seconds in a minute (60). The result (one light year) is about 9 500 000 000 000 kilometers (or 6 000 000 000 000 miles).

We know that the sun has planets, but we are not entirely certain that other stars have them. If an observer on Planet X revolving around a neighboring star looked at the sun with a telescope equivalent to our largest and most modern type, he would not be able to see the earth or the sun's other planets — they would be too faint. The sun would be just another star among thousands of others. A dweller on Planet X would be as unaware of us as we are of him.

To obtain an appreciation for the distances involved in an earlier example we shrank the earth to the size of a pea. Now let us imagine that the sun, which is nearly one million miles in diameter has shrunk to the size of a pea (6 millimeters in diameter or ¼ inch). On the same scale the earth would be the size of a speck of dust circling the pea at a distance of 50 centimeters (or 20 inches). Our moon would be a still smaller speck of dust circling the earth speck with only 1 millimeter separation. A star at 10 light years would be another pea and its planet a dust speck 50 centimeters from it *but with both 300 kilometers away!* When we talk about communicating with a civilization on a distant planet, we should try and keep in mind these relative distances. It is as though we are on one dust speck and the distant civilization on another speck 300 kilometers (200 miles) from us!

The sun is a relatively strong source of radio waves generated by virtue of its high surface temperature (about 6000 kelvins) and the high energies of electrons spiraling in its corona. It radiates about one million million watts of radio power. Should we not expect to detect such radiation from neighboring G-type stars? The answer is no, simply because the stars are a million times farther than the sun. The power received decreases as the square of the distance so the radio radiation would be reduced by one million million which makes radio emission from the G-type stars undetectable by present techniques. Some neighboring stars have been detected with radio telescopes, but these are either very hot B-type stars or flare

---

*An excellent discussion of the UFO phenomenon is given by Peter Millman (see references).

stars like UV Ceti. UV Ceti is a dwarf red star of type M, and it undergoes occasional outbursts increasing its radio power output by as much as one million fold.

If we can't detect the radio emission amounting to a million-million watts from a neighboring G-type star, how can we expect to receive intelligent signals from a transmitter of only, say, one million watts power on a planetary companion of the star?

The answer is that we could not unless the power is radiated in a very narrow bandwidth, and this requires that any information be transmitted at a slow rate. The simplest possible method of doing this is to simply turn a radio transmitter on and off slowly as when sending Morse code.

We may conclude from this reasoning that we should use a narrow bandwidth. But we also need to look in the right direction, on the right wavelength and at the right moment. There are other considerations but these can illustrate the general problem. Let us examine each of them in turn.

(1) *The right direction.* The beam of a radio telescope is very narrow. At least a million beams are required to cover the sky. Hence, we can't afford to direct our telescope haphazardly. We ought to select some points in the sky which are more likely than others for detecting intelligent signals and direct our antenna at them. These points might correspond, as discussed above, to Mars or to some stars like the sun in the solar neighborhood. What we need is a finding list. Such a list titled, "A List of Likely Objects," is given in the appendix.

(2) *The right wavelength or channel.* We should tune our receiver to the wavelength or channel of the distant transmitter; but we don't know what its wavelength is. It is like having a receiver with millions of channels and, hopefully, a signal on one of them but we don't know which one. Are there any wavelengths which are more likely than others? It turns out that there may be.

(3) *The right moment.* We should have our antenna pointed at the right place in the sky, be listening to the right channel, and if the distant civilization uses a large antenna with a narrow beam, we would want to be doing all of the above things properly when their beam is directed at us, that is, at the right moment. It is really more involved than this because of the time required for the signals to reach us. Suppose, for example, that a civilization 10 light years distant directed a powerful beam of radio waves at us for a whole year at a time corresponding to the year 1970 on the earth and then directed its beam elsewhere. To receive these signals we should not only do all of the right things mentioned above but do them at the right moment. This means doing them during the earth year 1980. If we listened in 1979 or 1981, we would detect nothing. In 1979 the signals would not yet have reached us, and in 1981 they would have passed us by.

Thus, even if we have everything else right but listen at the wrong moment, we will not be successful. It is clear that even with an advanced civilization within signalling distance, we might never know of its existence. So even if we observe a star for a minute, an hour, or even a year and get nothing we can not rule it out completely as a possibility.

If a distant civilization were to select the sun as a likely object and direct a radio beam continuously in its direction for thousands of years, our chances of detecting it would be greatly increased. But if the distant civilization did not choose to transmit at all, we might never be aware of its presence.

One procedure might be to start listening to the nearest stars, of a type like the sun, and then to extend the search gradually to more and more distant stars of this kind. Listening would be done at first on channels thought to be the most likely and the search extended later to other channels. With a systematic search we might gradually rule out the nearest stars as abodes of advanced civilizations and shift our search to those in the next distance bracket. If these yielded nothing, we would move to still more distant stars. At any point in this search about all we could say was that, if an advanced civilization existed somewhere out there, it must be farther than the stars we had already examined.

If we did detect signals from a distant civilization and wished to converse with it, there would be the problem of the "time delay." Suppose we were aware of a civilization on a planet circling a star 10 light years from us, and they were aware of us. If we said "Hello" today, we would have to wait 20 years for their reply. This assumes that they understood our message and answered immediately. It requires 10 years for our message to reach them and another 10 years for their answer to come back to us. Thus, conversation would be handicapped by a 20-year lag. So instead of attempting a dialogue, we might each try simultaneous monologues and gradually convey some knowledge of each to the other. But there would be a language problem, and it might require a long time to decipher and understand the messages. Thus, any getting-acquainted period could take a long time.

What about a journey to such a neighbor? At the speeds our Apollo ships travelled to the moon, a round trip would require millions of years. Even at the velocity of light (or radio waves), it would take 10 years. This velocity (670 million miles per hour) is Nature's speed limit. No higher velocity is possible. And vehicle speeds even remotely approaching this velocity would require a prohibitive amount of power. So it is likely that we will have to content ourselves to simple communication for a long time to come. At least our radio signals travel at Nature's limiting speed, and these we can generate in sufficient power to send over the required distances by techniques presently available on the earth.

There have been only a few attempts so far to search for intelligent signals. The first attempt called Project Ozma was made by Frank Drake in the summer of 1960 using the 85-foot (26-meter) diameter Tatel radio telescope at the National Radio Astronomy Observatory, Green Bank, West Virginia. He listened with 100 hertz bandwidth at 21 centimeters wavelength to Tau Ceti and Epsilon Eridani, two stars about 11 light years distant. Nothing was detected. Another attempt was made late in 1968 and early in 1969 by a Russian team using a 15-meter diameter radio telescope. They listened with 13 hertz bandwidths on a number of channels at 32 centimeters wavelength to 11 stars and with considerable audaciousness to M31, the Andromeda galaxy, two million light years from us! The Russian attempt is the first one on record made to detect intelligent signals from a source outside our galaxy. The Russian group observed the objects for periods of about one hour each. Nothing was detected. And at OSU a search has been conducted which I will tell about later.

In addition to these attempts to detect signals from distant civilizations, much thought and discussion has been devoted to the subject. A number of conferences have been held, many of them in Russia. Numerous books have been written, one of the more exhaustive treatises being "Intelligent Life in the Universe" by Shklovskii and Sagan mentioned earlier. More recently, Sagan has published a more popular account called "The Cosmic Connection."

In 1971 the National Aeronautics and Space Administration sponsored a study called "Project Cyclops" (after the mythical one-eyed giant) organized by Bernard Oliver, of the Hewlett-Packard Co., and John Billingham of NASA. The stated objective of Project Cyclops was "to assess what would be required in hardware, manpower, time and funding to mount a realistic effort, using present (or near-term future) state-of-the-art techniques, aimed at detecting the existence of extra-terrestrial (extra solar system) intelligent life." The term "realistic effort" was used in the context of one which has a high probability of success. To achieve this high probability an expenditure equivalent to that of the Apollo program is envisaged. Obviously before any hardware, such as a gigantic antenna, is constructed, there must be much thought, study and planning. Problems like those considered in this chapter are typical of the topics studied in much more detail in Project Cyclops.

Bob Dixon, of our observatory, participated in this project, especially in connection with the problems of data reduction and analysis. Enormous amounts of data would need to be sifted and analyzed in a project like Cyclops, and the only feasible way of doing this would be by using large fast computers.

Returning now to the matter of wavelength, it is important to determine, if possible, whether one particular wavelength or several specific wavelengths are more likely than others. One of the most important discoveries of radio astronomy is that atomic hydrogen gas in interstellar space can be detected by virtue of its radio emission at a wavelength of 21 centimeters.

Each atom of hydrogen consists of a proton as nucleus with a spinning electron orbiting around it. Once in a long while, measured in millions of years, the electron may abruptly flip, reversing its spin direction, and when it does it sends out a 21 centimeter wavelength radio signal. The single flip of one atom once in millions of years would pass unnoticed, like one chirp of one cricket, but the volume of space filled with hydrogen is so great that enormous numbers of flip signals join in a mighty chorus like the chirps of a vast horde of crickets.

Hydrogen gas appears to pervade all of space and, although its density is low, the total amount is immense. A distant advanced civilization should be aware of these "chirps" broadcast at a wavelength of 21 centimeters. So if a distant civilization wished to attract attention, reasoned Guiseppi Cocconi and Philip Morrison in 1959, might it not transmit on this channel or one close to it? Frank Drake thought so and listened on 21 centimeters the next year in his project Ozma. Since then, many other elements or molecules in space have been found to "chirp" or "broadcast" on other wavelengths or channels. Hydrogen, however, is more abundant and more widely distributed. Hence, its wavelength might be regarded as the most likely channel.*

Even if an advanced civilization broadcast at a fixed wavelength as measured at its transmitter, we would not, in general, receive the signal on the same wavelength, because the distant transmitter and we are in

---

*In selecting some wavelength on which to listen, we really are only guessing. Intelligent beings of a distant advanced civilization might not reason like we do, which brings us to the problem of *anthropocentrism*. This is a big word which means here that any method, plan, or strategy we develop will be from the viewpoint of man. Intelligent creatures which evolve on a distant planet may think very differently and so our strategy may not be relevant.

relative motion. This motion produces a shift in wavelength due to the doppler effect. This is the same effect which makes the pitch (or wavelength) of a locomotive or automobile horn change as it passes.

To compensate for this effect Bob Dixon has proposed, in an article in *Icarus,* a search strategy whereby we correct our receiving wavelength of the hydrogen line in any direction for our motion with respect to the center of our galaxy, the principal point of common reference for all galaxy dwellers. Assuming all beacons were also so corrected, we would then be tuned to exactly the right wavelength in whatever direction we looked for a beacon. Dixon's scheme specifies a *unique wavelength* for every beacon and every listener in the galaxy.

* * * * *

In all the searching and listening have any signals been received that suggested strongly that they were from a distant civilization? Yes, in 1967, a mysterious pulsing signal of this type was discovered with a radio telescope at the Cambridge University (England) radio observatory. A drama unfolded which was the most exciting development up to then in radio astronomy.

For some years radio astronomers at the University of Cambridge had been studying quasi-stellar radio sources or quasars by means of a scintillation effect. At meter wavelengths radio waves are distorted as they pass through electron clouds sprayed out by the sun. If the waves from a quasar pass through these clouds they fluctuate rapidly or scintillate but waves from other objects like ordinary galaxies do not. The reason is that quasars are of very small angular extent; they are veritable point sources in the sky whereas other objects tend to be more extended.* To facilitate the hunt for quasars Antony Hewish designed and built a new 4-meter wavelength radio telescope using 2048 dipole antennas arrayed over four and one-half acres.

The new array went into operation late in July 1967 with Antony Hewish supervising its operation. The task of analyzing the 400 feet of chart paper which spewed from the recorders each week was assigned to Jocelyn Bell, a young graduate student from Ireland, who had also helped construct the telescope.

For a while the records produced results as expected and many scintillating sources, presumably quasars, were noted. But one day in August, Jocelyn discovered something strange on the record which she described as "a bit of scruff," that is, something flaky or scaly in appearance. It looked like a scintillating or fluctuating source but it occurred near midnight when scintillation was usually absent. It lasted only a few moments and then was gone. Perhaps it was some kind of man-made interference. But by the end of August she had noted it six times, and each time that it occurred, the antenna was pointing at precisely the same place in the sky. This proved that it was not terrestrial interference but was indeed a signal from space. Perhaps it was from a flare star. Antony Hewish and his associates studied the records with great interest. But then for six weeks the signal was gone.

One day late in November Jocelyn Bell announced, "It's back." Inten-

---

*A similar effect occurs optically. Stars fluctuate in brightness or twinkle but planets do not because stars are minuscule points of light while planets have finite discs.

sive observations followed and it was discovered that the signal came as a regular succession of pulses at intervals of almost exactly one and one-third seconds.

How could this regular pulsing signal come from a natural astronomical object? Could it possibly be a message from a distant civilization? Half seriously, half jokingly the Cambridge group referred to the signal source as "L.G.M." for "Little Green Men." Wisely, Hewish refrained from any public announcement or publication of results until he and his associates had studied and interpreted the signal characteristics in more detail. During this period, similar type pulsing signals were discovered from three other points in the sky, each with a different pulsing rate. In all cases the regularity of the pulses was astonishing.

Then theory stepped into the picture and rapidly pulsating or rotating stars were considered as the cause. Much earlier Robert Oppenheimer (Chapter 8) and other theorists had predicted that when the nuclear fires in a star go out there would be an instability involving first an explosion and then a collapse of the remnant under gravitational attraction into a rapidly-rotating super-dense object called a neutron star. It would be so dense that one cubic centimeter of the star weighs as much as one cubic kilometer of lead. A beam of radio waves from this rapidly rotating star, like the beam of light from a lighthouse, would be observed as a pulse for each revolution of the star. By the time the first article by the Cambridge group appeared in February 1968, the visions of Little Green Men had vanished and the mysterious signals could be explained as a natural phenomenon. It was not long before the term *pulsar* was coined for the remarkable objects.

This is the story of the discovery of pulsars. It is interesting because if and when a signal, "a bit of scruff," is detected from an advanced civilization the circumstances of the discovery may have many similarities to this story. But there is one point of difference. Pulsars do *not* have the narrow bandwidth that we might expect for a signal from an advanced civilization.

Although many more pulsars have been found since, most are relatively "close," within 100 light years. Some are farther. One in the Crab nebula is at a distance of 3500 light years. This pulsar has been observed to pulse or flash simultaneously across optical, x-ray and radio wavelengths at the high rate of 30 times per second.

When the discovery of the first pulsars was announced, we wondered if we might be able to discover any new ones with Big Ear. Existing information indicated that they would be too weak at the wavelengths we were using at the time so we installed a receiver and a corner reflector feed antenna operating at the longer wavelength of one and one-half meters and during the spring and summer of 1968 we surveyed for pulsars while our regular sky survey was in progress at shorter wavelengths.

We didn't find any new pulsars although we had several false alarms which turned out to be either man-made interference or well-known radio sources pulsing or scintillating because of ionospheric irregularities. We concluded that a telescope of much larger aperture would be required for a productive pulsar search. However, we were able to detect some of the known pulsars and Don Smith did a masters thesis on our pulsar observations.

*   *   *   *   *

Should we expect a distant civilization to advertize its presence by sending out a beacon signal? We do not send out a beacon signal and probably would not send out an SOS even if our civilization were facing extinction. It might be more reasonable to search for signals which a distant civilization uses for its own purposes.

It is sometimes thought that since radio transmitters have been operating on the earth for over 50 years, notice of our presence has been given to all civilizations within the distance radio waves travel in 50 years. This couldn't be further from the truth. The earliest radio transmissions on earth of substantial power were at long wavelengths. These long-wave signals are completely trapped inside the ionosphere which surrounds the earth acting like a metallic spherical shell.

More recently, shorter wavelengths have been used, and these can escape through the ionosphere, but such radiation is incidental. All television stations, for example, employ antennas which direct most of the radiated power horizontally along the ground. Only a little is radiated upwards escaping into space.

There is, however, an exception. The powerful radar telescopes, such as the one at Arecibo, Puerto Rico, used for studying the sun, moon or nearer planets, send out radio beams which are so strong that echoes can be detected from Venus or Mars, allowing accurate determinations of the distance between us and the planet. An advanced civilization not too far away could readily pick up these radar signals if they happened to be in the line-of-sight of Mars or Venus, if they pointed their antenna at us and listened on the proper wavelength at the proper time. But the chances of this happening are very small.

The beam from a typical radio telescope covers only one-millionth of the sky. If the distant civilization had a similar beam and both its beam and ours were pointed at random, the chance that both beams were pointing at each other is only one in a million million. And with a million channels or wavelengths to choose from, the chances diminish to only one in a million-million-million that they will be aware of us or that, if they have radar telescopes, we will be aware of them.

A distant civilization might not even use radio to the extent we do. It might employ lines and cables for all telephone communication and its equivalent of radio and TV broadcasting. It might use low-frequency non-radiating induction lines buried in highways to communicate with surface vehicles, and light beam or infra-red communication for its aircraft or space vehicles. It may have been forced into this situation, because there are only a limited number of radio channels.

Radio channels on earth are already over-crowded, and it may not be long before we evolve a similar arrangement from sheer necessity. Thus, our chances of eavesdropping on a distant civilization are slim. The incidental radiation escaping from its planet would probably be weak and the bandwidth might not even be narrow, except for radar telescope signals, but as we have seen, the chances of detecting these are small.

If a civilization is intent on advertizing its presence, it could send out a beacon signal in all directions at once using a non-directional antenna. This would increase the chances of detection out to the same range provided the transmitter power were also increased a million fold.

We have been dealing in generalities. Now let's write down some numbers and find at what distance the Ohio State University 110 by 21 meter radio telescope with its 100 kelvin receiver might detect another civilization. If we assume that the distant civilization uses a one million watt transmitter, a 500-foot (152 meter) diameter antenna, and a bandwidth of 10 hertz at a wavelength of 10 centimeters, the OSU telescope would be marginally able to detect it at a distance of about 30 light years.

Although, the above assumptions may be "reasonable" ones, we really have no way of knowing what power, antenna size or bandwidth the distant civilization might employ. It is, however, a basis for the calculations. If it used less power than we assumed, our range would be less; if it used more power, our range would be more.

If our range is 30 light years, what are our chances of detecting a distant civilization? Bob Dixon estimates that there are about 40 stars of spectral class between F2 and K5 within 30 light years. (Eight of these are included in the "List of Likely Objects" given in the appendix.) He estimates further that there are about 1500 such stars within 100 light years and about one million within 1000 light years. If the probability of these stars having an advanced civilization is 1 in 100 000, then the chances of detecting an advanced civilization with the OSU radio telescope (on the basis of all the foregoing assumptions) is only 4 in 10 000 or four one-hundredths of one percent. However, if the distant civilizations employ enough more power that the range of our radio telescope is 100 light years our chances are increased to one and one-half percent.

Should we really make an effort to detect and communicate with a distant civilization? There could be many benefits. The distant civilization would probably be older and more advanced. It might be able to provide technological assistance like the U.S. now gives underdeveloped nations on the earth. But more important, "they" might tell us how they managed to adapt and survive on their planet, how they overcame the problems of overpopulation, pollution and war. More generally we might learn whether evolution tends to produce life forms on distant planets which are very similar to our own or very dissimilar.

What if the distant civilization we detect is but one of a number of sovereign groups on the distant planet? There are now over 140 sovereign nations on earth. Should U.S. radio observatories restrict their communication to but one of the distant groups and let the U.S.S.R. radio astronomers cultivate relations with another possibly rival group? This could lead to interstellar alliances where group A on planet 1 aligns with group B on planet 2 and group B on planet 1 aligns with group A on planet 2. We would not have solved any of the earth's problems; we would have compounded them.

For the Cyclops project an antenna is envisaged which is much larger than any built before on earth. The project is so enormous and expensive that it may only be practical if supported on an international basis. Perhaps it should be a United Nations project. Thus, it could have a unifying effect. Likewise a distant advanced civilization's signals may represent the combined effort of all the planet's inhabitants.

What if the distant civilization was not benevolent? It might be highly aggressive, hostile and threatening. Man has evolved to his dominant role on the earth because of his highly-aggressive characteristics. At the same time it is this aggressiveness which threatens his own annihilation. Somehow he must curb this tendency if he is to survive. It is likely that aggressiveness will be a characteristic of the distant civilization, at least, at some point during its evolution. Having survived for hundreds of thousands or millions of years, will the distant civilization have mellowed and become more benevolent, or will its malevolent characteristics have been perpetuated? These are basic questions, and I don't know the answers.

It is interesting to reflect that less than 10 000 years ago the earth was gripped in an ice age. Most of North America and much of the earth's surface was buried under enormous ice masses over a mile thick, like those now covering Greenland and Antarctica. Geological evidence indicates that there have been many ice ages with periods between when the climate was as warm or warmer than it is now. It is likely that some thousands of years hence conditions will favor another ice age unless we have advanced sufficiently in our knowledge of climatology and our ability to control the environment to prevent it. But if the ice age comes what effect will this have? Are distant civilizations subject to disturbances of this magnitude or catastrophies of greater magnitude? If ice ages occur once every 15 000 years, 67 occur in a million years. This could be a factor to contend with.

It is apparent that the problem of the existence of a distant civilization, of detecting it, and of communicating with it is highly complex. The problem contains many variables and uncertainties and in spite of our attempts to rationalize and understand it, we may be far off the mark. The problem may be considerably less difficult than we imagine or much more so.

The study or science of distant civilizations is very young. As studies continue, other ideas may emerge which could change our thinking entirely. We may be able to be much more selective in the stars added to our finding list making our search procedure more efficient. But it could be that we are searching for the wrong kinds of signals. What if the signals are sent in the form of beams of neutrons or in gravity waves? We have only progressed to a very primitive stage in dealing with these beams and waves. The future here is wide open.

We would be very conceited to believe that in all the vast universe we are unique — a real cosmic curiosity. But the answer to the question "Is man alone?" may be elusive. However, if a distant civilization is detected, it will be a new experience for mankind, a cultural monologue from, or possibly a dialogue with, a very old and advanced civilization with a story that would be important to know.

CHAPTER 24

THE SEARCH

Friday, the seventh of December 1973, the search began. We had completed observations for the seventh and final installment of the Ohio Sky Survey. Bob Dixon and Ed Teiga had worked for weeks setting up and testing the 8-channel filter unit which Bill Brundage had built nine years before. There was no fuss or fanfare; switches were set, recorders started and the data began to flow.

Our Big Ear was now listening for other-men on other-planets circling other-stars who might have built beacon stations to announce their presence.* The receiver wavelength was continuously tuned to the 21-centimeter hydrogen line doppler-corrected for galactic rotation according to Bob Dixon's search strategy. The 8-pen recorder drew eight lines on the paper chart as Big Ear's beam scanned the sky. A year later miles of charts had been spewed from the recorder and Bob Dixon, Ed Teiga and Dennis Cole, a graduate student, worked overtime to examine them but a full analysis of the data has not been completed as this is written and, meanwhile, more search observations continue.

We are searching for some kind of narrow-band signal that would appear in only one of the eight channels. If, in addition, it turned off and on in some systematic way this would be suggestive of an intelligent origin and we would then observe and analyze it in more detail.

If it could be established that the signals were indeed from other-men it would have the greatest psychological impact. It would be yet another step in the humbling of man as to the importance of his position in the universe. First, he found that the earth was not stationary but moved, that it was not at the center of the solar system, and then that the solar system was not at the center of our galaxy. Next he found that our galaxy was probably not at the center of the universe. And now he finds that he is not alone. He has competition elsewhere for the Almighty's attention and consideration!

Should the signal convey information about the other-men, the shock to our culture could grow but it is likely that the rate of acquisition of information will be slow, spread out over years, decades, centuries or millenia so there may be time to adjust. If not, the impact could make the "future shock" of Alvin Toffler mild by comparison.

---

*Our search is what some would call a "SETI program," where SETI is an acronym meaning "Search for Extra-Terrestrial Intelligence."

The message we receive would be a monologue. Modern man has been on the receiving end of many monologues. The records unearthed by archaeologists of ancient Babylonian, Egyptian, and Greek civilizations are monologues, much of them *unintentional*. We have learned much and been greatly enriched by this one-way communication from the past. By listening to and deciphering the old and tired signals of beings hundreds or thousands of light years distant we would become cosmic archaeologists.

If the other men wished to communicate with us, their attempt would be *intentional* and probably would involve the principle of *anti-cryptography,* by which they did everything possible to make their message easy to understand, the exact opposite of a secret or coded message which is made as difficult as possible to interpret.

If man elects to alert the other-men of his presence with a beacon of his own, this could take many years to build and centuries before the other-men learned of us if they are a hundred light years or more distant. We would need to do some very long range thinking and planning. A 5-year plan would be of no value. What man would need is a 500-year plan or a millenium plan.

There are many uncertainties. We are assuming that the other-men have built a beacon to announce their presence and that they have corrected its hydrogen-line wavelength for their motion with respect to the center of the galaxy. They may not have done either and there may not even be other-men. We do not know but that doesn't mean we shouldn't try to find out. It is not man's nature to turn away from and ignore a challenge.

If we knew our motion around the galaxy with high enough precision, we would need to search only on one channel using Dixon's strategy, but our uncertainty as to its exact value means that we need to search on a number of adjacent channels to avoid missing the signal altogether. A bonus of the search, if successful, would be learning the exact value of our motion if the beacon of the other-men were properly corrected for their motion, assuming that the other-men are more advanced and know their motion more accurately than we do ours. But Bob Dixon's strategy is not the only one.

Ben Zuckerman and Patrick Palmer have conducted observations with the radio telescopes at Green Bank in which they searched near the 21-centimeter hydrogen line wavelength in the direction of hundreds of nearby stars, of types like or similar to the sun. They corrected the wavelength for the difference in motion between us and the star instead of between us and the center of the galaxy.

Others suggest listening at wavelengths between the hydrogen or H line at 21 centimeters and that of the OH (hydroxyl radical) at 18 centimeters, a band of wavelengths popularly called the "water-hole" alluding both to the fact that H combined with OH makes water and that galactic civilizations might gather at this "hole" to talk with each other like animals of all kinds gather around an African water-hole to drink.

Ron Bracewell of Stanford University has reasoned along different lines. In his book, "The Galactic Club" he has suggested that other-men, instead of constructing beacons may have launched interstellar probes, like our Pioneers and Vikings, except much more sophisticated and able to travel vastly farther out into space until they approach other stars. From these vantage points they monitor what goes on and report back from time-to-time what they have discovered.

Suppose we do detect a beacon signal? How could it be possible to understand the other-men about whom we know absolutely nothing? Is there anything that we and the dwellers on another planet even have in common? To put it in a very esoteric way: Is there any common semantic frame of reference? The other-men and their planet may be entirely different but assuming the other planet revolves around a star somewhere in our own galaxy, we would have a knowledge of many of the details of our galaxy in common, the stars, pulsars and nebulosities, and, in addition, other galaxies and the rest of the universe. The idea of numbers or counting would be common.

We might suppose that the other-men could initiate their beacon transmission with a series of dots:

●   ●●   ●●●   ●●●●   ●●●●●   etc.

After repeating this sequence a number of times it could be followed by:

●●●   — —   ●

●●●   — —   ●●

●●●●   — —   ●●●

●●   — —   ●

●●●●   — —   ●

●●●●   — —   ●●   etc.

In this sequence a new symbol of two dashes (— —) has been introduced to convey the concept of *greater than* (each series of dots on the left is greater than the number to the right of the symbol). In a similar way the symbols meaning *less than,* or *equal to,* could be introduced, then the symbols for addition, subtraction, multiplication and division. Gradually more complicated mathematical concepts could be set forth. From approximations which were accurate and ones which were inaccurate the concepts of good and bad or good and evil could be developed and from there even more abstract and non-mathematical ideas advanced. Given enough time a language could be evolved and very complex notions or thoughts conveyed including information that if we tuned to a particular wavelength with a sensitive enough receiver of a certain design we might pick up a television signal they were sending which contained much more information.

It is unlikely that we would have discovered the television signal first because it would be wide band and much harder to find. The very narrow band beacon signal would have alerted us to their presence and their slow dots and dashes taught us a language with which to understand them.

Much has been written about such languages. The dot and dash example I have given is based on "Lingua Cosmica" by Hans Freudenthal, as set forth in his book "Lincos, Design of a Language for Cosmic Intercourse."

N.S. Kardashev of the U.S.S.R. has suggested that other civilizations may be grouped into three types: a *Type I* which has a beacon transmitter with a power something like that falling on its planet from its own sun or star, a *Type II* which has harnessed all the power of its star for a beacon and a *Type III* which puts out a power equal to that from all the stars in its galaxy. According to Kardashev's definitions we would be classed as a "type-zero" civilization. We have just achieved the technical capability of listening for beacons but we are a long way from harnessing a power equal to what falls on the earth from the sun and reradiating it all from a beacon. The total of the earth's power requirements for heating, transportation, manufacturing, lighting — everything — is less than one-hundredth of one percent of this and we are even having a crisis

49. With Bob Dixon discussing a map of the Ohio Sky Survey.

trying to meet it. To qualify as a Type I civilization we would need to put 10 000 times this power into a beacon.

Freeman Dyson of Princeton has proposed that an advanced civilization might construct a wall around its star to trap all of the star's power. It would be like building a shell at the earth's radius from the sun to completely enclose it. The interior of the shell would provide a surface area one billion times that of the earth's surface for man's agriculture, industry and housing. The construction of such a Dyson sphere would be but a step on the path of a civilization from Kardashev's Type I to Type II.

Gerard Oneill has studied what it would take to launch self-sufficient space stations of ten thousand to some millions of inhabitants each. These cylindrical stations, like huge Hindenburgs, one to twenty kilometers long, would be mostly constructed of material mined from the moon and asteroids. These stations could be proliferated almost endlessly as the material of the moon, asteroids and planets, other than the earth, were exploited. Eventually, the stations might be linked to form a Dyson sphere entirely enclosing the sun. It is suggested that other civilizations may have already embarked upon similar ventures.

But have we overlooked something? What about a civilization which stays on its own planet, adjusting to its environment by keeping in balance and harmony with it instead of spreading like a cancer across the galaxy? If we can't keep things on the earth in balance is it likely we can do it with a Dyson sphere and a population a billion times what the earth has now?

Maybe there aren't any Type I, II or III civilizations. It is possible that civilizations which have developed to advanced stages have stabilized and even with great power capability are not operating beacons but instead are listening like man is now beginning to do. In this case, it may be man who has to initiate the "conversation."

Or advanced civilizations may not last long. Thus, man has developed the capability of communicating by radio across interstellar space in only the last decade or so. Within a comparable period he has also developed the capability of annihilating himself by nuclear weapons or pollution or both. He is on the horns of a dilemma; will he be able to communicate before he self-destructs? He is in a perilous predicament with destruction as close as the push of a button. Philip Morrison of M.I.T. has warned that within a space of minutes "the entire industrialized world can be destroyed by tens of thousands of nuclear weapons. Eight hundred million people could be consumed in the resulting apocalypse and the entire ecology of the planet . . . seriously damaged. This problem is *the* single most serious problem facing mankind."

Curiously, the nations in the biggest danger are those wielding the greatest power while the groups most likely to survive such a catastrophe are the most primitive, aboriginal tribes. In the aftermath of a nuclear holocaust mankind might never recover.

However, while there is still time we, at least, can listen. In a talk to a Rotary Club I put it this way:

"The ancient Greeks did not have Rotary Clubs but I presume they had luncheon groups or supper clubs that were similar. Imagine with me, if you will, that 2000 years ago a speaker told a group in Athens that the earth extended far beyond the Aegean Sea and the Mediterranean and that there were tales of great civilizations in distant lands far, far away.

"Today, 2000 years later here in Ohio, I am suggesting to you that far out in space on a planet circling a distant star there may be an advanced civilization broadcasting signals which are passing through this room at this very moment. But in which direction should we point our antenna and to what wavelength should we tune our receiver? These are some of the questions whose full answers still elude us."

·

EPILOGUE

The search for other-men will go on whether Bob Dixon does it or others do it. Success may come tomorrow, next year, in a thousand years, or never. But regardless of the outcome, the search will be a venture of great consequence for man as he learns more about his celestial neighborhood and others who may possibly dwell there.

Probing the extreme depths of the universe will also continue, giving man a better understanding of the kind of universe he inhabits. At the time I built my first radio receiver with galena crystal and phosphor bronze catwhisker, astronomers were not sure if anything at all lay outside of our own galaxy. But Edwin Hubble took the first step and then the discovery of radio sources led to rapid leaps that propelled man in his exploration almost to the edge. To probe yet further and to learn more about the vast space between us and the edge are challenges that will eternally kindle man's curiosity as long as he is man. Astronomy presents man with the universe as his total environment and his endless frontier.

We are at a point in time between an infinite past and a boundless future. Our bodies are midway in size between the microscopic and the astronomical. There is a great wonder and deep mystery about it all. As the chronicler of the tale of "Big Ear" I haven't discovered the ultimate truths of the universe but I have experienced the thrill and excitement of playing a small part in the adventure of exploring the astounding, baffling, stranger-than-fiction cosmos in which we dwell.

50. The author of Big Ear.

APPENDIX

A "List of Likely Objects" to which we might direct a search is given in the table. The closer the object the more readily signals from it may be detected. Hence, the objects in the list are arranged in order of increasing distance. The list is divided into five regions: The *solar system,* the *solar neighborhood, our galaxy,* the *galactic neighborhood* (nearby external galaxies) and the *universe.* Distances are expressed in the time required for light or radio waves to travel from the object to us at the velocity of light or radio waves (186 000 miles or 300 000 kilometers per second).

The nearest object is Mars with a light or radio wave travel-time distance of 3 to 21 minutes depending on its position in its orbit with respect to the earth. The signal-to-noise ratio is very large which means that it would be very easy to detect on the assumption that the transmitter on Mars radiates one million watts with a 152-meter diameter antenna and that we are receiving with the OSU radio telescope.

The next object in the list is the star Alpha Centauri A of spectral class G4 at a distance of 4.3 light years, a big jump in distance from Mars. The signal-to-noise ratio of 17 dB (decibels) is large enough to make detection easy with the same assumptions regarding transmitting and receiving systems as above. The G4 designation refers to the spectral classification of Alpha Centauri A as explained in Chaper 23.

Further down the list we come to the star Beta Canum Venaticorum at 30.2 light years distance for which the signal-to-noise ratio is 0 decibels, which means that detection would be just marginal on the same assumptions regarding transmitting and receiving systems as above. However, there are many uncertainties about these assumptions and the distance for marginal detection might be much more than 30 light years or much less.

Going further down the table we find that at a distance of 1000 light years there are a million stars within range provided the transmitter power and/or antenna size were increased by an amount equivalent to 30 decibels.

The decibel (abbreviated dB) is a unit introduced years ago by the Bell Telephone Laboratories to express power ratios. It is a logarithmic unit and is convenient for expressing very large or very small ratios.

Taking the signal-to-noise ratios literally, the inference is that objects with positive dB values are within range of detection of the OSU radio telescope, but those with negative dB values are not. This is a gross oversimplification. Actually depending on whether the other-men use more or less than one million watts and whether their antenna is more or less than 152 meters in diameter, the range of the OSU radio telescope might be larger or smaller by amounts corresponding to plus or minus 50 dB (or more). This means that, on the one hand, the range may fall short of any object outside the solar system while, on the other hand it could extend to more than 1000 light years and encompass more than one million stars of spectral class similar to the sun. If the latter is the case, a curious thing happens. A finding list is no longer needed. With more than one million objects distributed evenly over the sky there will always be one in the beam of our radio telescope regardless of where it is pointed. In this situation it would be better to scan the sky systematically looking for signals and not concentrate on any point in the sky more than any other.

Thus, a search for signals from distant civilizations might be divided into phases. In *Phase 1* a finding list would be used and the solar system neighborhood searched out to distances of several hundred light years. This list would include many thousands of stars. If no success were achieved in Phase 1, then Phase 2 could be initiated. In *Phase 2* the entire sky would be scanned systematically bit by bit. The requirements of "The Right Direction," would be eliminated since in Phase 2 *any* direction could be the right direction. Our search with Big Ear described in Chapter 24, is a Phase 2 type of search.

If we pursue the above reasoning still further, we could enter a *Phase 3*. Thus, if our search distance became sufficient to encompass our entire galaxy, we would have more likely-objects in our antenna beam if we scanned in directions near the galactic plane. This is the band across the sky we refer to as the Milky Way.

Suppose our search distance were extended yet further to include the galactic neighborhood, that is, the nearest galaxies outside our own, such as the giant Andromeda or M31 galaxy. This could be called *Phase 4* and here once more we could use a finding list to advantage. The objects in this list would not be individual stars as in Phase 1 but entire galaxies such as M31, M81 and others, each containing thousands of millions of stars like the sun. Once again we would concentrate our search in the directions of these objects. The requirement of "The Right Direction," would again be important.

Finally, if our search distance goes far beyond the galactic neighborhood we find distant galaxies almost uniformly distributed in all directions over the sky, and a systematic search of the entire sky is once more appropriate. This could be *Phase 5*.

Actually the galaxies outside our own galactic neighborhood are not uniformly distributed in space but tend to form groupings called clusters. One of the largest clusters of galaxies is in the constellation Coma Berenices and is known as the Coma cluster. It is some 100 million light years distant and contains nearly one thousand galaxies. So a variant of the above scheme would be to introduce a Phase 4A between Phase 4 and Phase 5. This added phase would extend the search of Phase 4 from individual nearby galaxies to include at least some of the closer, larger clusters.

But signals from a planet revolving around one of billions of stars in one of a thousand galaxies in the Coma cluster would be 100 million years old when we received them and the civilization which sent them might have vanished long ago. Two-way communication would be unthinkable; it would take at least 200 million years for any reply! Although the signals would be electromagnetic relics from antiquity, forever speeding through space at the velocity of light like the ripples from a stone dropped in a pond, the impulses, if we could detect them, and their message, if we could interpret it, might be full of cosmic wisdom which could broaden and enrich our culture. It would be like translating a musty, tattered old book or deciphering an ancient scroll preserved for all time in a cosmic library.

Does listening for beacons of civilizations at such great distances make any sense at all? It depends entirely on your assumptions. For example, if the beacon were operated by a Kardashev Type I civilization the signal-to-noise ratio would be improved over the value in the table by 110 decibels and the range of the OSU radio telescope would be stretched to include our entire galaxy and some of the closer galaxies beyond it. And if the beacon were of a Type II civilization Big Ear could easily detect it anywhere in the universe!

In fact, it would have a booming signal (large signal-to-noise ratio).

As a final question one might ask why no Ohio radio sources are in the "List of Likely Objects." The answer is that no Ohio or other radio sources have been found to be stars similar to the sun. However, it is not inconceivable that one of the nearly 20 000 sources in the Ohio sky survey might ultimately turn out to be associated with a distant civilization.

> *　　　　*　　　　*　　　　*　　　　*

Explanatory note concerning the difference between radio waves generated by natural causes and radio waves produced by intelligent beings: Waves from most radio sources eminate from huge spinning clouds of electrons which gyrate in magnetic fields and produce radiation over broad bands of wavelengths. Interstellar clouds of many elements, such as hydrogen, and also molecules, such as ethyl alcohol, "chirp" at particular wavelengths which might result in very narrow band radiation were it not for the fact that most of these clouds are in turbulent swirling motion which tends to spread the observed radiation over broader bands of wavelengths. So a general characteristic of most natural radiation is that it is broad band or relatively so.

In contrast to radiation from the natural clouds, man-made radio waves are launched by antennas on which electrons oscillate along metal conductors producing, usually, very narrow band radiation. So a characteristic of man-made radiation is that it may be narrow band. Furthermore, the narrower the bandwidth, the further one can transmit with a given amount of power. Hence, if man were to build a beacon station it would be extremely narrow band and we presume that a distant civilization would do likewise. So when we detect a narrow band signal it becomes a prime candidate for further investigation to establish if it is indeed "artificial" or due to some natural phenomenon. If the signal also turns on and off in the manner of Morse Code dots and dashes it will be even more suspect of having an intelligent origin.

LIST OF LIKELY OBJECTS

Object	Distance (time)	Signal-to-Noise Ratio
Planets in Solar System		
Mars	3 to 21 minutes	+134 to +117 dB
Stars in Solar System Neighborhood (Phase 1)		
Alpha Centauri A (G4) (part of triple star system)	4.3 years	+17 dB
Epsilon Eridani (K2)	10.8	+9
Tau Ceti (G5)	10.9	+9
61 Cygni A (K3)	11.0	+9 double star
Epsilon Indi (K5)	11.3	+8
380 Ursae Majoris (M0)	14.7	+6
Omicron-2 Eridani A (K1)	16.1	+5 double star
70 Ophiuchi (K0)	17.3	+5
Rho Comae Berenices (G0)	27.2	+1
Beta Canum Venaticorum (G0)	30.2	0 dB
Eta Bootis (G0)	31.9	–1 dB
Iota Persei (G0)	38.8	–2
47 Ursae Majoris (G0)	44.7	–3
Psi Aurigae (G0)	48.6	–4
Pi Ursae Majoris (G0)	50.2	–4
Eta Herculis (G5)	61.6	–6
More distant stars but within our galaxy		
1 million stars (Phase 2)	Up to 1000 years	–30 dB
10 000 million stars (Phase 3)	Up to 80 000 years	–68
Galaxies in the Galactic Neighborhood (Phase 4)		
Andromeda galaxy (M31) 10 000 million stars	2 000 000 years	–95
More distant galaxies somewhere in the Universe (Phase 5)		
10 000 billion billion stars	Up to 10 billion years	–170 dB

THE METRIC SYSTEM

When Napoleon was advancing across Europe, his lieutenants were continually frustrated in their dealings to acquire food and supplies for his huge army of men and horses because they never knew what a pound of meat, a bushel of grain, a foot of lumber or a gallon of wine would amount to, all differing from one duchy or dukedom to the next. So Napoleon ordered that transactions be conducted in the metric system, a set of decimal units devised by the French Academy of Science and adopted by France in 1795.

As Napoleon invaded one country after another he introduced each to the metric system. Later when he retreated and a country replaced the French tricolor with its own flag, it did not change back to its old system of units; once metricated, it remained metric. It is likely that if Napoleon had crossed the English channel and invaded England, its conversion to the metric system would have occurred at that time instead of nearly two centuries later.

The metric system has many advantages. It is a decimal system throughout and free from such odd conversions as 12 inches to a foot, 16½ feet to a rod, 66 feet to a chain, 5280 feet to a mile and 231 cubic inches or 128 fluid ounces to a gallon. The units of length, area, volume and mass all have a simple decimal relationship and all of the electrical quantities we use daily, such as the volt, ampere, watt and kilowatt, are metric units.

The metric system became official, although not mandatory, in the U.S. in 1876, and subsequently the U.S. has on occasion come close to a complete conversion. The most recent act occurred in December 1975 when President Gerald Ford signed a bill establishing a national metric advisory board to help expedite conversion to the metric system by the U.S. but no compulsory provisions are included. There is no definite target date for complete metrication so the U.S. will continue to back into the metric system, inching gradually to millimeters while, as President Ford said, the U.S. has become "an island in a metric sea."

Countries which have metricated have done so with relatively few problems and little confusion and once the change was made many persons wondered why they hadn't converted earlier. As of 1976 the U.S. is the only sizable country in the world not already completely on the metric system or in the process of a scheduled conversion.

Changing to metric does not mean that vestiges of the English system can't remain for a long time. Football can continue to be played on a field 100 yards long and horse races run on a track measured in furlongs. Expressions like, "Give him an inch and he'll take a mile", will persist and their use will impart an added touch of quaintness like the words cubit, league, hogshead, kilderkin, puncheon or pennyweight now do. English units will become endowed with an aura or patina of antiquity which will add flavor to their use.

Gone but not forgotten will be such gems as, "An ounce of gold weighs more than an ounce of feathers but a pound of feathers weighs more than a pound of gold", resulting from the fact that gold is weighed in troy ounces (12 to a pound) while feathers are weighed in avoirdupois ounces (16 to a pound) with a troy ounce a bit bigger than an avoirdupois ounce. Gone but fondly recalled will also be 43 560 square feet to the acre, defined by King Henry VII as the area a man and team of oxen could plow between sunrise and sunset.

When you are accustomed to a system it is sometimes difficult to recognize the advantages of a better one. For example, when Britain converted its currency recently to a decimal system editorials appeared in U.S. newspapers congratulating Britain for changing its "12 pence makes a shilling and 20 shillings make a pound to a common sense decimal system similar to that employed in the U.S." Yet the U.S. editorial writers overlooked the fact that Britain was also converting to the metric system while the U.S. was still stuck with 12 inches to the foot, 3 feet to the yard, 1760 yards to the mile and 32 fluid ounces to the quart.

Metrication can provide employment making new rulers, wrenches, containers, signs and labels. It also offers the opportunity to standardize in new and better ways. For example, in Britain metrication has permitted adoption of fewer and simpler pipe and bolt sizes.

In the U.S. all scientific measurements have been done in metric units for decades and many industries, such as electrical, computer and pharmaceutical, are converted or rapidly converting. Conversion means there will no longer be the many fascinating but confusing grains, drams, links or pottles nor the problem of the differences between liquid and dry measure and between many U.S. and British units. But how long it will be before you can buy potatoes by the kilo(gram) instead of the pound or 21 by 28 (centimeter) typewriter paper instead of 8½ by 11 (inch) is unclear.

While conversion in the U.S. remains incomplete, it will be necessary to keep in mind that there are about 25 millimeters to the inch, about one and a half kilometers to the mile, a bit more than a quart of liquid in a liter and about two pounds to a kilogram. However, once conversion is complete, conversion ratios can be forgotten, except in historical situations, and we can simply think metric. Once we get used to it we will say "metric is so simple, metric is beautiful."

Big Ear was written during the U.S. transition from English to metric units. Although metric units appear frequently, I have not attempted to use them slavishly, often retaining an English unit simply because it seemed more appropriate or appealing. In many places the equivalent amount in the other system appears parenthetically.

Articles by John Kraus to which reference is made

"Some Characteristics of Ultra-High Frequency Transmission" with Henry Muyskens, *Proceedings* Institute of Radio Engineers, Sept. 1933.

"Radioactive Isotopes of Palladium and Silver from Palladium" with J. M. Cork, *Physical Review*, Oct. 15, 1937.

"Directional Antenna Systems for 14 Megacycle Operation", *R/9*, June 1935.

"A Small but Effective Flat-Top Beam Antenna", *RADIO*, March 1937.

"More on the Flat-Top Beam Antenna (By Popular Demand)", *RADIO*, June 1937.

"Rotary Flat-Top Beam Antennas", *RADIO*, Dec. 1937.

"Optional End-Fire Directivity with the Flat-Top Beam" with Robert R. Sprole, *RADIO*, June 1938.

"Directional Antennas with Closely-Spaced Elements", *QST*, Jan. 1938.

"Flat-Top Beam Antennas", *Television and Short-Wave World* (London), Feb. 1938.

"New Design Data on the Flat-Top Beam", *RADIO*, June 1938.

"Characteristics of Antennas with Closely-Spaced Elements", *RADIO*, Feb. 1939.

"The Square-Corner Reflector", *RADIO*, March 1939.

"Antenna Arrays with Closely-Spaced Elements", *Proceedings* Institute of Radio Engineers, Feb. 1940.

"The Corner Reflector Antenna", *Proceedings* Institute of Radio Engineers, Nov. 1940

"Multi-Wire Doublet Antennas", *RADIO*, May 1939.

"Multi-Wire Type Antennas", *RADIO*, June 1939.

"Compact-H Beam Antenna" with Harold E. Taylor, *RADIO*, Oct. 1939.

"Twin-Three Flat-Top Beam Antenna", *RADIO*, Nov. 1939.

"Multi-Wire Dipole Antennas", *Electronics*, Jan. 1940.

"Three Band Rotary Antenna", *RADIO*, Feb. 1940.

"The T-Matched Antenna" with Stocker S. Sturgeon,*QST*, Sept. 1940.

"The Double Twin-Three Beam Antenna" with Harold E. Taylor, *RADIO*, Oct. 1940.

"The Square-Corner Reflector Beam Antenna for Ultra-High Frequencies", *QST*, Nov. 1940.

"Diathermy Measurement Technique" with R. W. Teed, M.D., *Electronics*, Dec. 1940.

"Ultra-High Frequency Diathermy in Otolaryngology with Especial Reference to Dosage Measurement" with R. W. Teed, M.D., *Archives of Otolaryngology*, Oct. 1941.

"Principles of Direction Finding" with Andrew Alford and Ernest C. Barkofsky in "Very High Frequency Techniques", McGraw-Hill Book Co., 1947.

"Antennas for Direction Finders" With Hugh K. Clark, Ernest C. Barkofsky, and Gus Stavis in "Very High Frequency Techniques", McGraw-Hill Book Co., 1947.

"Helical Beam Antenna", *Electronics*, April 1947.

"Characterisitcs of Helical Antennas Radiating in the Axial Mode" with J. C. Williamson, *Journal of Applied Physics*, Jan. 1948.

"Measured Impedances of Helical Beam Antennas" with Otto J. Glasser, *Journal of Applied Physics*. Feb. 1948.

"Helical Beam Antennas for Wide-Band Applications", *Proceedings* of the Institute of Radio Engineers, Oct. 1948.

"Helical Beam Antenna", *Proceedings* Institute of Radio Engineers, March 1949.

"Helical Beam Antenna Design Techniques", *Communications,* Sept. 1949.

"The Influence of Conductor Size on the Properties of Helical Beam Antennas" with Thomas E. Tice, *Proceedings* Institute of Radio Engineers, Nov. 1949.

"The Ohio State Radio Telescope", *Sky and Telescope,* April 1953.

"New Techniques in Radio Astronomy" with Edward Ksiazek, *Electronics,* Sept. 1953.

"Radio Radiation from the Supergalaxy" with H. C. Ko, *Nature* (London), Sept. 19, 1953.

"Radio Map of the Milky Way" with H. C. Ko, *Sky and Telescope,* Nov. 1954.

"Galactic and Localized Source Observations at 250 Megacycles per Second" with H.C. Ko and S. Matt, *Astronomical Journal,* Dec. 1954.

"A Detailed Map of the Radio Sky" with H. C. Ko, *Nature,* Jan. 22, 1955.

"Radio Telescopes", *Scientific American,* March 1955.

"Radio Brightness Distribution Across the Andromeda Nebula", *Nature,* March 19, 1955.

"The Effect of Source Distribution on Antenna Patterns" with S. Matt, *Proceedings* Institute of Radio Engineers, July 1955.

"The Radio Position of the Galactic Nucleus" with H. C. Ko, *Astrophysical Journal,* July 1955.

"Radio Frequency Radiation from the Rosette Nebula" with H. C. Ko, *Nature,* July 30, 1955.

"Resolution, Pattern Effects and Range of Radio Telescopes", *Transactions on Antennas and Propagation* (Institute of Radio Engineers), July 1956.

"Radio Map of the Winter Sky", *Sky and Telescope,* 1955.

"Recent Results in Radio Astronomy at the Ohio State University" with H. C. Ko, R. T. Nash and D. Stoutenburg, *Proceedings,* Symposium on Radio Astronomy, Jodrell Bank, Manchester, England, Aug. 1955.

"Radio Noise from Jupiter", *Sky and Telescope,* 1956.

"New Design for Radio Telescopes of Large Aperture", *Sky and Telescope,* 1956.

"Radio Telescopes of Large Aperture and Low Cost", *Astronomical Journal,* May 1956.

"A Preliminary Study of the Magnitude Distribution of Celestial Radio Sources", *Astronomical Journal,* Nov. 1955.

"A New Radio Map of the Sky and a Model of the Galaxy" with H. C. Ko, *Astronomical Journal,* May 1956.

"Impulsive Radio Signals from the Planet Venus", *Nature,* July 7, 1956.

"Radio Signals from Venus at a Wavelength of 11 Meters", *Nature,* July 21, 1956.

"Apparent Radio Radiation at 11 Meter Wavelength from Venus", *Nature,* May 7, 1960.

"Some Observations of the Impulsive Radio Signals from Jupiter", *Astronomical Journal,* May 1956.

"The Radio Sky", *Scientific American,* July 1956.

"Recent Observations with the Ohio State University Radio Telescope" with H. C. Ko, R. T. Nash and D. Stoutenburg, *Astronomical Journal,* May 1956.

"Radio Telescope Antennas of Large Aperture", *Proceedings* Institute of Radio Engineers, Jan, 1958.

"A Note on Some Signal Characteristics of Sputnik I" with J. S. Albus. *Proceedings* Institute of Radio Engineers, March 1958.

"Detection of Sputniks I and II by CW Reflection" *Proceedings* Institute of Radio Engineers, March 1958.

"Sputnik I's Last Days in Orbit" with E. E. Dreese, *Proceedings* Institute of Radio Engineers, Sept. 1958.

"A Map of the Cygnus Region at 915 Megacycles per Second" with J. J. Eaton, *Astrophysical Journal,* March 1959.

"The Ohio State University 360-ft Radio Telescope", *Nature,* Aug. 1959.

"The Satellite Ionization Phenomenon" with R. C. Higgy and W. R. Crone, *Proceedings* Institute of Radio Engineers, April 1960.

"Evidence of Satellite-Related Ionization Effects between Hemispheres", *Proceedings,* Institute of Radio Engineers, Nov. 1960.

"Some Characterisitcs of the Ohio State University 360-foot Radio Telescope" with H. C. Ko and R. T. Nash, *Transactions on Antennas and Propagation* (Institute of Radio Engineers), Jan. 1961.

"Observations of Ionization Induced by Artifical Earth Satellites" with R. C. Higgy, D. J. Scheer and W. R. Crone, *Nature,* Feb. 1960.

"Observations of Satellite-Related Ionization Effects between 1958 and 1960" with Martti Tiuri, *Proceedings* Institute of Radio Engineers, Oct. 1962.

"Ionospheric Disturbances Associated with Echo I as Studied with 19-Megacycle per Second Radar" with Martti Tiuri, *Journal of Geophysical Research,* Oct. 1963.

"The Satellite Ionization Phenomenon as Studied by CW-Reflection and Pulse Radar Techniques" in "Interactions of a Space Vehicle with an Ionized Atmosphere", S. F. Singer, editor, Pergamon Press, 1965.

"Is the Satellite Ionization Phenomenon Responsible for the Decametric Radiation from Jupiter?" with Martti Tiuri, *Astronomical Journal,* Nov. 1965.

"The Large Radio Telescope of the Ohio State University", *Sky and Telescope,* July 1963.

"Recent Advances in Radio Astronomy", *Spectrum* (Institute of Radio Engineers), Sept, 1964.

"Radio and Radar Astronomy and the Exploration of the Universe", *Transactions on Antennas and Propagation* (Institute of Radio Engineers) Dec. 1964.

"A Backward Angle-Fire Array Antenna", *Transactions on Antennas and Propagation* (Institute of Radio Engineers), Jan, 1964.

"Wave Velocities on the Grid Structure Backward Angle-Fire Antenna", with Keith Carver, *Transactions on Antennas and Propagation* (Institute of Radio Engineers), July 1964.

"A Map of the M31 Region at 1400 Megacycles per Second", *Nature,* June 1, 1963.

"Maps of M31 and Surroundings at 600 and 1415 Megacycles per Second", *Nature,* April 18, 1964.

"Does M31 Have a Halo?", *Nature,* June 20, 1964.

"Maps of the Perseus Region at 600 and 1415 Megacycles per Second" with R. S. Dixon and S. Y. Meng, *Nature,* Feb. 20, 1965.

"A New High Sensitivity Study of the M31 Region at 1415 Megacycles per Second" with R. S. Dixon and R. O. Fisher, *Astrophysical Journal,* May 1966.

"Preliminary Results of a 21-Centimeter Line Investigaion of M33" with S. Y. Meng, *Astronomical Journal,* April 1966.

"Neutral Hydrogen Survey of the Andromeda Galaxy" with W. D. Brundage, *Science,* July 22, 1966.

"21-Centimeter Observations of High Velocity Hydrogen Clouds" with S. Y. Meng, *Astronomical Journal,* June 1970.

"The Ohio Survey: I" with D. J. Scheer, *Astronomical Journal,* May 1967.

"The Ohio Survey: II" with R. S. Dixon, *Astronomical Journal,* Aug. 1968.

"The Ohio Survey: III" with L. T. Fitch and R. S. Dixon, *Astronomical Journal,* June 1969.

"The Ohio Survey: IV" with J. R. Ehman and R. S. Dixon, *Astronomical Journal,* May 1970.

"The Ohio Survey: V" with R. K. Brundage, R. S. Dixon and J. R. Ehman, *Astronomical Journal,* Nov. 1971.

"The Ohio Survey: VI" with J. R. Ehman, R. S. Dixon and C. M. Ramakrishna, *Astronomical Journal,* Feb. 1974.

"The Ohio Survey: VII" with C. P. Rinsland, R. S. Dixon and M. R. Gearhart, *Astronomical Journal,* Nov. 1974.

"The Ohio Survey, Supplement 1" with B. H. Andrew, *Astronomical Journal,* March 1971.

"The Ohio Survey, Supplement 2" with C. P. Rinsland and R. S. Dixon, *Astronomical Journal,* Oct. 1975.

Ohio Specials: "Spectra of OQ208 and other Centimeter Wavelength Radio Sources" with D. J. Scheer, *Astronomical Journal,* Sept. 1967.

Ohio Specials: "Radio Sources with Peaked Spectra" with D. J. Scheer, R. S. Dixon, L. T. Fitch and B. H. Andrew, *Astrophysical Journal Letters,* April 1968.

Ohio Specials: "Spectral Data on Some Ohio Radio Sources" with B. H. Andrew, *Astrophysical Journal Letters,* Jan. 1970.

Ohio Specials: "Radio Sources with Flat Spectra" with B. H. Andrew, *Astrophysical Journal Letters,* Jan. 1970.

Ohio Specials: "Ohio Source Spectra: List II" with B. J. Wills and B. H. Andrew, *Astrophysical Journal Letters,* Nov. 1, 1971.

Ohio Specials: "Spectra of Some Ohio Radio Sources: List III" with E. K. Conklin, B. H. Andrew and B. J. Wills, *Astrophysical Journal,* Oct. 15, 1972.

Ohio Specials: "Spectra of Some Ohio Radio Sources: List IV" with B. H. Andrew, J. R. Ehman and M. R. Gearhart, *Astrophysical Journal,* Oct. 1, 1973.

Ohio Specials: "Spectra of Some Ohio Radio Sources: List V" with M. R. Gearhart and B. H. Andrew, *Astrophysical Journal Supplement,* March 1976.

Ohio Specials: "Optical Identification of Ohio Radio Sources with Peculiar Spectra" with J. R. Thompson and B. H. Andrew, *Astrophysical Journal,* Oct. 1968.

Ohio Specials: "Identification of Radio Sources from the Ohio Survey" with M. M. Radivich, *Astronomical Journal,* Oct. 1971.

Ohio Specials: "Optical Identification of Ohio Survey Radio Sources" with M. R. Gearhart, J. M. Lund and D. J. Frantz, *Astronomical Journal,* Sept. 1972.

Ohio Special: "Radio and Optical Observations of the Source OZ-252" with B. H. Andrew, S. van den Bergh and E. H. Conklin, *Publications of the Astronomical Society of the Pacific,* Feb. 1971

Ohio Specials: "Radio Spectra of OH471 and OQ172" with M. R. Gearhart, B. H. Andrew, Glen Blake, Paul Scott, Martin Ryle, S. Ya. Braude, N. K. Sharykin, I. N. Zhouck, A. H. Bridle, E. K. Conklin, J. N. Douglas, O. Hachenberg, M. Thiel, Pierre Kaufmann, C. R. Purton, P. A. Feldman, K. A. Marsh, Mark Stull, Kent Price, J. W. Warner, G. Assousa and B. Balick, *Nature,* June 21, 1974.

"Radio Source Counts from the Ohio Survey" with B. J. Harris, *Nature,* Aug. 1970.

"Ohio Radio Sources in Clusters of Galaxies" with Patricia C. Boeshaar, *Astrophysical Journal,* May 1971.

"Radio Source Counts from the Ohio Survey" with B. J. Harris, *Bulletin of the American Astronomical Society,* 1970.

"Ohio Source Counts" with B. J. Harris, *Nature Physical Science* (London), April 5, 1971.

"Ohio Survey Statistics", *Nature Physical Science,* March 6, 1972.

"Radio Spectra and Red Shifts of 179 QSOs" with Mirjana Gearhart, *Astronomical Journal,* Jan. 1975.

Ohio Special: "OE110: A New Faint BL Lacertae Object," with Alex Smith, Robert Leacock, P. L. Edwards, J. T. Pollack, R. L. Scott, Mirjana Gearhart and Erich Pacht, *Astrophysical Journal Letters,* June 1, 1976.

Ohio Special: "OX-192: A New Highly Variable BL Lacertae Object", with Eric Craine, Peter Strittmatter, Santiago Tapia, Bryan Andrew, Gladys Harvey, and Mirjana Gearhart, *Astrophysical Letters,* June 15, 1976.

"The Ohio Sky Survey and Other Radio Surveys" in "Vistas in Astronomy" edited by Arthur Beer, Pergamon Press, 1976.

Books by John Kraus

"Elements of Electromagnetics", Long's College Book Co., Columbus, 1949 (179 pages).

"Antennas", McGraw-Hill Book Co., New York, 1950 (553 pages).

"Electromagnetics", McGraw-Hill Book Co., New York, 1953 (604 pages).

"Radio Astronomy", with chapter on receivers by Martti Tiuri, McGraw-Hill Book Co., New York, 1966 (486 pages).

"Electromagnetics", second edition, with Keith Carver, McGraw-Hill Book Co., New York, 1973 (828 pages).

Foreign editions of these books include translations into Japanese, Russian and Spanish

General References

Boeke, Kees, "Cosmic View: The Universe in 40 Jumps", John Day Co. N.Y., 1957.

Bracewell, Ronald N., "The Galactic Club: Intelligent Life in Outer Space", Scribner, N.Y., 1975.

Baker, Kenneth, Ohio State Journal, Columbus, Feb. 14, 1952.

Brown, G. H., "Directional Antennas", *Proceedings* IRE, Jan. 1937.

Cambridge Surveys
   1C: M. Ryle, F. G. Smith, and B. Elsmore, *Monthly Notices* of the Royal Astronomical Society, 1950.

   2C: J. R. Shakeshaft, M. Ryle, J. E. Baldwin, B. Esmore, and J. H. Thomson, *Memoirs* of the Royal Astronomical Society, 1955.

   3C: D. O. Edge, J. R. Shakeshaft, W. B. McAdam, J. E. Baldwin, and S. Archer, *Memoirs* of the Royal Astronomical Society, 1959.

   4C: J. D. H. Pilkington and P. F. Scott, *Memoirs* of the Royal Astronomical Society, 1965; J. F. R. Gower, P. F. Scott, and D. Wills, *Memoirs* Royal Astronomical Society, 1967.

Carswell, R. F., and Strittmatter, P. A., "Redshift of OH471", *Nature,* April 6, 1973.

"CETI: Communication with Extraterrestrial Intelligence" Carl Sagan ed, MIT Press, 1973.

Cleeton, C. E., and Williams, N. H., "Electromagnetic Waves of 1.1 cm Wavelength and the Absorption Spectrum of Ammonia", *Physical Review,* Feb. 15, 1934.

Cocconi, Giuseppe and Morrison, Philip, "Searching for Interstellar Communications", *Nature,* Sept. 19, 1959.

Craine, Eric R. and Warner, John W., "Optical Variations of OJ287, ON231, and OQ208", *Astorphysical Journal Letters,* Jan. 1973.

Cyclops: "Project Cyclops, A Design Study of a System for Detecting Extraterrestrial Life", J. Billingham, editor, NASA/Ames Research Center, Moffett Field, California, 1972.

Dixon, Robert S., "A Master List of Radio Sources", *Astrophysical Journal Supplement,* July 1970.

Dixon, Robert S., "A Search Strategy for Finding Extraterrestrial Radio Beacons", *Icarus,* 1973.

Drake, Frank D., "How Can We Detect Radio Transmissions from Distant Planetary Systems?", *Sky and Telescope,* Jan. 1960.

Drake, Frank D., "Project Ozma", *Physics Today,* April 1961.

Dyson, F. J., "Search for Artificial Stellar Sources of Infrared Radiation", *Science,* June 3, 1960.

Freudenthal, Hans, "Lincos, Design of a Language for Cosmic Intercourse", North-Holland Publishing Co., 1960.

Gorshkov, A. G., and Popov, M. V., "A New Galactic Population of Radio Sources" (The Ohio Specials), *Astronomical Circular* of the Academy of Science, U.S.S.R., Sept. 18, 1972.

Greenstein, Jesse L., and Schmidt, Maarten, "The Quasi-Stellar Radio Sources 3C48 and 3C273", *Astrophysical Journal,* July 1, 1964.

Hart, I. B., "Makers of Science", Oxford University Press, 1923.

Hewish, A., Bell, S. J., Pilkington, J. D. H., Scott, P F., and Collins, R. A., "Observations of a Rapidly Pulsating Radio Source", *Nature*, Feb 24, 1968.

Hey, J. S., "The Radio Universe", 2nd ed., Pergamon Press, 1976.

"Interstellar Communication", A. G. W. Cameron ed., Benjamin, 1963.

Hubble, Edwin, "The Realm of the Nebulae", New Haven, 1936.

Hubble, Edwin, Halley Lecture, "Red Shifts in the Spectra of Nebulae", May 8, 1934. Oxford Press, 1934.

Jansky, Karl G., "Electrical Disturbances Apparently of Extraterrestrial Origin", *Proceedings* Institute of Radio Engineers, Oct. 1933.

Jansky, Karl G., "A Note on the Source of Interstellar Interference", *Proceedings* Institute of Radio Engineers, Oct. 1935.

Kardashev, N. S., "Transmission of Information by Extraterrestrial Civilizations", *Soviet Astronomy (Astronomicheskhi Zhurnal)*, March-April, 1964.

Marshall, Catherine, "A Man Called Peter", McGraw-Hill, 1951.

Millman, Peter M., "Seven Maxims of UFOs", Royal Astronomical Society of Canada Journal, vol. 69, 1975.

Mills, B. Y., "The Distribution of the Discrete Sources of Cosmic Radio Radiation" *Australian Journal of Scientific Research* (Series A), 1952.

Morrison, Philip, Letter, Federation of American Scientists, Oct. 1975.

Oneill, Gerard K., "The Colonization of Space", *Physics Today*, Sept. 1974.

Oppenheimer, Robert, and Volkoff, G. M., "On Massive Neutron Cores", *Physical Review*. Feb. 15, 1939.

Oppenheimer, Robert, and Snyder, H., "On Continued Gravitational Contraction", *Physical Review,* Sept. 15, 1939.

Poincare, Henri, "La Valeur de la Science", Cheval Aile, Geneva, 1946.

Reber, Grote, "Cosmic Static", *Proceedings* Institute of Radio Engineers, Feb. 1940.

Reber, Grote, "Cosmic Static", *Astrophysical Journal,* June 1940.

Sagan, Carl, "Cosmic Connection", Doubleday, 1973.

Shklovskii, I. S., and Sagan, Carl, "Intelligent Life in the Universe", Holden-Day, 1966. Sagan's comparison of the attitudes of the saucerian and the scientist is given in Chapter 2.

Schmidt, M., and Matthews, T. A., "Redshifts of the Quasi-Stellar Radio Sources 3C47 and 3C147", *Astrophysical Journal,* Feb. 15, 1964.

Shapley, Harlow, Press release from Cambridge, Massachusetts, Nov. 6, 1954.

Stull, Mark, "Observations of Ohio Radio Sources at 430 MHz", *Astronomical Journal,* May 1973.

Sullivan, Walter, "We Are Not Alone", McGraw-Hill, 1964.

Toffler, Alvin, "Future Shock", Bantam Books, 1971.

Warner, John W., "Radio Sources in the Ohio Survey and Zwicky Compact Galaxies", *Astrophysical Letters,* 1972.

Wampler, E. J., Robinson, L. B., Baldwin, J. A., and Burbidge, E. M., "The Redshift of OQ172", *Nature,* June 8, 1973.

Watson, James D., "The Double Helix", Mentor, 1968.

Figure Credits

Jeff Bates (49), Walter Buhl (4), Madeline Drexler (50), Clayton Fletcher (43), Bill Foley (20), Helskinki Institute of Technology (37, 38), Paul Horn (21), Mel Ivory (6, 10), Jack Kraus (42), NASA (19, 46), National Geographic Society-Palomar Observatory Sky Survey (44), F. Ouradnik (5, 7, 8, 9, 11, 15), Ohio State University Photography Department (22, 23*, 24, 27, 28, 29, 40) (*23 from rendering by Louis Kail), Henry Pagean (13, 36), Charles Piatt (32, 33), Tom Root (34, 35), K. A. Strand (47), TRW Corp. (17), United Features Syndicate, Inc. (48), USAF (18). Photographs not creditied above are by the author.

Acknowledgement

For all the help, encouragement and suggestions my deep appreciation and accolades to Mary Jo Arnold, Patricia Beebe, Reed Crone, Robert Dixon, Madeline Drexler, Mira Gearhart, Alice Kraus, Jack Kraus, Janice Kraus, Nelson Kraus, Valerie Kraus, Donna LaRue, John Pfeiffer, and Hazel Snyder.

The author is the Taine G. McDougal Professor of Electrical Engineering and Astronomy at the Ohio State University and Director of the Ohio State-Ohio Wesleyan Radio Observatory.

INDEX